Software
Design
for
Real-time
Systems

Software Design for Real-time Systems

J.E. COOLING

Department of Electronic and Electrical Engineering,
University of Technology, Loughborough

CHAPMAN AND HALL

University and Professional Division

LONDON • NEW YORK • TOKYO • MELBOURNE • MADRAS

UK	Chapman and Hall, 2–6 Boundary Row, London SE1 8HN
USA	Van Nostrand Reinhold, 115 5th Avenue, New York NY10003
JAPAN	Chapman and Hall Japan, Thomson Publishing Japan, Hirakawacho Nemoto Building, 7F, 1–7–11 Hirakawa-cho, Chiyoda-ku, Tokyo 102
AUSTRALIA	Chapman and Hall Australia, Thomas Nelson Australia, 480 La Trobe Street, PO Box 4725, Melbourne 3000
INDIA	Chapman and Hall India, R. Seshadri, 32 Second Main Road, CIT East, Madras 600 035

First published 1991

© 1991 J.E. Cooling

Typeset in 10/12 Sabon by Selectmove Limited, London
Printed in Great Britain by T.J. Press, Padstow, Cornwall

ISBN 0 412 34180 8
0 442 31174 5 (USA)

British Library Cataloguing in Publication Data

Cooling, J. E. (Jim E)
  Software design for real-time systems.
  1. Real time computer systems. Software. Design
  I. Title
  005.12

  ISBN 0–412–34180–8

Library of Congress Cataloging-in-Publication Data
available

To Nieve and Niall
Le grá agus gach déa-ghuí

Contents

Acknowledgements

CONTRIBUTORS

Paul Robinson (Rolls-Royce and Associates Ltd) and Mike Bushell: for making the formal methods chapter readable, interesting and understandable. This book would have been a much lesser text without their contributions.
Janet Redman: for producing such a good set of diagrams, on time, as specified, and with good humour.

ADVICE AND ASSISTANCE

Steve Mallon (British Aerospace Dynamics plc): who gave so much time and effort for the development of the CORE and MASCOT examples.
Len Griffiths (British Aerospace Dynamics plc): for generously providing the CORE and MASCOT tool facilities.
Bill Smith (British Aerospace Dynamics plc): for his patience and time in showing how MASCOT 3 is handled by professionals.
Richard Kaiser and Phil Sulley (Yourdon International Ltd.): for the time and assistance to develop the YSM examples.
John Cameron (Michael Jackson Systems Ltd.): for his help in the JSD work.
Stuart Frost (ISS Ltd.): for his time and effort in the development of the HOOD example.
Pamela Webster (RPM Systems): for her enthusiastic and informative efforts in producing diagrams for the ATRON debugger text.
And to many others who helped along the way by providing comments, technical information, photos, etc.

CRITICS AND ASSESSORS

My good friend Alan Cuff: for encouragement, support and incisive (if sometimes occasional) proofreading.
Niall and Jo: for taking the time to wade through the draft manuscript, and for their many useful and fresh ideas.
Two anonymous reviewers: for their highly detailed, painstaking and extensive review effort. It has been much appreciated.

SUSTENANCE AND RELAXATION

Arthur Guinness and Sons Ltd.
Hi-fly windsurfing boards.

And finally, for my wife Pauline: who, during the last 20 months, coped with my long, isolated, writing sessions, plausible (to me) excuses for avoiding house maintenance, and constant failures to do jobs on time.
Thank you love.

JIM COOLING
Loughborough

Preface

WHAT IS THIS BOOK ABOUT?

In recent times real-time computer systems have become increasingly complex and sophisticated. It has now become apparent that, to implement such schemes effectively, professional, rigorous software methods must be used. This includes analysis, design and implementation. Unfortunately few textbooks cover this area well. Frequently they are hardware oriented with limited coverage of software, or software texts which ignore the issues of real-time systems. This book aims to fill that gap by describing the total software design and development process for real-time systems. Further, special emphasis is given to the needs of microprocessor-based real-time embedded systems.

WHAT ARE REAL-TIME COMPUTER SYSTEMS?

Real-time systems are those which must produce correct responses within a definite time limit. Should computer responses exceed these time bounds then performance degradation and/or malfunction results.

WHAT ARE REAL-TIME EMBEDDED COMPUTER SYSTEMS?

Here the computer is merely one functional element within a real-time system; it is not a computing machine in its own right.

WHO SHOULD READ THIS BOOK?

Those involved, or who intend to get involved, in the design of software for real-time systems. It is written with both software and hardware engineers in mind, being suitable for students and professional engineers.

AT WHAT LEVEL IS IT PITCHED?

Few assumptions are made about the background of the reader. Ideally he will have a broad grasp of microprocessor systems, a basic understanding of programming and an appreciation of elementary digital logic. These aren't essential, but they help in understanding the reasoning used at many points in the text. Some experience of assembly language and high-level language programming would also be helpful here.

HOW IS THE BOOK ORGANIZED?

In general there is a logical progression from start to finish (this shows an original mind at work!). Chapters have, where possible, been written to stand alone. Thus some repetition and duplication will be found. Occasionally, forward referencing will be met, but this is used mainly as a pointer to future topics.

The book opens by describing what real-time systems are, their structures and applications, and the impact of these on software design in general. This should be especially useful to readers having a software background only.

Following this is a section which shows clearly why a professional approach to software design is imperative to achieve reliable, safe and correct operation of real-time systems. It explains why and how software errors occur, what qualities are desirable (e.g. feasibility, suitability, robustness, etc.), discusses error avoidance and defensive programming and finishes by looking at design styles.

The problems of deducing and defining system specifications and performance requirements are covered, incorporating the relatively new topics of rapid and animation prototyping. This leads into design proper, the purpose being to lay foundations for later work. It covers the basic concepts of design, including modularization, structured programming, functionally structured designs and object-oriented methods. Supporting these design methods are diagramming techniques, described in two parts. First, the conceptual aspects of diagramming are covered, involving context, entity relationship, dataflow, process structure, program structure and event-dependent diagrams. Then specific methods are illustrated, including (amongst others) Yourdon, Jackson, Warnier-Orr, Nassi-Schneiderman and Petri-Net techniques. Later the specific design methodologies of Jackson Structured Design (JSD), Yourdon/Ward-Mellor, Mascot and HOOD are explained.

Formal methods for specification and design are becoming more and more important in critical real-time systems. Here the fundamentals of the subject are set out, together with a general look at VDM and Z. Simple examples are given to illustrate the basics of these techniques.

Another topic which has taken on much greater significance is that of high-level programming languages. To reflect this the requirements, importance and constructs of such languages for real-time systems are described in some detail. A survey of languages is given, together with a comparative assessment of Ada, C, Pascal and Modula-2. The role of assembly language programming is discussed.

The use of real-time operating systems and fast executives is spreading rapidly in the real-time field. A full chapter is given over to this, covering the basics of the subject, including scheduling, mutual exclusion, intertask communication and memory management. A brief review of standard silicon-based executives is given.

The last stage of the development process, that of producing debugged ROMmed code, is covered extensively. Software debugging on host and target systems, debugging in host/target combinations, the use of performance analysis tools, PROM programmers and emulators and microcomputer development systems are described.

Finally, the relevance and importance of system test and documentation is shown, from functional specification through module description and test operations to maintenance documents. The importance and implementation of configuration control methods are discussed.

HOW SHOULD THE BOOK BE READ?

If you are new to real-time microprocessor-based systems start with chapter 1. Then the following sequence is recommended:
Chapters 2, 3, 4, 5, 6, 10, 11, 12.
Chapters 4, 5, 6 and 10 have a basic unifying theme: software design principles and practices. Chapters 3 and 12 have much in common concerning requirements analysis and specification.
Chapters 7, 8, 9 and 11 are very much self-contained.

Glossary

ADC	Analogue-to-digital
ANSI	American National Standards Institute
APSE	Ada Project Support Environment
CASE	Computer-Aided Software Engineering
CORE	Controlled Requirements Expression
CP/M	Control Program Microcomputer
CP/M-86	Control Program Microcomputer/8086 version
CPU	Central Processing Unit
CT	Control Transformation
DAC	Digital-to-Analogue Converter
DDT	Dynamic Debugging Tool
DFD	Data Flow Diagram
DMA	Direct Memory Access
DOS	Disk Operating System
DP	Data Processing
DPT	Design Process Tree
DSD	Design Structure Diagram
DSP	Digital Signal Processor
DT	Data Transformation
EEPROM	Electrically Erasable Programmable Read-Only Memory
EPROM	UV Erasable ROM
ERD	Entity Relationship Diagram
FIFO	First-In First-Out
HCI	Human–Computer Interaction
HOOD	Hierarchial Object Oriented Design
HOOD-PDL	HOOD Program Design Language
IBM	International Business Machines
ICE	In-Circuit Emulator
IIH	Interactive Information Handling
I/O	Input–Output
IPSE	Integrated Project Support Environment
ISO	International Standards Organization

JSD	Jackson System Development
JSP	Jackson Structured Programming
MASCOT	Modular Approach to Software Construction, Operation and Test
MDS	Microcomputer Development System
MS-DOS	Microsoft DOS
MTBF	Mean Time Between Failures
MTTR	Mean Time To Repair
NMI	Non-Maskable Interrupt
ODS	Object Definition Skeleton
OED	*Oxford English Dictionary*
OOD	Object-Oriented Design
OPCS	Operation Control Structure
OS	Operating System
OTPROM	One-Time PROM
PC	Personal Computer
PD	Process Descriptor
PDF	Program Development Facility
PROM	Programmable Read-Only Memory
PSD	Program Structure Diagram
QA	Quality Assurance
RAM	Random Access Memory
RISC	Reduced Instruction Set Computer
ROM	Read-Only Memory
RTOS	Real-time Operating System
SBC	Single-Board Computer
S-H	Sample-Hold
SOR	Statement of Requirements
SP	Structured Programming
STD	State Transition Diagram
TCB	Task Control Block
TOD	Time-of-Day
VDM	Vienna Development Method
VDU	Visual Display Unit
YSM	Yourdon Structured Method

Chapter One

Real-time systems – setting the scene

Thirty years ago software development was widely seen as consisting only of programming. And this was regarded more as an art than a science (and certainly not as an engineering discipline). Perhaps that's why this period is associated with so many gloomy tales of project failure (Brooks, 1975). The industry matured. Along the way we had new languages, real design methods, and, in 1968, the distinction between computer science and software engineering.

The microprocessor arrived circa 1970 and set a revolution in motion. But experienced software people played little part in this. For, until the late 1970s, most developers of microcomputer software were electronic, electrical or control engineers. And they proceeded to make exactly the same mistakes as their predecessors. Now why didn't they learn from the experience of earlier workers? There were three main reasons for this. In the first place, there was little contact between electronic engineers (and the like) and computer scientists. In the second place, many proposed software design methods weren't suitable for real-time applications. Thirdly, traditional computer scientists were quite dismissive of the difficulties met by microprocessor systems designers. Because programs were small the tasks were trivial (or so it was concluded).

Over the years the industry has changed considerably. The driving force for this has been the need to:

- Reduce costs.
- Improve quality, reliability and safety.
- Reduce design, development and commissioning timescales.
- Design complex systems.
- Build complex systems.

Without this pressure for change the tools, techniques and concepts discussed in this book would probably still be academic playthings.

Early design methods can be likened to hand-crafting, while the latest ones are more like automated manufacture. But, as in any industry, it's no good automating the wrong tools; we have to use the right tools in the right place at the right time. This chapter lays the groundwork for later work by giving a general picture of real-time systems. It:

- Highlights the differences between traditional computer applications and real-time systems.

- Looks at the types of real-time systems met in practice.
- Describes the environmental and performance requirements of embedded real-time systems.
- Describes typical structures of modern microprocessor-based equipments.
- Shows, in general, how software design and development techniques are influenced by these factors.

The detailed features of modern software methods are covered in later chapters.

1.1   CATEGORIZING COMPUTER SYSTEMS

How are computer systems categorized? There are many answers to this, sometimes conflicting, sometimes overlapping. But if we use speed of response as the main criterion, then three general groups emerge:

- Batch: I don't mind when the computer results arrive, within reason (the time taken may be hours or even days in such systems).
- On-line: I would like the results within a fairly short time, typically a few seconds.
- Real-time: I need the results within a definite short time scale (typically milliseconds to seconds), otherwise the system just won't work.

Let's consider these in turn.

An example of a modern batch system is shown in Fig.1.1. Methods like this are used where computing resources are expensive and/or scarce. Here the user usually pre-processes all programs and information, perhaps storing data on a local computer. At some convenient time this job is passed over the data link to the remote site (normally a number of jobs are transmitted as a single group). When all jobs are finished the results are sent back to the originating site. Transmission times may be scheduled to use cheap rate periods if a public communication network is used.

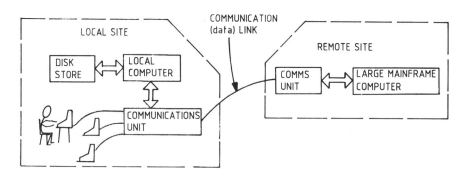

Fig.1.1 Modern batch system

On-line computer systems are widely used in banking, holiday booking and mail-order systems. Here, access to the system is made using terminals (Fig.1.2). Local processing of data isn't normally done in this instance. Instead, all transactions are handled by the central computer in a time-sliced fashion. Routing and access control is the responsibility of the front-end processor and local multiplexers.

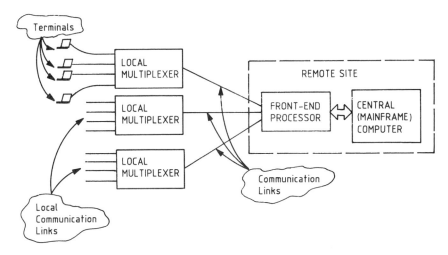

Fig.1.2 Typical on-line computer system

In the data processing (DP) field, 'on-line' and 'real-time' often have the same meaning. But on-line systems (sometimes called 'soft real-time' systems) aren't always time-critical. If the answer is a bit slow in coming, well, so what? Another trait of on-line applications is that response times depend on the amount of activity. All systems slow down as load builds up, sometimes seizing-up at peak times. For time critical – 'hard' real-time – systems this type of response is unacceptable (hence forward 'real-time' implies 'hard real-time'). As an example, consider the use of a computer to control the cruising speed of a car (Fig.1.3).

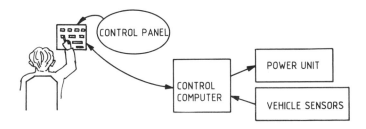

Fig.1.3 Real-time computer system

Here the driver dials in the desired cruising speed. The cruise control computer notes this, and compares it with the actual vehicle speed. If there is a difference, correcting signals are sent to the power unit. The vehicle will either speed up or slow down, depending on the desired response. Provided control is executed quickly the vehicle will be powered in a smooth and responsive manner. But if there is a significant delay in the computer, a kangaroo-like performance occurs. Clearly, in this case, the computer is worse than useless; it degrades the car's performance.

In this text 'real-time' is taken to imply time-bounded response constraints. Should computer responses exceed specific time bounds then performance degradation and/or malfunction results. So within this definition, batch and on-line systems are not considered to operate in real-time.

1.2   REAL-TIME COMPUTER SYSTEMS

1.2.1   General

From what's been said so far it can be seen that, for real-time systems, one factor is dominant: timeliness. This particular ingredient sets them apart from batch and on-line applications – but tells us little about the structure of such computer systems. So, before looking at modern real-time systems, it's worth digressing to consider the set-up of a typical mainframe/mini installation (Fig.1.4).

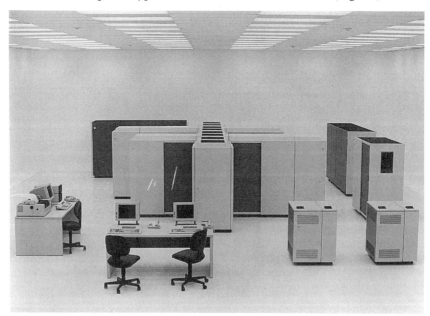

Fig.1.4 Mainframe computer installation – IBM 3090 Model with vector facility (reproduced with permission from IBM UK Ltd)

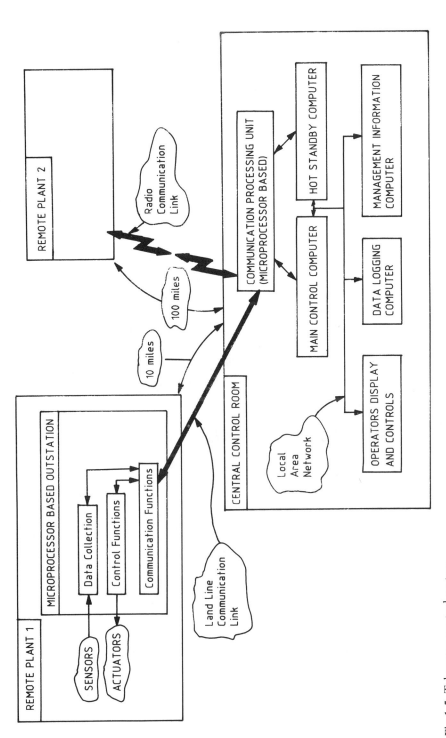

Fig.1.5 Telemetry control system

Walk into the DP department of almost any large organization and this is what you'll see. There will be a machine which may be used for a number of jobs. But for every one of them the same configuration is used; only the programs change. Often the physical environment is a controlled one, including air-conditioning. Peripheral devices include terminals, printers, plotters, disks, tapes, communication links; and little else. Common to most mainframe installations is the use of hundreds of megabytes of disk and tape storage. The installation itself is staffed and maintained by professional DP personnel. It requires maintenance in the broadest sense, including that for upgrading and modifying programs. In such a setting it's not surprising that **the computer** is the focus of attention and concern.

Fig.1.6 Rapier missile system (reproduced with permission from British Aerospace plc)

By contrast, real-time systems come in many types and sizes. The largest, in geographical terms, are telemetry control systems, Fig.1.5. Such systems are widely used in the gas, oil, water and electricity industries. They provide centralized control and monitoring of remote sites from a single control room. Smaller in size, but probably more complex in nature, are missile control systems, Fig.1.6. Another instance of a complex real-time application is the command and control systems of modern naval vessels (Fig.1.7). Moving down in size, the weapon management system of Fig.1.8 is a good example of a fast, highly reliable application. On the industrial scene, there are many installations which use computer-based standalone controllers. Typical of these is the unit of Fig.1.9. Finally, there are many uses of microcomputers for smaller, dedicated purposes. Applications include vending machines, printer controllers, anti-lock braking, burglar alarms; the list is endless.

Fig.1.7 Submarine control system console (reproduced with permission from Dowty Maritime Systems Ltd.)

Fig.1.8 Weapon management system (reproduced with permission from Computing Devices (Eastbourne) Ltd.)

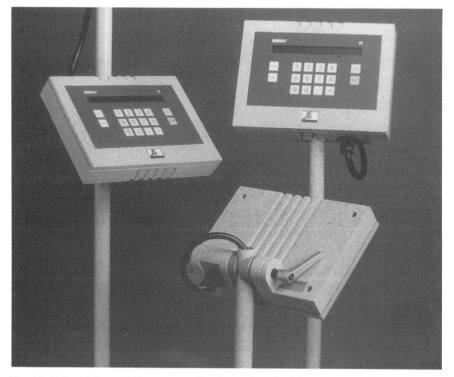

Fig.1.9 Industrial stand-alone controller (reproduced with permission from JB Micro-systems Ltd.)

These examples differ in many detailed ways from DP installations, such factors being discussed below. There are, though, two fundamental points. First, as stated above, the computer is seen to be merely one component of a larger system. Second, the user does not normally have the requirements – or facilities – to modify the programs on a day-to-day basis. In practice most users won't have the knowledge or skill to re-program the machine.

1.2.2   Characteristics of embedded systems

Embedded computers are defined to be those where the computer is used as a component within a system: not as a computing engine in its own right. This definition is the one which, at heart, separates embedded from non-embedded designs (note that, from now on, 'embedded' implicitly means 'real-time embedded').

Embedded systems are characterized (Fig.1.10) by:

- The environments they work in.
- The performance expected of them.
- Their interfaces to the outside world.

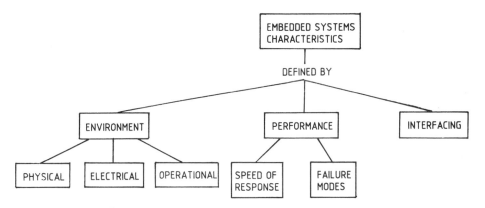

Fig.1.10 Embedded systems characteristics

(a)   Environmental aspects
Environmental factors may, at first glance, seem to have little bearing on software. Primarily they affect:

- Hardware design and construction.
- Operator interaction with the system.

But these, to a large extent, determine how the complete system works – and that defines the overall software requirements. Consider the physical effects of:

- Temperature.
- Shock and vibration.

- Humidity.
- Size limits.
- Weight limits.

The temperature ranges commonly met in embedded applications are shown in Fig.1.11. Many components used in commercial computers are designed to operate in the band 0–30 degrees centigrade. Electronic components aren't usually a problem. Items like terminals, display units, floppy and hard disks are the weaknesses. As a result, the embedded designer must either do without them or else provide them with a protected environment – which can be a costly solution.

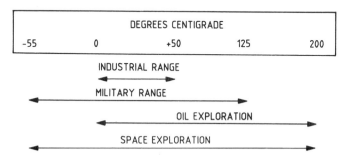

Fig.1.11 Typical temperature specifications

When the requirements to withstand shock, vibration and water penetration are added, the options narrow. For instance, the ideal way to re-program a system might be to update the boot floppy disk in the computer. But if we can't use a floppy disk in the first place on environmental grounds, then what?

Size and weight are two factors uppermost in the minds of many embedded systems designers. For vehicle systems, such as automobiles, aircraft, armoured fighting vehicles and submarines, they may be **the** crucial factors. Not much to do with software, you may think. But suppose a design requirement can only be met by using a single-chip micro (section 1.3.4). Further suppose that this device has only 256 bytes of Random Access Memory (RAM). How does that affect our choice of programming language?

The electrical environments of industrial and military systems are not easy to work in. Yet most systems are expected to cope with extensive power supply variations in a predictable manner. To handle problems like this we may have to resort to defensive programming techniques (chapter 2). Program malfunction can result from electrical interference; again, defensive programming is needed to handle this. A further complicating factor in some systems is that the available power may be limited. This won't cause difficulties in small systems. But if your software needs 10 Megabytes of dynamic RAM to run in, the power system designers are going to face problems.

Let's now turn to the operational environmental aspects of embedded systems. Normally we expect that when the power is turned on the system starts up safely and correctly. It should do this every time, **and** without any operator intervention. Conversely, when the power is turned off, the system should also behave safely. What we design for are 'fit and forget' functions.

In many instances embedded systems have long operational lives, perhaps from ten to thirty years. Often it is required to upgrade the equipment a number of times in its lifetime. So, the software itself will also need upgrading. This aspect of software, its maintenance, may well affect how we design it in the first place.

(b) Performance
Two particular factors are important here:

- How fast does a system respond?
- When it fails, what happens?

(i) The speed of response
All required responses are time critical (although these may vary from milliseconds to seconds). Therefore the designer should predict the delivered performance of the embedded system. Unfortunately, with the best will in the world, it may not be possible to give 100% guarantees. The situation is complicated because there are two distinct sides to this issue – both relating to the way tasks are processed by the computer.

Case one concerns demands to run jobs at regular, pre-defined intervals. A typical application is that of closed-loop digital controllers having fixed, preset sampling rates. This we'll define to be a 'synchronous' task event (synchronous with some real-time clock – Fig.1.12).

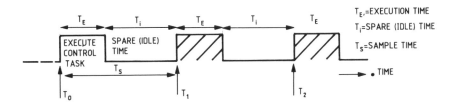

Fig.1.12 Computer loading – single synchronous task

Case two occurs when the computer must respond to (generally) external events which occur at random ('asynchronous'). And the event must be serviced within a specific maximum time period. Where the computer handles only synchronous events, response times can be determined reasonably well. This is also true where only **one** asynchronous event drives the system (a rare event) Fig.1.13.

When the system has to cope with a number of asychronous events, estimates are difficult to arrive at. But by setting task priorities, good estimates of worst case performance **can** be deduced (Fig.1.14).

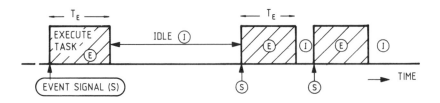

Fig.1.13 Computer loading – single asynchronous task

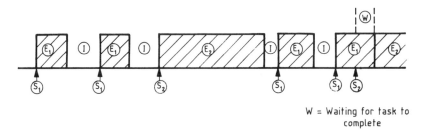

W = Waiting for task to complete

Fig.1.14 Computer loading – multiple asynchronous tasks

Where we get into trouble is in situations which involve a mixture of synchronous and asynchronous events – which is what we normally have in real-time designs. Much thought and skill are needed to deal with the response requirements of synchronous and asynchronous tasks when using just one processor.

(ii) Failures and their effects

All systems go wrong at some time in their lives. It may be a transient condition or a hard failure; the cause may be hardware or software or a combination of both. It really doesn't matter; accept that it **will** happen. What we have to concern ourselves with are:

- The consequences of such faults and failures.
- Why the problem arose in the first place.

Because a system can tolerate faults without sustaining damage doesn't mean that such performance is acceptable. Nuisance tripping out of a large piece of plant, for instance, is not going to win many friends. **All** real-time software must therefore be designed in a professional manner to handle all foreseen problems, that is, 'exception' handling (an exception is defined here to be an error or fault (chapter 2) which produces program malfunction. It may originate within the program itself or be due to external factors). If, on the other hand, software packages are bought-in, their quality must be carefully assessed. Recently one well-known personal computer operating system was seriously proposed for use in real-time applications. Yet users of this system often experience unpredictable behaviour, including total system hang-up. Could this really be trusted for plant control and similar applications?

In other situations we may not be able to cope with unrectified system faults. Three options are open to us. In the first, where no recovery action is possible, the system is put into a fail-safe condition. In the second, the system keeps on working, but with a reduced service. This may be achieved, say, by reducing response times or by servicing only the 'good' elements of the system. Such systems are said to offer 'graceful degradation' in their response characteristics. Finally, for fault-tolerant operation, full and safe performance is maintained in the presence of faults.

(c) Interfacing

The range of devices which interface to embedded computers is extensive. It includes sensors, actuators, motors, switches, display panels, serial communication links, parallel communication methods, analogue-to-digital converters, digital-to-analogue converters, voltage-to-frequency converters, pulse-width modulated controllers, and so on. Signals may be analogue (d.c. or a.c.) or digital; voltage, current or frequency encoding methods may be used. In anything but the smallest of systems, hardware size and cost is dominated by the interfacing electronics. This has a profound effect on system design strategies concerning processor replication and exception handling.

When the processor itself is the major item in a system, fitting a back-up to cope with failures is feasible and sensible. Using this same approach in an input-output (I/O) dominated system makes much less sense (and introduces much complexity).

Conventional exception handling schemes are usually concerned with detecting internal (program) problems. These include stack overflow, array bound violations and arithmetic overflow. However, for most real-time systems a new range of problems has to be considered. These relate to factors such as sensor failures, illegal operator actions, program malfunction induced by external electrical interference, etc. Detecting such faults is one thing; deciding what to do subsequently can be an even more difficult problem. Exception-handling strategies need very careful consideration to avoid system or environmental damage (or worse – injury or death) when faults are encountered.

1.3   THE COMPUTING ELEMENTS OF REAL-TIME SYSTEMS

1.3.1   Overview

The most commonly-used computing device in modern real-time systems is either a microprocessor or one of its derivatives. Currently there are three distinct groups within the micro field: the microprocessor, the microcomputer and the specialized computing machine (Fig.1.15). To use these effectively the software designer should have a good understanding of their features. After all, what might be the best design solution using one type may be inappropriate (or even unusable) on a different one.

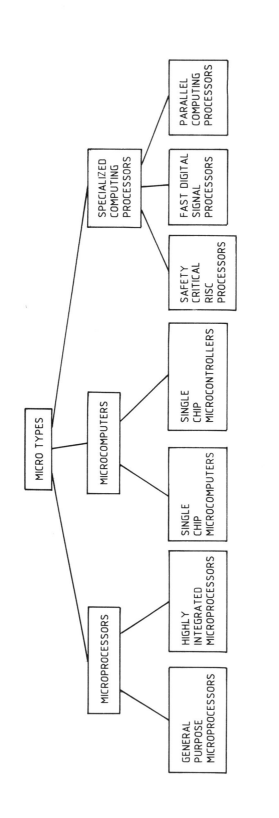

Fig.1.15 Microprocessor based computing elements of real-time systems

1.3.2   General purpose microprocessors

General purpose microprocessors are the largest single group, including the well-known Zilog Z80 and Z8000, Intel XX86, Motorola 680XX and the National 32XXX series processors. Bit slice processors such as the AMD 29000 also belong to this category.

By itself the processor is only one element within the microcomputer system. To turn it into a computing machine certain essential elements need to be added (Fig.1.16). The program code is carried in read-only memory (ROM), mostly in ultra-violet erasable programmable ROM (EPROM). This is a non-volatile device which normally needs to be removed from the computer for erasure and re-programming. However, where in-circuit re-programming is required, code is located in electrically erasable programmable ROM (EEPROM). When large production quantities are concerned, mask-programmable devices are used. In this case the program is set in the memory by the chip manufacturer; as such it is unalterable. Nowadays this market sector usually uses single chip microcomputers rather than general purpose ones.

All data which is subject to change is located in read-write or random access memory (a confusing title, as almost all memory locations can be accessed randomly). This includes program variables, stack data, process descriptors and dynamic data structures.

The final element is the address decoder unit. Its function is to identify the element being accessed by the processor.

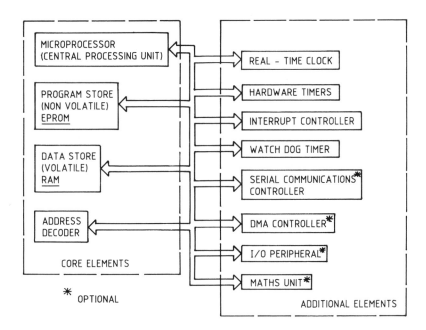

Fig.1.16 Elements of a microcomputer system

Taken together, these items form the heart of the microcomputer. However, to make it usable at all, extra elements need to be added. For a real-time computer the following are essential:

- Interrupt controller.
- Real-time clock.
- Hardware timers.
- Watchdog timer.

Items which should also be considered at the design stage include:

- Serial communications controller.
- Direct Memory Access (DMA) controller.
- Input-Output (I/O) peripheral.
- Maths unit.

These may be essential in some systems but not in others.

(a) Interrupt controller

As pointed out earlier, real-time systems must support both synchronous and asynchronous tasks. In most designs guaranteed response times are obtained by using interrupts.

(b) Real-time clock

The function of the real-time clock is to provide a highly accurate record of elapsed time. It is normally used in conjunction with an interrupt function. Real-time clocks shouldn't be confused with calendar clocks (although they may be used for calendar functions). When an operating system is incorporated within the software the clock acts as the basic timing element (the 'tick').

(c) Hardware timers

Accurate timing, especially that involving long time periods, cannot normally be done in software. Without the timing support of the tick in the operating system, hardware timers have to be used. Even where an operating system is used, these timers provide great flexibility. Generally these are software programmable (Fig.1.17), both in terms of timing and modes of operation (e.g. square-wave generation, 'one-shot' pulse outputs and retriggerable operation).

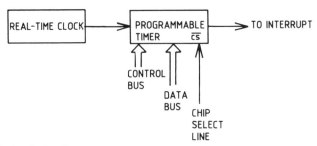

Fig.1.17 Timing in hardware

(d) Watchdog timer

The purpose of the watchdog timer is to act as the last line of defence against program malfunction. It normally consists of a retriggerable monostable or one-shot timer, activated by program command (Fig.1.18).

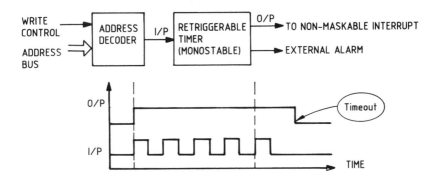

Fig.1.18 Watchdog timer

Each time the timer is addressed it is retriggered, the output staying in the 'normal' state. If for any reason it isn't retriggered then time-out occurs, and the output goes into alarm conditions. The usual course of action is to then generate a non-maskable interrupt (NMI), so setting a recovery program into action. In some instances external warnings are also produced. In others, especially digital control systems, warnings are produced and the controller then isolated from the controlled process.

Address decoding of the watchdog timer is, for critical systems, performed over all bits of the address. In these circumstances the address is a unique one; hence retriggering by accident is virtually eliminated.

(e) Serial communications controller

The overall system structure may require the use of a serial communication network, as in distributed control applications. Even where this isn't needed, it is well worthwhile to design in an RS232 compatible communication channel (EIA, 1969). This can be used as a major aid in the development and debugging of the application software (chapter 11).

(f) DMA controller

The DMA controller (Fig.1.19) is used where data has to be moved about quickly and/or in large amounts. Typical data transfer rates are in excess of 1 MByte/sec. DMA techniques are widely used in conjunction with bulk memory storage devices such as floppy and hard disks. For most real-time systems they are used where high-speed serial communication links (>1 MBit/sec) have to be supported.

In normal circumstances the controller acts just as any other slave device, being controlled by the processor. However, when a DMA request is generated by a peripheral device, control is taken over by the DMA controller – the micro being disconnected from the system. Precise details of data transfer operations are usually programmed into the controller by the micro.

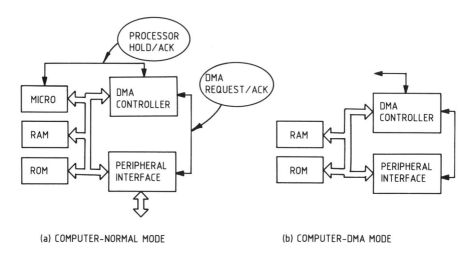

(a) COMPUTER-NORMAL MODE   (b) COMPUTER-DMA MODE

Fig.1.19 DMA operation

(g) I/O peripheral

I/O peripherals are used either as controllers or as interfacing devices. When used as a controller their function is to offload the I/O processing, control and high-speed transfer work from the processor itself. The Intel implementation, the 8089 I/O processor (Intel, 1985(a)), may be configured to share all the resources of the main processor (Fig.1.20). In other words, it works in parallel with the micro itself, using system resources as and when required.

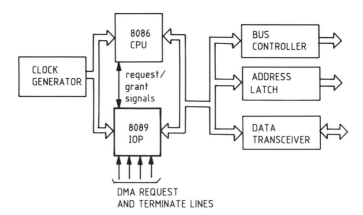

Fig.1.20 Implementation of an intelligent I/O controller

In other applications I/O devices are used to provide compact, simple and low-cost interfaces between the processor and peripheral equipment. Input/output pins are user programmable to set up the desired connections to such equipment. These interface chips function as slave devices to the processing unit (Fig.1.21). Typical of such devices is the Intel 8255 Programmable Peripheral Interface (Intel, 1985(a)).

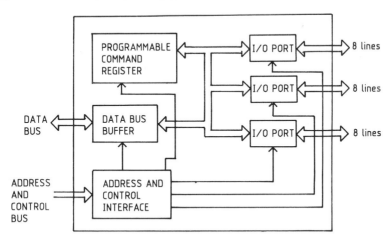

Fig.1.21 I/O interface peripheral

(h) Maths unit

Mathematical operations, once we get beyond 8-bit working, are very time consuming. This is especially true of floating point functions, where the words may be as long as 80 bits. In order to speed up computations the system may be augmented by a special maths computing unit. As with the I/O processor, two distinct methods can be used. The first, typified by the Intel 8087 (Intel, 1985(a)), is to incorporate a co-processor. This works alongside (in parallel) with the micro, responding to program instructions as required. When high level language programming is used, 8087 instructions are generated automatically by the compiler. This considerably simplifies the programming task as no explicit 8087 instructions are used in the source code.

The second method is to use a maths chip as a slave processor. This is treated as a standard peripheral by the micro, all operations being determined by instructions from the processor itself. Arithmetic operations need to be explicitly handled by the programmer. One widely used device of this type is the Intel 8231 Arithmetic Processing Unit (Intel, 1985(a)). In general, the trade-offs are cost, speed and flexibility. It is important to realize that co-processors are designed to integrate with specific microprocessors (e.g. 8087/8086, 80287/286, 68881/68020, 68882/68030). They are not stand-alone devices. In contrast, slave processors may be used with virtually any micro.

1.3.3   Highly integrated microprocessors

Highly integrated processors are those which contain many of the standard elements of a microcomputer system on a single chip. Typical of these are the Intel 80186, 80188 and the Hitachi 64180 (Fig.1.22). Note this doesn't contain memory devices (RAM or ROM): hence it doesn't qualify for the title 'microcomputer'.

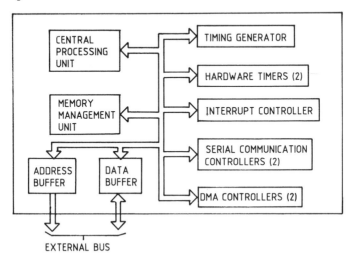

Fig.1.22 Highly integrated processor – Hitachi 64180

A comparison of Fig.1.16 and Fig.1.22 shows just what can be achieved on one chip. Naturally, such processors are more expensive than the basic general purpose device. However, the integration of many devices onto one chip usually reduces overall system cost. Moreover, it makes a major impact on board-packing densities. It also reduces manufacturing and test costs. In short, these are highly suited for use in embedded systems design.

1.3.4   Single chip microcomputers

The architecture of single chip micros is such that complete microcomputers can be implemented without using additional components. Using a single-chip solution reduces the:

- Package count.
- Size.
- Overall costs.

One widely used device of this type is the Intel 8751 microcomputer (Fig.1.23).

By now all the on-chip devices will be familiar. Note that interfacing to the outside world may be carried out through the I/O port sub-system. This is a highly flexible structure which, in smaller systems, minimizes component count. But with only 4 kBytes of EPROM and 128 bytes of RAM, it is clearly intended for use in small systems (the memory size can, of course, be extended by using external devices).

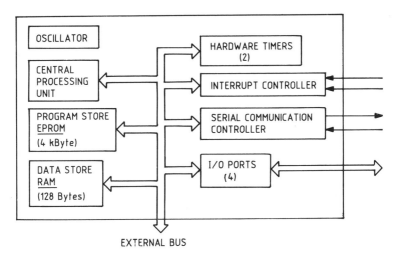

Fig.1.23 Single chip microcomputer – Intel 8751

1.3.5   Single chip microcontrollers

Microcontrollers are derivatives of microcomputers, but aimed specifically at the embedded control market. Like the single chip microcomputer, they are designed to provide all computing functions in a single package. The interfacing hardware, internal register structure and the instruction set are usually optimized for use within fast real-time systems. An example of such a device is the Intel 80196 microcontroller, Fig.1.24 (Intel, 1985(b)).

From the hardware point of view, the most obvious additions relate to I/O interfacing. Analogue signal handling is provided by an on-chip data acquisition sub-system. This consists of a 10-bit analogue-to-digital converter (ADC), a sample-hold (S-H) module and an 8-channel analogue multiplexer. Standard switch control functions are available via I/O ports; additionally, pulse-width modulated output control signals may be generated by the controller. An independent timer sub-system is implemented (the 'high-speed I/O') to support specialized real-time requirements. These include:

- Pulse and frequency measurements (inputs).
- Pulse output control (output).
- ADC conversion synchronization (internal).
- Hardware support for software delays (internal).

The interrupt structure is comprehensive, handling up to 21 sources, including eight external devices.

The on-chip ROM size is 8 kBytes, with 232 bytes of RAM space available for variable data.

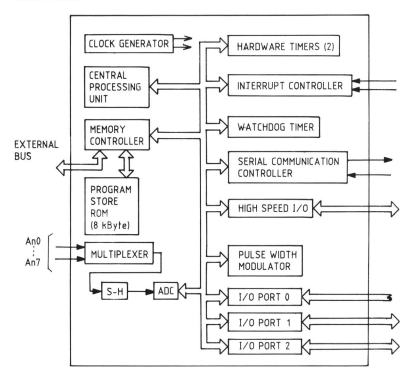

Fig.1.24 Single chip microcontroller – Intel 80196

1.3.6   Specialized computing processors

Many types of specialized processors exist. Those most frequently met in practice are used for:

- Safety-critical computing (using Reduced Instruction Set Computers – RISC).
- Parallel computing.
- Fast digital signal processing.

(a)   RISC for safety-critical systems
Examples of safety-critical applications are aircraft fly-by-wire control, nuclear reactor systems, mine-winding gear and the like. Although these systems are quite diverse they have one feature in common. Should anything go wrong the results may be catastrophic.

Many safety-critical systems are relatively simple and straightforward. Where digital controllers are used, the computing requirements are quite modest. In normal circumstances the single chip micro would be the best device to use in the design. Unfortunately, these are considered to have significant drawbacks, including excessive complexity, incomplete specifications and little inbuilt handling of exceptions. On the other hand, with a RISC machine, it is possible to formally (i.e. mathematically) verify its performance. For this reason, RISC architecture is preferred in safety-critical applications.

One microprocessor designed for such applications is the VIPER, the Verifiable Integrated Processor for Enhanced Reliability (Kershaw, 1985), Fig.1.25. Its main features are:

- The processor logic can be described in formal mathematical terms.
- It is easily testable.
- Floating-point operations are excluded on the grounds of complexity, inexactitude and resistance to formal verification. Instead, 32-bit integer arithmetic is used.
- Interrupts are excluded, as such programs make formal verification virtually impossible. All task handling is done via polling techniques.
- Dynamic memory allocation is prohibited.

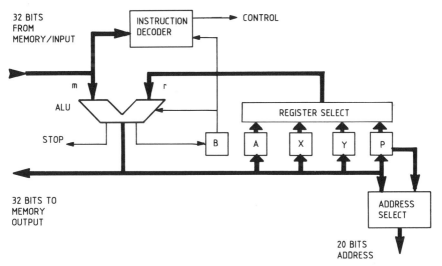

Fig.1.25 RISC processors – the VIPER

(b) Parallel computing processors

All the processors described up to now have one thing in common; they use the von Neumann structure. This has proved to be fundamentally sound and durable (hence its widespread use). However, by its very nature this architecture has a built-in bottleneck in the processing structure. To achieve very high throughputs different structures must be used, the most common approach being to parallel up a number of computing elements.

One microprocessor which has been designed specifically to tackle this problem is the Transputer (INMOS, 1986). Its basic structure and connection within a parallel processing array are shown in Fig.1.26.

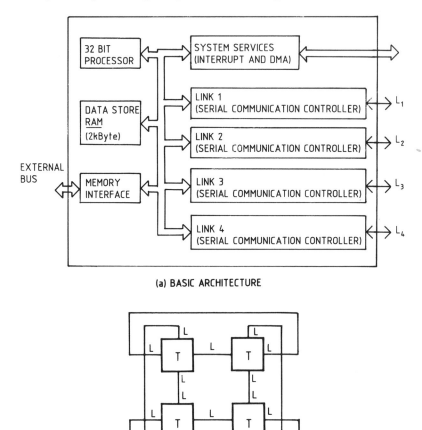

(a) BASIC ARCHITECTURE

(b) MULTIPROCESSOR ARRAY

Fig.1.26 Parallel computing processor – the Transputer

Central to the design is the provision of four fast (20 MBits/sec) serial communication links. These act as the connecting channels within the multiprocessor structure, giving rise to a loosely coupled architecture. High-speed maths operations, low latency (input to output delay) and fast process switching is achieved through the use of a 32-bit RISC architecture. Note that it may also function as a high performance, stand-alone processor.

For single processor operation, programming may be done using conventional languages. However, for multiprocessor designs, the language should inherently support the parallel structure of the system.

(c)   Fast digital signal processors

There are numerous applications which require the use of fast processing of analogue signals. These include speech processing, instrumentation, tele-communications, radar, sonar and control systems. In the past such processing has been done using analogue techniques. But because of the disadvantages of analogue processors (filters) designers have been moving over to digital techniques. The requirement here is for relatively low-cost devices which have extremely high throughputs. This has resulted in the Digital Signal Processor (DSP), optimized for digital filtering calculations. Such calculations are typified by sets of multiply and add (accumulate) instructions, the so-called 'sum of products' computation.

To achieve high processing speeds the basic computing engine is organized around a high-speed multiplier/accumulator combination (Fig.1.27). In these designs the von Neumann structure is replaced by the Harvard architecture, providing separate paths for instructions and data. The system form shown in Fig.1.27 is fairly typical of digital signal processors. The Texas Instruments TMS320 range of DSPs are representative of this type of machine (Texas Instruments, 1986). Obviously, specific details vary from processor to processor; for a general overview of the types available and their structures see Shaw (1987).

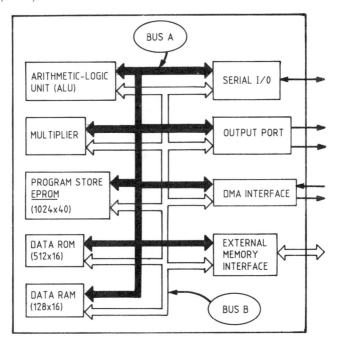

Fig.1.27 Digital signal processor structure

Programming DSPs is a demanding task, especially as few high-level language compilers are available for these. The instruction sets are optimized to perform fast and efficient arithmetic. Among these instructions are those which invoke complex multipurpose operations. Added to this is the need to produce compact and efficient code if the whole program is to fit into the on-chip ROM. And finally, there is the need to handle extensive fixed-point computations without running into overflow problems. It has been said that, in DSP programming, '90% of the effort goes into worrying about where the decimal point is' (Dettmer, 1986).

1.4   SOFTWARE FOR REAL-TIME APPLICATIONS — SOME GENERAL COMMENTS

In the following chapters the total design process for real-time systems is described. We'll be looking for answers to questions such as:

- What needs to be done?
- How should we specify these needs?
- What methods do we use to satisfy the system specifications?
- How can we show that the design solution is correct?
- How do we get programs to work correctly in the target itself?

Before doing this, let's consider some general problems met in real-time systems work, and also dispel a few myths along the way. Don't believe everything you read – question any unsupported assertions (even in this book).

The quotations used below have been made (in print) by experienced software practitioners.

'For real-time systems . . . programs tend to be large, often on the order of tens of thousands or even of hundreds of thousands of lines of code.' This generalization is wrong, especially for embedded systems. Here programs are frequently small, having object code sizes in the range 2–40 Kbyte. One major mistake frequently made by computer scientists is to apply the rules of the large system to that of the small one.

'At the specification stage . . . **all** the functional requirements, performance requirements and design constraints **must** be specified'. In the world of real-time system design this is an illusion. Ideas like these have come about mostly from the DP world. There, systems such as stock control, accounting, management reporting methods and the like **can** be specified in their entirety before software design commences. In contrast, specifications for real-time systems tend to follow an evolutionary development. We may start with an apparently clear set of requirements. At a much later stage (usually some time after the software has been delivered) the final, clear, but quite different, specifications are agreed.

'Software costs dominate . . .'. Not necessarily true. It all depends on the size of the job, the role of software within the total system, and the number of items to be manufactured.

'Software is one of the most complex things known to man . . . Hundreds of man-years to develop the system XX . . .'. Well, yes, software is complex. But let's not go overboard about it. Just consider that the development of a new nuclear propulsion system for submarines took more than 5000 man-years (at a very conservative estimate). And it involved large teams, skilled in many engineering disciplines, and based at various geographically separate sites. Is this an 'easy' task compared with software development?

'Software, by its nature, is inherently unreliable'. I think the assumption behind this is that software is a product of thought, and isn't bounded by natural physical laws. Therefore there is a much greater chance of making mistakes. This is rather like saying that, as circuit theory underpins electronic design, hardware designs are intrinsically less prone to errors. Not so. Delivered hardware is generally free of fault because design, development and manufacture is (or should be) rigorous, formal and systematic. By contrast, software has for far too long been developed in a sloppy manner in cottage industry style. The industry has lacked design formality, has rarely used software design tools, and almost completely ignored the use of documentation and configuration control mechanisms.

The final point for consideration concerns the knowledge and background needed by embedded systems software designers. Until quite recently there has been an intimate bond between microprocessor hardware and software. It was (and in many cases, still is) essential to have a very good understanding of the hardware: especially so for the I/O activities. So, most software designers are typically electronic engineers with a knowledge of software, or software engineers with a knowledge of electronics. Pure software graduates have been virtually locked out of this area of work. Now, though, we are coming up against a shortage of designers with the right mix of skills. Moreover, larger and larger jobs are being implemented using microprocessors. As a result of all this activity software design methods are changing. Now the design philosophy is to provide a 'software base' for handling hardware and system specific tasks. This is sometimes called 'foundation software', which is quite an apt term. Programmers can then build their application programs on the foundation software, needing only a minimal understanding of the system hardware. The greatest impact of this has been in the area of real-time operating systems (chapter 9).

REFERENCES

Brooks, F.P. (1975), *The Mythical Man-Month*, Addison-Wesley, ISBN 0–201–00650–2.

Dettmer, R. (1986), Digital signal processors, *Electronics and Power*, February, pp124–128.

EIA (1969), Interface between data terminal equipment and data communication equipment employing serial binary data interchange, *EIA Standard RS-232*, Electronics Industries Association, Engineering Dept., Washington DC 20006.

INMOS (1986), *The Transputer Family*, product information booklet 72 TRN 05600, March, INMOS Ltd., Almondsbury, Bristol BS12 4SQ, UK.

Intel (1985(a)), *Microsystems Components Handbook – Microprocessors and Peripherals*, Intel Corporation, 3065 Bowers Avenue, Santa Clara, CA 95051.

Intel (1985(b)), *Microcontroller Handbook*, Intel Corporation, 3065 Bowers Avenue, Santa Clara, CA 95051.

Kershaw, J. (1985), Safe control systems and the VIPER microprocessor, *RSRE Memorandum No. 3805*, Royal Signals and Radar Establishment, Malvern, Worcs., UK.

Shaw, C. (1987), Choosing a digital signal processor, *Electronic Product Design*, November, pp41, 42.

Texas Instruments (1986), Digital signal processing applications with the TMS 320 family – theory, algorithms and implementations, *Application Note*, Texas Instruments, Bedford MK41 7PA, UK.

Chapter Two

The search for dependable software

Many steps have to be taken to combat the problems of poor software. Proper system specification, defined design methods, high-level language support and good development tools all contribute toward a solution. But to appreciate their use (instead of merely knowing what they do), we must understand what they aim to achieve. To answer that we need to know where, why and how software problems arise. Then at least we can define the features of software and software design which can eliminate such problems.

The aims of this chapter are to:

- Show where, why and how software errors arise.
- Explain why, in the real world, development of fault-free systems cannot be achieved.
- Distinguish between correct, reliable and safe software.
- Establish that dependable software should be a primary design aim.
- Highlight the importance and influence of the software operating environment.
- Establish the basics of good software.
- Describe the need for, and use of, defensive programming.
- Show that, in a professional software design environment, codes of practice are a key element.

2.1 WHAT DO WE WANT IN OUR SOFTWARE?

In an ideal world, what do we look for in our software? There are many answers to this question, but, more than anything else, one stands out: the production of totally fault-free software. We look for that because, we reason, given such software, our systems should work exactly as planned. But will they? Unfortunately not necessarily so, as will be shown later. When designing software a total system view must be taken. There are too many opportunities to get designs and implementations wrong; it isn't just confined to the code writing stage.

In this chapter we'll first look at the root problems of such errors. Then we'll define the qualities of software which attempt to eliminate these. One must be realistic about them, however. Given the current state of design tools it is impossible to guarantee the delivery of fault-free systems (on a personal note, I believe that totally fault-free systems are a myth).

Therefore, if fault-free systems are unattainable, what should we aim for? A different, realistic, criterion is needed, that of 'dependable software', having the qualities shown in Fig.2.1.

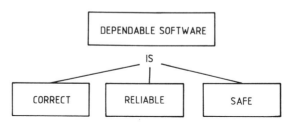

Fig.2.1 Qualities of dependable software

Many people, when asked to define fault-free software, talk about 'correct' software. But what **is** correct software? *The Dictionary of Computing* (1984) defines correctness as 'the static property that a program is consistent with its specification'. In other words, if we check the code against the job specification, it does exactly what is asked of it.

On the other hand, reliability is concerned with the intended **function** of the system. The IEEE definition of software reliability is 'the extent to which a program can be expected to perform its intended function with required precision' (IEEE, 1979). That is, it defines how well a program carries out the required task when asked to do so. Thus it is a measure of the dynamic performance of the software.

Can a correct program be unrealiable? Conversely, can an incorrect program be reliable? The answer in each case is, surprisingly, **yes.** Consider the first question. Let's suppose that a program has been checked out statically and shown to be correct. Subsequently, when installed in a system, it behaves in an unexpected way. In this situation it hasn't performed its intended function. So the program is deemed to be unreliable. This really means that the design specification wasn't right in the first place.

Now let's turn to the second one. Assume that we've written a program to implement a control algorithm in a closed loop control system. This should produce results with a given, predefined, accuracy. If it fails to do this then clearly it is incorrect. Yet, if the errors are small, the control loop will work quite well. In this instance it performs its intended function satisfactorily. Thus the program is deemed to be reliable.

The terms 'safe software' and 'reliable software' are often used loosely to mean the same thing. They are, in fact, very different. In extreme cases, the aims of reliability and safety may conflict. Where software is designed with safety in mind, it is concerned with the **consequences** of failure. Such consequences usually involve injury or death and/or material damage. Reliability is concerned with failures *per se*. A system can be 100% reliable, yet be totally unsafe. And, as a ludicrous example, a system can be 100% safe but 0% reliable if it is never switched on.

All designs aim for high reliability (it goes without saying that we would like our programs to be correct as well). By contrast the emphasis put on safeness depends on each particular task (various measures of 'safeness' are given in reference IEE88). Any real system will throw up a fault at some point in its life. Therefore, we need to decide at the design stage exactly **how** the system should behave when faults occur: that is, fail-hard, fail-soft or fail-safe (Fig.2.2).

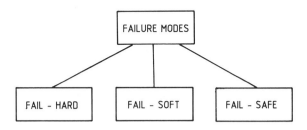

Fig.2.2 System failure modes

Hard failures are those which, while they persist, may well cause the whole system to grind to a halt. These problems are often met in personal computers. In such applications they usually don't cause damage (though they are extremely irritating). This failure mode may well be acceptable in low-cost software.

Fail-soft systems are designed to keep on working with faults present, but with reduced system performance. For instance, some automobiles use simplified back-up engine management systems to cater for failures of the main unit.

Fail-safe systems make no effort to meet normal operational requirements. Instead they aim to limit the danger or damage caused by the fault. Such techniques are applicable to aircraft weapon stores management systems, nuclear reactor control equipment and the like.

Most real-time software needs some attention paid to its safety aspects. In many applications hard software failures are tolerable because external devices are used to limit their effects. For more stringent functions, or where external back-ups aren't available, fail-soft methods are used. Finally, fail-safe methods are generally used only in safety-critical operations, a small but important area of real-time systems design. These account for less than 1% of all the real-time software in service in the UK (based on personal research).

On a last note, although we talk about 'unsafe software', in fact only hardware can do physical damage.

2.2   SOFTWARE ERRORS

2.2.1   Overview

In this text a software error is defined to be 'any feature of a program which produces a system malfunction'. This is a very broad definition, really quite unfair to software developers. In many instances of system misbehaviour the code is blameless; but we still talk of 'faulty software'. What it does, though, is emphasize that it isn't sufficient to eliminate errors at the software design stage; other factors need to be taken into account (Fig.2.3). These are looked at in more detail below.

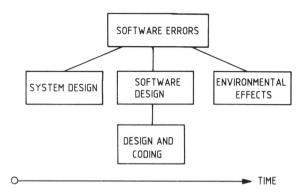

Fig.2.3 Types of software errors

2.2.2   System design errors

System design takes place right at the front end of a project. Quite often software engineers are excluded from this stage. Many system designers have the attitude of 'well, we'll go out and buy a box to control the plant (once we've worked out how to put it together)'. Mistakes made here usually show only when system trials begin (or worse still, when the system is in service). It doesn't matter whether we're talking about mechanical, electrical or software designs; getting it wrong at this point can have dramatic consequences. For instance, on one new type of Royal Navy destroyer the radar mast was located just aft of the funnel. During sea trials the paint burnt off the mast. Only then was it realized that the design was only suitable for steam propulsion, not gas turbines (as fitted).

During the system design phase the designer has to make many assumptions about the system and its operational environment. These form the basis for the specification against which the software is designed. If this is wrong then everything else from then on is also wrong (no matter how many times the program is validated and verified). The following examples illustrate this:

'A wing-mounted missile on an F18 aircraft failed to separate from the launcher after ignition because a computer program signalled the missile retaining mechanism to close before the rocket had built up sufficient thrust to clear the missile from the wing. An erroneous assumption had been made about the length of time that this would take. The aircraft went violently out of control' (Leveson, 1986).
'HMS Sheffield radar system identified an incoming Argentinian Exocet missile as non-Soviet and thus friendly. No alarm was raised. The ship was sunk with considerable loss of life' (SEN1, 1983).

The moral for the software designer is to make the software flexible because you never know when you'll need to change it.

2.2.3   Design and coding errors

Design and coding errors fall into four categories, Fig.2.4.

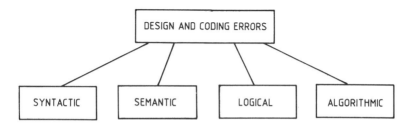

Fig.2.4 Errors in the design process

In software design, a concept is translated into computer code without any sign of a physical product. In essence it is an intellectual effort by the designer. Thus errors introduced at this point must be due to faulty thinking about the problem. The only way we can catch mistakes of this type is to force the designer to externalize his thinking (a rather up-market way of saying 'get it out of him'). That is the essence of modern software design practices.

(a)   Syntax errors
The *Oxford English Dictionary* defines syntax to be 'the grammatical arrangement of words in speech or writing' (Fig.2.5).

In software terms, syntax is the definition and arrangement of program symbols that the computer will accept. Such symbols include program words and delimiters – semi-colons, full stops (periods), brackets, etc.

There are two distinct types of syntax error. In the first, the wrong symbol is used. In the second the symbol is used wrongly. As an example of the first suppose that, in a Modula-2 program, we write:

```
          VAR
      ShaftSpeed: INTEGER:
```

Here the final delimiter, ':', is incorrect. It should be ';'. Mistakes like this are, almost without exception, picked up by the compiler. So although they're frustrating, no damage is done.

However, consider writing

$$X = Y. . .$$

in a C program when what was wanted was:

$$X == Y . . . . .$$

Both are valid constructs; yet they produce quite different results. If it so happens that the statements are accepted by the compiler then the program is guaranteed to malfunction. This may not appear to be all that significant, except that:

> 'a misplaced comma in one NASA program sent a Voyager spacecraft
> towards Mars instead of Venus' (Hamilton, 1986).

Problems like these fall into the general category of 'errors of user intent'. They can be extremely difficult to identify because programs which contain them appear to be correct.

Fig.2.5 A problem of syntax

The best way to combat syntax errors is to use the right language for the job. This doesn't mean that one, and only one, language should be used. It's more a question of having the right basic features to support good design practices (discussed later). Nowadays, unless there are special reasons, code should be written in a modern high-level language (HLL). The text produced is compact and readable, two very good reasons for using such languages. Furthermore, the less we write, the fewer chances there are of making mistakes. And the less there is to read, the easier it is to grasp its meaning. On top of this, modern HLL compilers usually have powerful error-checking features. Executable code produced in this way should be syntactically quite trustworthy – but never forget that compilers themselves can have residual errors.

(b)   Semantic errors
Semantics 'relate to the meaning in language' (*Oxford English Dictionary*). Semantic errors (Fig.2.6) can arise in two ways. First, we may not properly understand what the software is supposed to do. So we end up translating the wrong solution into code. Second, we may understand the problem but translate it wrongly into code. This second point is the one most often talked about under the heading of semantic errors (the *Dictionary of Computing* defines these to be 'programming errors that arise from a misunderstanding of the meaning or effect of some construct in a programming language').

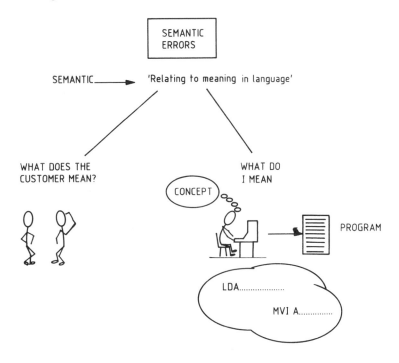

Fig.2.6 A problem of semantics

An example of the first type of mistake is that which resulted in an accident involving a chemical reactor (Kletz, 1982). Due to human and software problems a reactor overheated, discharging its contents into the atmosphere.

Afterwards, during the accident investigation, the system specifications were examined. In these the programmers were told if a fault occurred in the plant, they were to leave all controlled variables as they were and sound the alarm. But it was also found that they didn't properly understand this directive. Did this mean that the valve which controlled the flow of cooling water to the reactor should freeze its position? Or, should the temperature of the reactor itself be held steady? The systems engineers clearly thought they'd specified the second response. Unfortunately the programmers had done it the other way round.

Problems caused by not having a full and proper understanding of programming languages are very common. Mistakes are made mostly by inexperienced programmers. But they also crop up when software teams begin to use new programming languages. An example of such a mistake was made by a fairly experienced assembly language programmer when using an HLL for the first time. The design task was to produce a series of recursive filter algorithms, implemented as procedures. But because he didn't appreciate the difference between static and dynamic variables, these algorithms just refused to work.

Both problems described here are also 'errors of intent'. As pointed out earlier, these are extremely hard to catch before software is tested. To eliminate the first we need to set down an agreed design specification. And to do that we have to extract full and correct information from the system designers. **Then** we have to show them that we understand it.

Having a set specification helps us attack the second issue. From such specifications we can produce the source code. This can then be checked against the original requirement to verify that it is correct. In safety-critical systems we may have to use formal mathematical techniques in the verification process. The more complex the language the more likely it is that blunders will be made (and the longer it'll take to find them). Assembly language working certainly produces many more problems of this type compared with HLLs.

(c)   Logic errors

These are also errors of user intent, made during program design and coding phases (Fig.2.7). As a result these programs don't behave in a logically correct manner. This can show up in a number of ways. For instance, the program may appear to run correctly but keeps on giving the wrong answers. Doing post-checks instead of pre-checks leads to this. Forgetting to preset variables produces similar results; we may violate assumptions upon which the logic operations are built. In other cases systems hang-up as a result of carrying out illogical actions. Infinite loops and deadlocks in multi-processing/tasking are well known examples. Mistakes of logic aren't always found in test. And when they do show the results can be costly:

'Mariner 18 lost due to missing NOT statement in program' (SEN2).

It's important to realize that logical errors are easily made. And, when programs are coded in assembly language, the errors are quite difficult to detect before the test stage. Fundamentally this is due to the highly detailed nature of low-level coding methods. When using these it is almost impossible to see the **structure** of the logic. Hence it is difficult to spot logical errors just by reading through the source code. By contrast, when using a high-level language, such errors are less likely to be made in the first place; the inbuilt constructs ('while-do', 'repeat-until') force us to do the right thing. Even when mistakes **are** made they are much easier to find and correct because of improved program readability.

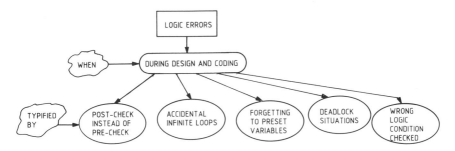

Fig.2.7 Logic errors – when and what

(d)   Algorithmic errors

These occur during mathematical operations (Fig.2.8), for a variety of reasons. In some situations basic mathematical rules are broken, as in trying to divide by zero. In other cases the capabilities of the computer system are exceeded. Every machine has limits on the size and range of its number system, affecting:

- The largest number which the machine can hold.
- The smallest number.
- The ratio of the largest to the smallest number which can be manipulated simultaneously.
- The degree of precision (resolution) of numbers.
- The range of values which input/output devices handle.

What are the effects of algorithmic errors? Here are some examples:

'A Shuttle laser experiment failed because the computer data was in nautical miles instead of feet' (SEN3).
'Gemini V splashed down 100 miles off target when the program used 360 degrees for the Earth's rotation in one day' (SEN4).
'The Vancouver Stock Exchange Index rose by 50% when two years of round-off errors were corrected' (SEN4).

Algorithmic errors are a significant factor in control system and signal processing work. When coding is done at assembler level it is a painstaking and time-consuming task. These tasks are much more controllable and testable when working in an HLL. But the designer still needs to understand fully the number system used by his machine.

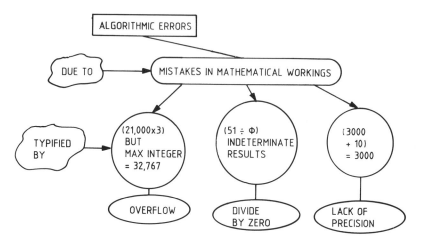

Fig.2.8 Algorithmic errors

2.2.4   Environmental factors

This is a broad-ranging topic because it concerns how software behaves within its normal working environment. Far too often designers regard software as something which is complete in itself. They forget that it is just one part of a larger process. And, in most real-time applications, this involves not only hardware but also humans. For such designs it's not good enough to produce software which is correct. We must also ensure that the system in which it is incorporated also works correctly.

These problems often surface for the first time when full system testing is carried out. In other cases they lie dormant for long periods until the right set of circumstances occurs; then they can strike catastrophically. There is **no** way that we can eliminate environmental problems at the design stage; there are just too many different ways in which they can occur (see below). All we can do is to minimize the number of potential trouble-spots by deep and extensive design analysis. It also helps, as a matter of sanity, to accept Murphy's law ('anything that can go wrong, will').

'A computer issued a "close weapons bay door" command on a B-1A aircraft at a time when a mechanical inhibit had been put in place in order to perform maintenance on the door. The "close" command was generated when someone in the cockpit punched the close switch on the control panel during a test. Two hours later, when maintenance was completed and the inhibit removed, the door unexpectedly closed. Luckily nobody was injured. The software was later altered to discard any commands not completed within a certain time frame, but this situation had never been considered during testing' (Frola and Miller).

'A mechanical malfunction in a fly-by-wire flight control system set up an accelerated environment for which the flight control computer was not programmed. The aircraft went out of control and crashed' (Frola and Miller).

'Just before the Apollo 11's moon landing, the software sent out an alarm indicating that it was overloaded with tasks and had to reset itself continually to service critical functions. The program was still functional, so the landing went ahead. Later it was found that an astronaut had mistakenly been instructed to turn on a sensor that sent a continuous stream of interrupts to the processor, causing the overload' (Hamilton).
'An F16 autopilot flipped the plane upside down whenever it crossed the equator' (SEN2). The fact that this occurred in a simulator doesn't lessen the gravity of the mistake.
'In one case, a 62 year old man died abruptly during treatment. Interference from the therapeutic microwaves had reset his pacemaker, driving his already injured heart to beat at 214 times a minute. It couldn't do it.' (SEN5).

2.2.5   Why do we get poor software?

There isn't a formal definition for 'poor' software. This term is meant to cover all aspects of the problem, including software which is:

- Incorrect.
- Unreliable.
- Unsafe.
- Late.
- Expensive.

The last two items are usually closely bound up with the first three.

What gives rise to poor software? Many answers to this question will by now be obvious. What doesn't always show is that, frequently, more fundamental problems exist. There are three general aspects to this (Fig.2.9).

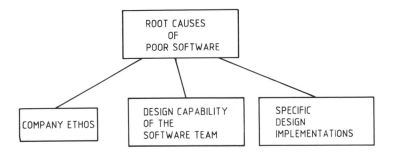

Fig.2.9 Poor software – the reasons

(a)   Company ethos
This is all tied up with how software activities are understood at a senior level within a firm. Basically, the characteristic spirit of a company determines how well jobs are done. A company with negative attitudes has:

- Poor senior management response to problems.
- Lack of formal and rigorous company software design and documentation procedures.

- Inadequate tools.
- Lack of professionalism and discipline in the software team.

If senior management doesn't (or doesn't want to) understand the needs of software development then poor software becomes endemic. No effort is made to bring formality and rigour into the design and development process. No specifications are set for documentation. No provision is made for the costs of design documentation. Development tools are obtained only with the greatest of difficulty, often much later than needed. The inevitable consequences are that design teams become demoralized. Good people opt out, either by leaving or just by giving in to the system. It is no accident that one very large company which epitomizes these qualities has, in the last two years, lost money, contracts and prestige in large amounts. It has had government contracts terminated. It has had one of its major projects investigated and evaluated by a rival software house (this being paid for by a highly disillusioned customer). And its software effort on one defence project was described as being run by 'one man and his dog'.

(b) Design capability

Management decisions have a strong bearing on the levels of competence and expertise achieved by software teams. You don't get good software by accident. It requires experienced, professional and dedicated designers. And you don't hold such people without the right support and encouragement from senior management. Indicators of a suspect design team are:

- Lack of appreciation of software complexity.
- Little formal documentation.
- Little use of software design tools.
- No system prototyping.
- Designing from scratch (no re-use of software).

These directly affect just how well individual jobs are handled.

(c) Specific design implementations

Given the situation outlined above, it isn't surprising that inferior software designs commonly have:

- Hazy system requirements specifications.
- An overrun on time.
- An overrun on budget.
- Faulty delivered software.
- Negligible documentation.

Contributory factors are:

- Simultaneous development of hardware and software.
- Incorrect trade-off of resources.

Let's look at how these all combine to turn a software project into a nightmare.

In the first place it's not unusual to find that nobody can define exactly what the system is supposed to do. Everybody thinks they know what should happen, but frequently these just don't add up. Because little is committed to paper during the design stage such discrepancies fail to surface.

As the design progresses, three factors cause it to become late. It often turns out that the software is much more complex than first envisaged. Second, much more effort is required. Finally, implementing it without decent software design tools makes it a long (and often error-prone) task. And, because no use is made of re-usable software, **all** of it has to be designed from scratch.

The overall system may involve new hardware. This presents the software designers with a task over and above that of writing the application software; that is, the need to develop programs to interface to the physical level, the 'system' software. It's not enough just to allow for the time and effort needed to do this. In these circumstances the development phase takes on a new dimension. System programs can't be tested out until the hardware is ready. And application software can't be fully tested until both these are completed. Concurrent development of hardware, system software and application software is a recipe for long, long development timescales.

During this period various trade-offs have to be made which affect the resulting software. For instance, an early decision concerns the choice of a programming language. This has a profound impact on productivity, visibility and, ultimately, dependability. At the same time the hardware–software balance has to be decided on. Later, specific effects of the language have to be checked out, concerning items such as memory usage and program run-time. It takes experience and knowledge to get these right.

All of these combine to make the job late, and as a result it costs more than planned. And, the first set of software is delivered as the final item: there is no prototyping effort as in normal engineering design. So it is not surprising that the software fails to work correctly on delivery. It then takes a massive effort to eliminate all the faults (this last item seems to be a way of life in much commercial software; it has been said that some firms regard customers as extensions to their software teams, acting as fault finders).

The factors outlined above influence the general nature of software design in a company. As an analogy, visualize management as providing hygienic facilities, the software teams being hygiene attendants. If facilities are poor then the attendants are unlikely to produce a safe environment – no matter how hard they work. The end result is that the user's health is under threat.

2.2.6   Testing — how useful?

The testing of software is a contentious issue, particularly for safety critical applications. Testing **is** an important part of the development process but its limits must be recognized. Design flaws can often be picked up early on by running the program in an emulated environment. Consider, for instance, where source code is written, compiled and linked using a personal computer (PC). It may be possible to exercise it subsequently under the control of the PC operating system. The behaviour of the program can be examined and any faults rectified. But there is a limit to what we can do at this point; some errors will always get through to the final hardware. Unfortunately, these errors tend to be the really difficult ones to sort out. The only solution then is to use specialized test gear such as In-Circuit Emulators.

There are sound objections to using tests for proving that software works. Consider the flow-chart example (Fig.2.10) set out by Boehm (Jensen and Tonies, 1979).

The questions are:

- How many paths through this section of program?
- How long would it take to check out each and every path?

The answers are 10^{20} and about 4000 years at one path per nanosecond.

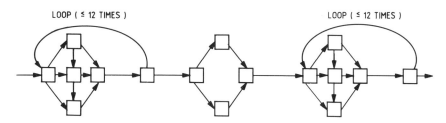

LOOP (≤ 12 TIMES)   LOOP (≤ 12 TIMES)

Fig.2.10

This shows that statements which say that 'full and complete testing of the program has been carried out' must be treated with scepticism. Fortunately, in practice, things are not quite so gloomy. Usually a smaller number of tests exercises a sufficient, statistically significant number of paths through the program (Jensen and Tonies). While this is very encouraging it has a profound implication. That is, testing of this kind cannot **prove** that the software is error-free.

There is a second, more fundamental, point implicit in this technique. What we have tested is the **correctness** of the program. But this, as has already been pointed out, is not sufficient. Correctness testing only shows how well the program meets its specification. It cannot point out where the specifications may be wrong. Further, such testing is static. We really need to verify that it will behave **reliably**. Consequently, many real-time systems developers use simulation as a test method. This gives much greater confidence in the behaviour of the software. But it still leaves questions unanswered because:

- Most testing is done by simulation of the environment.

- It is difficult to provide realistic test exercises and set-ups.
- In many cases the test strategy is based on assumptions about the total system and its environment. There is no guarantee that these are right.
- It is difficult to predict and simulate all failure modes of the system. Hardware failures complicate the matter.
- The behaviour of the software may vary with time or environmental conditions. This requires testing to be dynamic.
- Following on from this, it may become impossible to carry out complete and exhaustive tests for real-time systems.

Don't get paranoid about software problems. Be assured that all engineering project managers would instantly recognize the difficulties listed above. Just be realistic about what can and can't be achieved by the testing of software.

2.3   THE BASICS OF GOOD SOFTWARE

2.3.1   General

'Good' software is dependable, is delivered on time and is done within budget. Whether we can achieve this depends on many factors. Some relate to major sections of the development process. Others affect quite specific design activities.

What then, do we need to do to create a quality software product? At the minimum, we should:

- Develop a clear statement of requirements for the software.
- Ensure that the design solution is capable of achieving this.
- Organize the development so that the project is manageable.
- Organize the development so that the time scales can be met.
- Make sure that the design can be changed without major rewrites.
- Design for testability.
- Minimize risks by using tried and trusted methods.
- Ensure that safety is given its correct priority.
- Make sure that the project doesn't completely rely on particular individuals.
- Produce a maintainable design.

Mind you, there is a bit of the 'wish' element here.

Let's now look at items which determine precisely how well we can achieve these aims.

2.3.2   Specification correctness

There is only one way to make sure that the software specification is right. Talk to the user. Explain what you're doing. Put it down on paper in a way that he can understand. Get to know the job yourself. Keep on talking to the user. And never delude yourself that requirements' documents are set in concrete.

In reality they never stop changing.

Specification methods and related topics are covered in detail in chapter 3.

2.3.3   Feasibility and suitability

Here we seek to answer the general questions 'will it work?' (feasibility) and 'how well?' (suitability). Specifically we need to assess the:

- Time allowed to complete tasks.
- Accuracy and completeness of input information.
- Required accuracy of mathematical operations.
- Operator interaction with the system.
- Special operating conditions, such as data retention on a power loss.
- Power supply parameters.
- Special performance parameters, such as radiation hardness.

It may seem that decisions concerning the last two items should be left to hardware engineers. But these can have a major impact on the software development. For instance, if a battery-powered system is specified then a CMOS processor will probably have to be used. Likewise, if radiation hardness is required it may be that bi-polar technology has to be used. Any choices made must take into account their effects on the software aspects of the project. So they need consideration at the feasibility design stage.

We then need to consider the overall hardware and software structure, and determine:

- Is the language correct for the job?
- Are there proper support tools for the chosen language?
- Is there enough code and data store space?
- Will task execution times meet their specifications?
- If, at test time, task execution times are excessive, how can we handle the problem?
- Will the system be able to respond sufficiently fast to asynchronous events?

This part of the development process isn't easy to get right. It is carried out at an early stage when there are many unknowns in the project. Frequently the size of the problem is under-estimated. Combine that with the usual optimism of designers and it's not surprising that so many projects have problems.

2.3.4   Modularization

One of the most highly refined structures for the handling of major projects in set time scales is that of the military (Fig.2.11).

The military command structure is hierarchical, grouping men together as a set of distinct units (or 'modules'). Without this structure all we'd have would be a disorganized rabble. But with it, the organization becomes manageable and effective. With this simple chain of command, control is easy to maintain.

Large jobs can be tackled by the group as a whole. Yet, at the lowest level, the jobs taken on by separate platoons are 'visible'. Individual progress and performance can be monitored and assessed. When troubles arise they can be dealt with quickly and effectively.

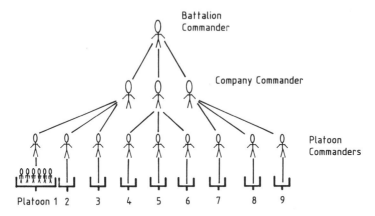

Fig.2.11 Hierarchical modularized structure

Software which is organized in a modular way exhibits the same properties:

- The overall project is manageable and flexible.
- Low-level tasks can be made small enough for one person to work on.
- Software can be designed as a set of parallel (concurrent) actions.

Even within the work of one person, modularization gives the same sort of benefits.

What is not so obvious is that modularization can make a program very stable. That is, localized changes produce very little of a ripple-through effect in the program as a whole. For exactly the same reasons a modular program is much easier to test and maintain (but this is also closely tied up with program design methods, chapter 4).

2.3.5   Portability and re-usability

Most manufacturers of microprocessor systems produce a range of products (Fig.2.12). Typically these range from simple single board computers (SBCs) through multiple rack units. In many cases a number of microprocessor types are used. To a lesser extent different operating systems may be in use. If each configuration requires unique software, development is expensive and time-consuming – and threatens to generate a whole new range of software faults. Ideally we would like one set of programs capable of running on all configurations – fully portable software. Portability is a measure of the effort needed to transfer programs between:

- Computers which use different processors.

- Different configurations based on the same processor.
- Configurations which use different operating systems.
- Different compilers, given the same language and same hardware.

If programs need a complete rewrite before being transferred they are totally non-portable.

It is true that, in the past, most real-time software was non-portable. Now there is much greater emphasis on portability, especially for professional work. There are still many barriers to achieving this goal, the major ones being:

- Computer hardware.
- Number representation, range and precision.
- Programming language.
- Operating system structures.
- Communication structures and protocols.

For embedded systems, fully portable software can never be attained. The stumbling block is that hardware structures almost always differ from job to job. But, given the right design approach and the right programming language, very high levels of portability **can** be achieved.

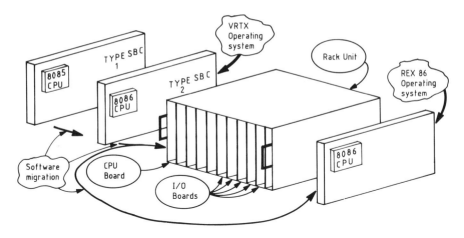

Fig.2.12 Microprocessor system configurations

Re-usability is a measure of how easily we can use existing software, especially that which is tried and trusted. Doing this saves us from (to quote a very hackneyed but true cliché) 're-inventing the wheel'. There's no doubt that high portability produces high re-usability (and vice versa).

What exactly do we gain by having portable and re-usable software libraries? The advantages are that:

- Design and coding times are reduced.
- Development effort is reduced.
- Less manpower is needed.

- Less debugging is needed (use of proven software).
- Costs are reduced.
- Correct and reliable designs are more easily achieved.

Standard libraries are not a universal remedy for poor design techniques. They must be organized in terms of clearly defined functions and be easy to use. Otherwise they are likely to make it more, and not less, difficult to implement a design.

One of the most important factors affecting portability and re-usability is the programming language used for the design.

2.3.6   Error avoidance and defensive programming — robust programs

How can we deal with error situations? Start off by accepting that, in any real project, mistakes **will** be made. Therefore we need to design software to limit the effects of such mistakes – damage limitation. But to do this we must have some idea of the general (and sometimes specific) nature of error sources. Exactly how, when, why and where do these problems arise? Generally they are due to:

- The human factor.
- Computational problems.
- Hardware failure.

(a)   The human factor
The problem can originate outside the system due to the behaviour of people (assuming they can interact with the software). For instance, consider using a processor as a controller for a closed loop control system. Normally the controller is expected to carry out tasks additional to that of controlling the loop. So, under normal conditions, the control task runs at regular and preset times; other tasks are executed in the remaining time. Assume that the operator can set the system sampling rate as desired. If he sets this too fast the processor will execute nothing but the loop control algorithm; all other tasks are ignored. Despite the fact that the software may be faultless, the system fails to work correctly.

(b)   Computational problems
One of the well-known mistakes here is not allowing for invalid mathematical operations. These, such as dividing by zero, produce indeterminate results. Other items, such as going outside the correct limits of array bounds, also fall into this category.

(c)   Hardware failure
The following example typifies the problems of hardware failure. A control program instructs an analogue-to-digital converter to begin conversion. It then polls the converter, looking for the end of conversion signal. But for some

reason the converter fails to generate this signal. The result is that the program just sits there *ad infinitum* (or until the power is switched off); control of the system is completely lost.

The technique used to handle these situations is called 'defensive programming'. Fundamentally, this method accepts that errors will occur, originating inside the computer system and/or external to it. It aims to:

- Prevent faults being introduced into the system in the first place.
- Detect faults if they do occur.
- Control the resulting response of the system.

Software which behaves like this combines the attributes of fault resistance with fault tolerance.

In the case of (a) above we could limit the range of sample times which are accepted as valid. In (b) and (c) we can't control the occurrence of a fault. Instead, once having detected the fault, we must put the system into a safe mode ('exception handling'). An ideal design includes a specific test and a corresponding response for each possible error condition. In practice this is very unlikely to be achieved. But, for real-time systems, this isn't our chief concern. If we can identify the cause of the problem, fine. But it's usually much more important to respond to faults quickly, safely, and in a deterministic manner.

All these factors are summed up in a quality called the 'robustness' of the program. This is defined by the *Dictionary of Computing* as 'a measure of the ability of a system to recover from error conditions, whether generated externally or internally, e.g. a robust system would be tolerant to errors in input data or to failures of internal components. Although there may be a relationship between robustness and reliability, the two are distinct measures: a system never called upon to recover from error conditions may be reliable without being robust; a highly robust system that recovers and continues to operate despite numerous error conditions may still be regarded as unreliable in that it fails to provide essential services in a timely fashion on demand'.

2.3.7   Design codes of practice — style, clarity and documentation

First, it is important not only that software specifications and the corresponding design solutions are correct; they must be seen to be so. Second, the resulting program must be understandable and unambiguous. And not just to the original designer. Finally, the ability to assess the effects of program modifications easily and quickly is very desirable.

These items are not so concerned with how well we do a design (design quality is considered to be an implicit requirement). Rather, it relates to the quality and completeness of design methods and documentation.

Design style defines the way in which the development as a whole is tackled. It covers all aspects of the work, from initial feasibility studies to post-design services. Most engineering firms have, for many years, used 'codes of practice' to establish design styles. In large organizations such practices are fairly formal; small companies can afford to work informally. The purpose is to create working conditions and attitudes which:

- Encourage the production of high quality work.
- Ensure that time scales are met.
- Ensure that budgets are met.

Codes of practice may be written for detailed as well as general design activities. For instance, one software house which used C as a programming language was concerned about the quality of their existing implementations. As a result company standards were issued limiting the language constructs that its programmers could use. The purpose of this was to:

- Eliminate unsafe programming practices.
- Get rid of 'clever' (i.e. obscure) programming tricks.
- Produce understandable programs (clarity).
- Avoid the use of special language extensions (affects portability).

This aspect of design is normally termed 'programming style'.

Clarity is not just restricted to program writing; it is essential that the design as a whole should be easy to understand. At all stages we should be able to answer the 'what, why and how' questions. This is why good, clear, comprehensive documentation is such an important item.

2.3.8   A final comment

It is only in the last few years that the ideas and methods described here have been put into action by the software industry (STARTS, 1987). Much still remains to be done, especially in view of the 'cottage industry' mentality of many developers. It's not as if professionals didn't recognize the problems of software design and development. In fact, many tools and techniques have been proposed with a fervour normally associated with evangelical rallies. Most of the early developments came from the DP field. Unfortunately, they proved to have little to offer for real-time work. Now the sheer size of the software problem (time, cost, reliability, etc.) is acting as the driving force for the development of new tools. Integrated project support environments, design formality, documentation standards and high standards of professionalism (as exhibited by software engineers) are all combining to raise software quality standards.

REFERENCES

Dictionary of Computing (1984), Oxford University Press, Oxford, UK, ISBN 0–19–853905–3.

Frola, F.R. and Miller, C.O. (1984), *System Safey in Aircraft Management*, Logistics Management Institute, Washington, D.C., January.

IEE88 (1988), Draft report on safety-critical systems employing software, Joint IEE/BCS study, UK Department of Trade and Industry reference IT/24/27/39, November.

IEEE Computer Society Standards Committee (1979), *Computer Dictionary* (ed. Martin H. Weik), IEEE Computer Society.

Jensen, R.W. and Tonies, C.C., (1979) *Software Engineering*, Prentice-Hall International Inc., ISBN 0–13–822148.

Kletz, T. (1983), Human problems with computer control, hazard prevention *Journal of the System Safety Society*, March/April, pp24–26.

Leveson, N.G. (1986), Software safety: why, what, and how, *ACM Computing Surveys*, Vol. 18, No. 2, June, pp125–163.

Hamilton, M.H. (1986), Zero-defect software: the elusive goal, *IEEE Spectrum*, March, pp48–53.

SEN1, ACM Software Engineering Notes, **Vol.8**, No.3.

SEN2, ACM Software Engineering Notes, **Vol.5**, No.2.

SEN3, ACM Software Engineering Notes, **Vol.10**, No.3.

SEN4, ACM Software Engineering Notes, **Vol.9**, No.1.

SEN5, ACM Software Engineering Notes, **Vol.5**, No.1.

STARTS Guide (1987), *Software Tools for Application to Large Real-time Systems – Part 1: The Software Engineering Context*, NCC Publications.

Chapter Three

First steps – requirements analysis and specification

One of the most difficult tasks in any project is to establish precisely what the system requirements are. This is a problem faced by project managers from time immemorial, who recognize that getting it right at the start of a job is of the utmost importance. Engineers have long realized that a disciplined, organized and formalized approach must be used when evaluating systems requirements (whether that's always been practised is another matter). This hasn't been done through a sense of 'doing the right thing'. No. Experience, frequently painful, has shown that such methods are necessary. In particular, with projects of any real size, they are absolutely essential.

What is the situation concerning software projects? Considering the number of major failure stories in circulation, the answer must be 'pretty awful'. In the past this situation has frequently been condoned on the grounds that software is inherently highly complex; one can't expect anything else in such projects. This is nonsense. The real problem was that anything smacking of organization and discipline was considered to impinge upon the programmer's creativity. Eventually, though, the point came when such an approach to professional software couldn't be tolerated any longer. Consequently, requirements analysis and software specification are now regularly practised as a formal aspect of quality software design. The purpose of this chapter is to:

- Distinguish between mythical and realistic software life cycle models.
- Show where requirements analysis and software specification (the requirements stage) fits into the life cycle.
- Highlight the importance of the requirements stage.
- Explain why and how mistakes are made during this period.
- Discuss practical analysis and specification methods.
- Introduce the topic of software prototyping.

In reality this isn't about software; it's project engineering.

3.1   THE SOFTWARE LIFE CYCLE

3.1.1   Introduction

There is a long path between recognizing the need for a product and satisfying this need. Many activities take place along this 'life cycle' path, involving system, software and hardware designers. In an attempt to formalize the process, models have been developed describing what the process consists of and how it functions. Although these cover all aspects of system development they have generally become known as 'software life cycle models'. Software engineering textbooks describe these in varying degrees of detail, such descriptions usually being quite plausible. Regrettably many suffer from the 'wish' syndrome – as in 'I wish it was like this' – ignoring the realities of life. Consequently, models usually belong to one of two distinct groups – mythical and real. And, for the inexperienced engineer, it can be difficult to tell them apart on a first meeting.

3.1.2   A mythical model of the software life cycle

The simplistic 'waterfall' structure shown in Fig.3.1 is an example of a mythical software life cycle model. Let's see how this model is supposed to function.

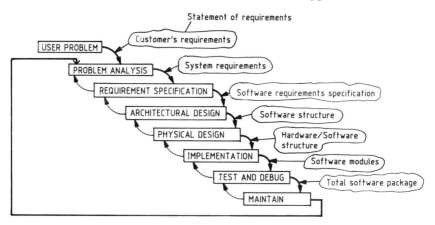

Fig.3.1 The mythical software life cycle model

The process begins when a prospective customer arrives looking for a solution to a clearly-defined requirement. Frequently this is a desire to automate an existing manual system, such as accounts handling, stock control, or bookings and reservations. The computing task is seen primarily as a software one, even though hardware forms part of the design solution. Hardware is subordinated to software because the equipment fit is usually based on standard items, configured specifically for each application. Moreover, by using standard hardware, there isn't a need to develop system software; the primary objective is the production of application software only.

At this point the software house sends its top men – the system's analysts – to investigate the client's existing system. Their objectives are to:

- Analyse the problem presented to them (i.e. the existing system).
- Establish precisely what the new system is supposed to do.
- Document these aspects in a clear and understandable way.

The output from the problem analysis phase is the system's requirements' document. Using this the system's analysts, together with senior software designers, define what the software must do to meet these requirements. This includes the:

- Objectives of the software.
- Constraints placed on the software developers.
- Overall software work plan.

Such features are described in the software specification document, issued at the end of the requirements specification phase. Note that usually there is iteration around the analysis and specification loop, to resolve errors, ambiguities, etc. Note also that similar iterations take place at all stages in the model.

Only now does software design commence, in a neatly compartmentalized manner, Fig.3.2. Experienced designers, working with a clear, complete and correct software specification document, begin software architectural design. Their purpose is to identify and model the overall software structure, based on the software specification supplied to them. The resulting software structure document defines the essential components of the system, how these fit together and how they communicate. In essence it describes an abstract model of the software, ignoring implementation aspects (i.e. processor hardware, communication links, etc.).

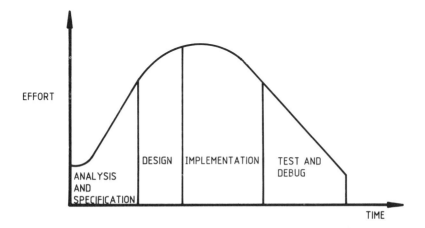

Fig.3.2 Project effort distribution – another myth

During the next stage, that of physical design, the abstract structure is partitioned or 'mapped' onto actual system hardware. In some applications this may be a complex task – but it is considerably simplified by using standard hardware. The outcome of this work is a hardware/software structure defining document, forming the input to the implementation phase. The function of **this** phase is to take the physical design structures and translate them into source code. Once the code is written it can be tested and debugged. Normally this is first done on a host development system; later it is tested in the target system (in most cases the host and target computers are identical).

One of the assumptions underlying this simplistic approach is that system hardware requires configuration, installation and commissioning: but not development. It also assumes that such activities proceed in parallel with the design task; that the hardware is fully functional when application software tests commence on the target system. Such testing is, of course, always needed to show that the finished code performs as specified. Thus the integration of software and hardware is a straightforward and fairly painless task.

Once the customer is convinced that the system performs as required it is put into operational use; the maintenance phase begins. This involves two major factors. First, not all errors are detected during the testing phase; such residual bugs need to be eradicated from the software. Second, upgrades and enhancements are usually demanded by the customer during the life of the system. Minor changes involve tinkering with the source code (the minor iteration). But significant alterations take us back to the analysis stage of the life cycle model, the major iteration loop.

3.1.3   A more realistic model of the life cycle

So, what's wrong with the model described so far? It seems reasonable, clearly describing the major activities and outputs relating to software production. It also defines what these involve, where they occur and how they relate to each other. Quite true. The problem is not with the definition and use of the individual activities. These are perfectly valid, forming a sound basis for software design methodologies. Fundamentally it is due to many underlying false assumptions within this model, the first relating to the customer's requirements.

Most real-time software designs form part of larger systems (it's also worth pointing out that software costs dominate hardware costs only if a very narrow view of hardware is taken, i.e. the computer installation itself). In such applications it isn't a case of putting processor-based equipment into a company to perform a computing task; the problems are much more complex. Moreover, although there may be a single end user, other bodies often have vested interests in the project. It isn't easy to generalize about real-time developments because projects are so diverse. But let's take the following example which shows how complex the situation **can** become.

Assume that the Defence Staff have perceived a potential air warfare threat.

Decisions are made to develop a new air interceptor fighter aircraft to counter this, its requirements being stated in very general terms. At this stage the need is seen, but the solution isn't. Studies are then carried out by defence procurement agencies, research establishments and the end user. Aircraft and avionic companies are invited to bid. They in turn perform tender studies which involve **their** system suppliers (e.g. flight control, weapon management, etc.). Only at this level are hard decisions made concerning mechanical, electrical, electronic and software systems, etc.

One can define system requirements at each and every point in this chain. The content of such requirements and the issues involved vary from level to level. So when we talk about requirements analysis, we have to define precisely the issues which concern us. In this text attention is focused on the lowest level discussed above.

The customer (in this case the aircraft manufacturer, say) has a perceived need, and is looking for a way to meet this need. Internal discussions within the company – and possibly external studies by consultants – lead to the production of an informal specification of requirements (Fig.3.3).

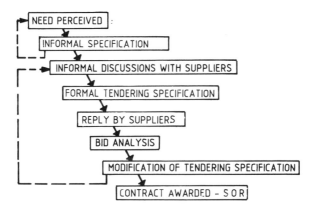

Fig.3.3 Formulating the user statement of requirements (SOR)

These are firmed up in terms of concepts, achievable targets, outline costs, etc. during informal discussions with potential suppliers of equipment. The process is repeated until the customer is sure that his requirements are realizable, both technically and financially – and within his desired time scales. Eventually he produces a formal tendering document requesting bids by suppliers. Replies are analysed, the responses usually leading to changes in the tendering document. This is then re-issued in modified form, requesting further bids. Finally, a single supplier is identified as the best contender and nominated for the job. When contracts are awarded, the tendering document is converted into a statement of requirements (SOR) for the task. This then becomes the binding legal document for all further developments.

Note that even before the design process proper begins many decisions have already been made. These concern system structure, performance targets, size, weight, time scales, as well as project management functions. So although work hasn't yet started many constraints apply to the job – compounded by one major factor. The specifications **always** change in such complex systems. This is an immutable rule which can't be proved but always holds true. It is inherent in the evolutionary aspects of the design process.

So, we start the life cycle with what appears to be a complete, correct and full statement of requirements of the problem; in reality, it is nothing of the sort. It is, though, the best we can do given the nature of the problem. Consequently much greater effort is needed at the requirements analysis stage to clarify the customer's requirements. The effect of this is to introduce a new major iteration step between the analysis and problem definition (the SOR) stages, Fig.3.4.

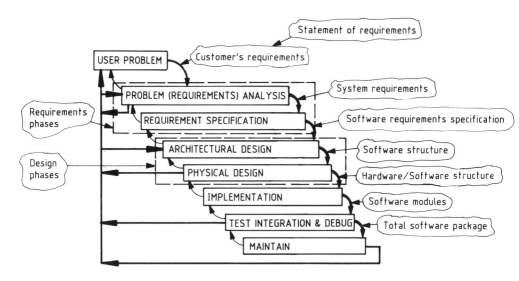

Fig.3.4 A realistic software life cycle model

The steps through requirements specification and architectural design tend to follow the earlier pattern. In practice there may be a major change in design methodology between these steps (chapter 10). Problems encountered in these stages are usually reasonably easy to solve, unless they are fundamental (for instance, it just won't work). It's at the physical design stage that some really difficult problems surface, involving computer power, speed, memory, size, weight and cost. If the designer had a free hand there wouldn't be a problem; but he hasn't. Constraints set at the tendering phase act as a straitjacket, limiting the designer's choices. If the effects are significant they usually lead to a major iteration, going right back to the user problem. Surprisingly, critical problems at the physical design level can often be eliminated by making simple changes to the SOR.

During the implementation phase minor changes may be made in the physical design structure. For instance, tasks may be partitioned in more efficient ways, better modular structures formed, etc. Generally this part of the work doesn't raise real difficulties, provided proper development tools are available. However, the next set of major stumbling blocks occur in the test, integration and debug phase. This is a wide ranging activity which includes:

- Testing software in a host environment.
- Testing software in a target environment.
- Integrating separately designed software packages.
- Integrating software and hardware.
- Integrating subsystems.
- System trials.
- System commissioning.

This phase, which embraces much more than just software, is often **the** major activity in the development of processor-based systems, Table 3.1 (Farnan, 1975).

Table 3.1   Distribution of software effort (%)

	Requirements and design	Implementation	Test, debug and integration
SAGE	39	14	47
NTDS	30	20	50
GEMINI	36	17	47
SATURN V	32	24	44
OS/360	33	17	50
TRW Survey	46	20	34

There are many reasons for the size of this activity. Testing and debugging software in a target environment is a difficult and time-consuming process. This is compounded by the fact that target systems are usually quite different from the hosts. Integration of systems, whether software, electronic, mechanical, etc. is always fraught with problems. Some system testing **can** take place in a simulated environment. Mostly it has to be done within the real environment, with all its attendant problems. Like, for instance, operating hundreds of miles from base, with limited test facilities, working long hours in arduous conditions, trying to meet near impossible time scales. Grave problems may be found for the first time at this stage, particularly concerning processing power (not enough), available memory size (too small) and response times (too slow). Solving these involves iteration back to the architectural design stage (at the very least). In really dramatic cases it may be impossible to meet the user requirements under any circumstances. So we need to go right back to the SOR to try to resolve the problem.

Maintenance aspects are similar to those described earlier, only the whole process is more difficult to carry out. It may be tedious to hunt for bugs in an accounts recording system. By contrast, trying to pin down a fault in the flight control software of a supersonic fighter can be a Herculean task. Upgrading systems can also present major problems. With DP systems the emphasis is on software upgrading; for real-time applications it includes software, hardware, subsystems and even whole systems.

Lack of precision in the initial SOR, together with continual changes in this document, alters the way a project progresses. Project effort distribution becomes more like that shown in Fig.3.5 than that of Fig.3.2.

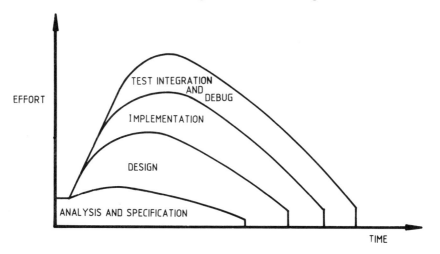

Fig.3.5 Project effort distribution – reality

This is a simplified model; precise details vary from project to project (Key, 1986). But they all exhibit one common feature: the overlapping of phases. This implies a much higher degree of interaction between stages than that predicted by the simple waterfall model. It also highlights the need for firm, organized project management and formal quality assurance techniques (chapter 12).

The model of Fig.3.4 describes the concrete aspects of software development for real-time systems. In the past few companies formalized this process; generally their methods evolved in an *ad hoc* way. Now, though, more rigour is gradually being introduced, reinforced by the use of modern tools and techniques (chapter 10). Designers now realize that the total process can be defined as a series of sub-processes, each having clearly defined attributes (even if, in practice, it isn't always possible to have clear boundaries). The rest of this chapter concentrates specifically on the front-end stages of analysis and specification; other aspects are discussed later in the text.

3.2   THE IMPORTANCE OF THE REQUIREMENTS STAGES

Why are the front-end stages so important? Because they have a profound effect on overall software error rates and productivity. And these are closely related to system costs.

Let's first consider software errors. There's no need to ask where they occur. The answer, as pointed out in chapter 2, is **everywhere**. More importantly, what is the distribution of these occurrences? Fig.3.6, based on statistics obtained by Tom DeMarco (1978), gives a good general guide.

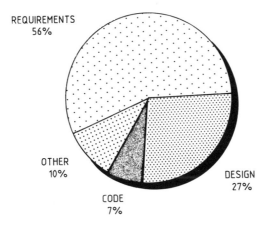

Fig.3.6 Distribution of software errors

It's not surprising that high error levels occur in the requirements phase. It is, after all, a highly complex procedure to specify fully the requirements of a system. More on this later.

A second important point is the cost impact of these errors. Fig.3.7 illustrates this, again using statistics from DeMarco (1978).

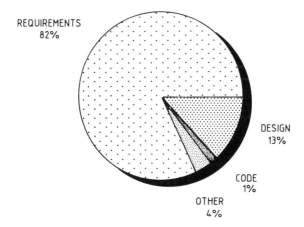

Fig.3.7 Cost of rectifying software errors

Given that Fig.3.6 is correct, this shouldn't be a surprise. Any mistake made at the beginning of a project affects all subsequent phases, a 'ripple-down' effect. So when requirements errors are discovered at the final stage of development, corrections have to be made throughout the complete design. The resulting corrective costs are extremely high. Mistakes made in later stages have much less impact. In theory there should be no ripple-up effect; in practice, though, this **can** happen. For instance, suppose a major error occurs at the physical design level. It may actually be easier to change the software specification and structure rather than redesign the physical level.

The second issue, cost, is very closely bound up with the first one. Mistakes take time to find and correct. Therefore as the error rate increases the amount of deliverable code per unit time decreases – with consequent cost penalties.

It should now be clear that the requirements stage is the most important aspect of the life cycle process. Unfortunately, many customers and suppliers fail to realize exactly how important it is. Getting this wrong can produce dreadful downstream effects. Most situations are recoverable – at a cost. But there are also well documented cases where whole projects have been ditched as a result of requirements errors. Paradoxically, this stage has the fewest development and support tools within the total software toolset.

3.3   MAKING MISTAKES — SOURCES AND CAUSES

3.3.1   A general comment

Why and how do we make mistakes? Fig.3.8 attempts, in a light-hearted way, to highlight some of the issues involved. It may be simplistic but it does get to the heart of the matter. Because it shows that three major factors are at work here:

- How we convert what we think into what we say.
- How we express ourselves.
- How we convert what we see (receive) into thought.

How do these apply to the requirements stage of a project? Let's first look at the customer–supplier relationship in more detail, as modelled in Fig.3.9.

This model also applies to the system designer–software designer relationship. So rules derived to enhance customer–supplier interactions can also be applied later in the software development cycle.

The first step in procuring any new system is to define exactly what is needed. The customer, using his acquired knowledge and available information, formulates a set of requirements. These are communicated (by whatever means are suitable) to the supplier. He in turn evaluates these requirements, and produces a design solution based on the evaluation. This looks simple enough. But then why is it that the delivered product often fails to match up with what was wanted in the first place? The answer, of course, is that it isn't simple at all.

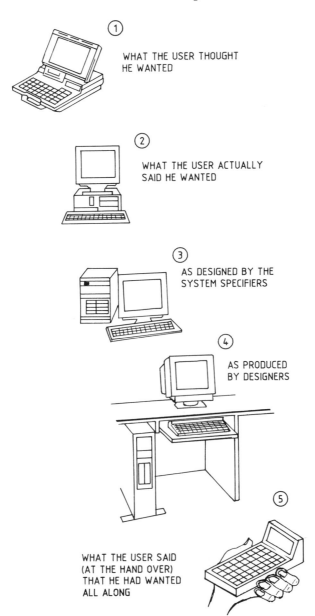

Fig.3.8 Making mistakes

It's important to recognize the source of these mismatch problems because then we can:

● Understand the weaknesses of informal systems (past–current practice).

- Appreciate the use of formal analysis/specification tools (current–future practice).
- Perceive the reasons for developing prototyping systems (mainly future practice).

There are four major reasons why mismatch problems occur (Fig.3.10).

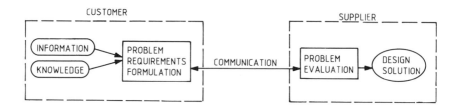

Fig.3.9 Simplistic view of the customer–supplier relationship

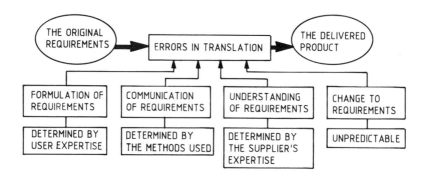

Fig.3.10 Sources of requirements/deliverables mismatch problems

First, we don't formulate the requirements properly. Secondly, we don't communicate these requirements correctly. Thirdly, we fail to understand properly these improperly communicated requirements. Finally, because requirements continually change, not all changes may be acted on correctly. How much effect do these errors have, and how significant are they? It depends mainly on two factors: expertise and methods. Experienced people make fewer mistakes and are more likely to find errors in other people's work. Unfortunately this is a process we can't automate; there is no substitute for good people. What we **can** do is produce tools which help in formulating and analysing problems and communicating ideas. Furthermore, it is essential that these tackle the root causes of errors (Fig.3.11), otherwise they're useless.

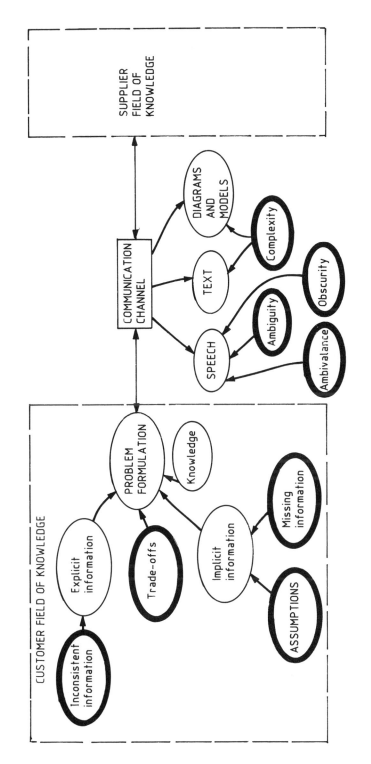

Fig.3.11 Causes of requirements/deliverables mismatch problems

3.3.2   Problems in formulating specifications

First let's consider what goes on when the customer attempts to put together an SOR. In an ideal situation full information relating to the requirement is explicitly defined. In reality the requirement document is based on explicit information, implicit information and knowledge. Further, in putting together a specification, many conflicting demands are made by involved parties; hence trade-offs must be made. Each aspect has associated problems. And problems are compounded by specifying requirements which appear to be clear and reasonable – but actually are quite imprecise (and sometimes untestable). For instance, what does 'mimic displays shall be clear and uncluttered' mean? How does one define 'clear' and 'uncluttered'?

(a)   Explicit information
This may seem a clear-cut situation. True, but the major problem here is inconsistency of the information supplied. Specification documents are usually weighty items (in both a physical and literary sense). It can be extremely difficult to identify conflicts in such circumstances.

(b)   Implicit information
Implicit information is that which, to the specifier, appears to be present in, or deducible from, the SOR – but isn't. In some instances it is a simple case of missing information. In others, information is omitted or overlooked because assumptions are made concerning the supplier's understanding of the requirements. For instance, the operational temperature range of an equipment might be omitted from its specification. But because the application is an avionic one, say, everybody knows what this requirement is. Really?

(c)   Knowledge
This is a difficult area to describe precisely; there are many facets to it. Problems arise because the customer has a much greater knowledge of the system than the supplier; and much of it is unstated. For instance, there is always some relationship between the system being specified and other systems. The specifier has a good understanding of this, and aims to ensure that system integration is achieved correctly. Unfortunately the supplier is unlikely to have the same knowledge. Hence, during software design, decisions are made which seem perfectly correct for the system being constructed – yet may adversely affect other systems.

There is usually some overlap between this aspect and that of implicit information. The following example, relating to a very large computer-controlled rotating machine, illustrates this point. On initial trials the protection system kept shutting the machine down during start-up operations. It turned out that nobody had bothered to tell the software designers that the machine took a full minute to run up to speed – the assumption was that everybody knew about this. Unfortunately the software engineers didn't, and invoked an underspeed trip far too early in the run-up process.

Another factor, that of balance of judgement, can have significant cost and performance effects on the final product. Consider, for instance, where a particular requirement is extremely difficult to satisfy. The supplier isn't in a position to judge its importance; it's just another target to be met. So the target is achieved – but only with the greatest of difficulty, possibly affecting both software and hardware. Yet the customer may be the only person who knows that the requirement isn't especially important. Thus the specification could well be relaxed, with attendant savings of time and money.

3.3.3   Problems in communicating requirements

Four basic methods can be used to communicate information: speech, text, pictures and physical models. Models tend to play a much greater role in the later stages of system development, and their importance cannot be under-estimated. It's well known that car manufacturers build models of new vehicles – but less well known is that a full scale wooden mock-up was built of the Swiftsure class nuclear powered hunter-killer submarine. For software systems different, non-physical models, are needed. This topic is discussed further in the section on prototyping.

One view of the communication process is that information is transmitted along a communication channel from sender to receiver. In the ideal world, what is sent is also what is received. But in reality this isn't true; information is corrupted by 'noise' along the way. The major sources of noise are:

- Ambiguity – I don't know what it means.
- Ambivalence – it could mean either this OR that: or both.
- Obscurity – it just isn't clear at all, I'm quite confused.
- Complexity – I hear what you say but I'm now totally confused.

Speech (and here is implied face-to-face contact) is probably the most important and significant communication process. Yet it is the one most prone to noise corruption. It's impossible to eliminate this noise – it is part of human nature. One must accept that there are inherent problems in speech communication; therefore other methods are needed to compensate for them.

Text description is, after speech, the most common method of communicating information. It too suffers from the problems outlined above, but generally these are easier to correct. Unfortunately, as a result of trying to eliminate these deficiencies, textual material becomes extremely complex (have a look at some legal documents). For technical systems we frequently end up with specification documents which are massive, dull and virtually unusable. Some authors of specification documents have an unshakable belief in their effectiveness – even when experience proves the contrary point.

Pictures (diagrams) are one of the most effective means of communicating information (just think of the amount of money spent on eye-catching television advertisements). Diagrams have two major advantages over other forms of communication. First, they let us express our thoughts easily. Second, they make it much easier (compared with text descriptions) to assimilate information. Engineers have used this as a primary communication tool for centuries; yet for years it was almost entirely neglected by the computer science community.

The role of diagramming is discussed in much more detail in chapter 5. Suffice it to say that, as far as specification methods are concerned, diagrams are becoming an important technique. Note that in this context structured text is considered to be a diagram.

Finally, this description has only considered information flow from the customer to the supplier. In practice it is a two-way process – with all the consequent noise corruption effects on return messages.

3.3.4   Problems in understanding requirements

Even if the specifications delivered by the customer are totally correct, unambiguous, etc., mistakes are still going to be made. First, the supplier interprets the specifications from his point of view (or 'domain'). This is usually very different from that of the customer. Second, difficulties arise as he attempts to convey his response to the customer. He has exactly the same problems as those experienced by the customer when formulating the specification. Is it surprising then that the customer may not quite understand what the supplier is doing, how he's doing it and why he's doing it in a particular way? Therefore it is essential that the supplier uses techniques which make his work meaningful: both to him and to the customer.

3.4   A PRACTICAL APPROACH TO ANALYSIS AND SPECIFICATION

3.4.1   General aspects

What is the fundamental purpose of the analysis and specification – the requirements – phase? It is to define **what** a proposed system is to do, not **how** it is supposed to do it; 'how' is the function of the design process. However, in practice there isn't always a sharp boundary between requirements and design. And the problem is compounded because some design methods make little distinction between the two. We can see why these overlap by considering the make-up of the requirements work-stage, Fig.3.12.

The first part of this process is concerned with analysing and recording the system **requirements**. Note this well. Many traditional (i.e. DP) descriptions discuss the analysis of systems, but you can only analyse a system if one already exists.

In the initial run-through, design factors shouldn't affect the outcome of the analysis work. Using the information acquired during the analysis phase the software requirements are now specified. Constraints are usually applied here: programming language, design methods and documentation procedures, for instance. Now this is the point where design aspects **do** enter the process. There isn't much point in specifying a software requirement if the required system can't be:

- Achieved.
- Completed within the required time scale.
- Done within budget.

Implementation difficulties, actual or anticipated, cause us to review and re-analyse system requirements. As a result the software specifications are, if necessary, changed to a more sensible form. In some cases though, it may be impossible to do this and still meet the original system requirements. Consequently a further review of the SOR must be carried out. Where possible this document should be amended to take implementation factors into account. This is a normal and accepted part of any development process – most problems can be tackled in this way. Occasionally obstacles arise which are impossible to overcome within the given requirement objectives. There are only two courses of action. Either major changes are made to these objectives, or else the whole project must be abandoned.

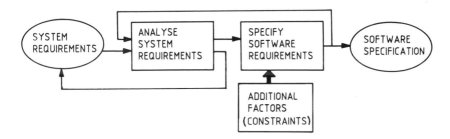

Fig.3.12 The requirements phases – analysis and specification

We've already said that requirements and design may not be easy to separate. But they **are** very distinct parts of the development process. Therefore the software developer should always strive to treat them in this way. The main attributes of the requirements phase are the:

- Basic strategy used.
- Acquisition and presentation of information.
- Information content.
- Choice of method and tool support.

The first question to answer is what the specification document should contain. Sensibly it should provide a good description of the intended system, Fig.3.13. This description includes system:

- Function.
- Performance.

- Interfaces.
- Constraints.

Interfaces include those which connect to the physical environment – the 'real world' – and to other software entities.

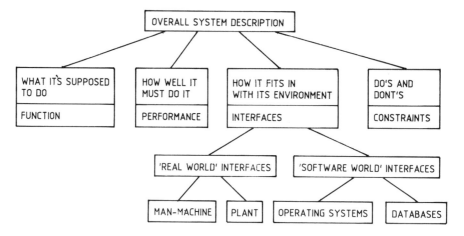

Fig.3.13 Overall system description

The description/document must be structured so that it can be understood both by the customer and the supplier. This means, most definitely, that it should not use obscure notation, complex structures or definitions using computer language terms. This latter approach has been advocated by a number of authors (Sommerville, 1989). It may be a very useful technique for the architectural design stage – but it cannot be recommended as a way of stating system requirements. We really need methods which are:

- Formal (that is, there are defined rules which must be obeyed).
- Visible (no implicit information).
- Expressive (easy to state what we mean).
- Understandable (making communication simpler).
- Easy to use (an obvious need, yet frequently ignored).

We also need proper tools to support these methods. In structural terms three specific functions should be present in any requirements tool: elicitation, representation and analysis (Fig.3.14).

These cover the actions of gathering information, formally recording this information, and then checking it for consistency, conflicts and completeness. Such information is derived from a variety of sources, including users (humans), equipment data and formal documents such as the SOR. It should be appreciated that only the customer can provide this information. In an ideal world these three actions would be performed once, as a set of sequential operations. In practice the process is an ongoing one, with regular overlapping of actions. There are constant iterations through these steps as new data is acquired, ideas refined, and old information modified or discarded.

What's been described so far takes place in all engineering projects. Requirements-handling strategies in engineering are usually quite formalized: but only on a company basis. The techniques are well known and practised, adapted as necessary to suit particular local conditions. Specific prescriptive methods, which can be applied across a variety of applications, are virtually unknown. This hasn't been a problem though, because of the rigour and discipline inherent in engineering projects. Unfortunately, in the past (only the past?), rigour and program development have been mutually exclusive events. To rectify this situation – at least as far as the requirements phases are concerned – a number of methods have been developed. Some have been designed for very specific uses; others intended for general usage. A review of the mainstream ones is given by Finkelstein and Potts (1985). The following section describes the concepts underlying one particular method intended for general use.

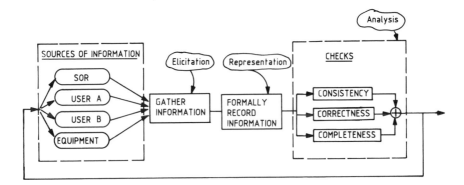

Fig.3.14 Requirements elicitation, representation and analysis

3.4.3   Automated tools and viewpoint analysis

Defined **methods** are fine. They are the first step in formalizing analysis and specification techniques. Unfortunately there is one problem on which methods themselves make little impact: information complexity. How can we really be sure that, when dealing with complex requirements, information is:

- Consistent (we haven't made mistakes in gathering and recording the data)?
- Correct (there aren't wrong or conflicting requirements laid down within the requirements themselves)?
- Complete (items haven't been omitted)?

It's extremely difficult, time-consuming and tedious to do this manually. Clearly, automated tools are needed. Then the question arises: what can we sensibly automate? Ideas, concepts, meaning: all are beyond automation. We can only work with facts. Now, systems can be described in terms of their internal data, the data flow through them, and actions performed on this data. To a large extent we can automate this description, as shown in Fig.3.15.

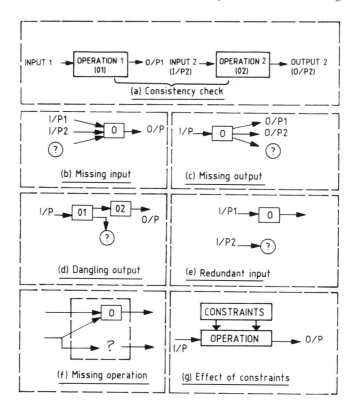

Fig.3.15 Automated checking rules

First we describe individual operations within the system, together with their inputs and outputs. It is then possible to check for consistency between operations, as in Fig.3.15a. Assume, for instance, that the requirements specification defines that the output of operation 01 acts as the input to 02. Thus both output1 and input2 represent the same entity. If during the recording process different entities are assigned to these, the error can be quickly identified – provided all information is held in a common store. Thus any automated tool has at its heart a common database.

Many other errors can be picked up in this way. These include:

- Missing inputs; Fig.3.15b (an operation, to produce the desired output, needs three inputs; but only two are provided).
- Missing outputs, Fig.3.15c (an operation must produce three outputs to satisfy system structure and operation; however, only two are specified in the SOR).

- Dangling outputs, Fig.3.15d (specified operations produce outputs which aren't used anywhere).
- Redundant inputs, Fig.3.15e (inputs are specified in the SOR, but no operations are performed on these within the system).
- Missing operations, Fig.3.15f (inputs are provided, outputs are expected, but no operations are specified in the requirements document).

Constraint effects can also be introduced, Fig.3.15g. We can, for instance, define that:

- Operations may be controlled by specific enabling/disabling conditions.
- Selection of operations may be required.
- Repeated activation of operations may be invoked.

Now this is splendid – but its effectiveness depends on how well we can define the set of operations in the first place. One concept which has been highly effective here is that of viewpoint analysis.

The notion of viewpoints is based on common sense; that is, we all see things from our own point of view. Consider a system which consists of a propulsion engine driving a ship's propeller via gearing and shafting, Fig.3.16.

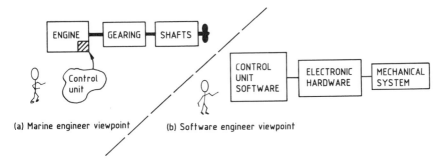

Fig.3.16 Viewpoint concept

Attached to the engine is a digital control unit, its function being to modulate engine speed. To the marine engineer the controller is insignificant when compared with the mechanical systems. Yet the software engineer responsible for the controller programs may have a totally different perception of the situation. He may regard software as **the** single most important item in the whole system, electronic hardware being a poor second. Mechanical systems almost disappear from sight.

The viewpoint analysis concept recognizes that systems cannot be adequately described from a single point of view; many must be taken into account. By setting out a system description as seen from all relevant viewpoints, consistency, correctness and completeness can be monitored. We can then produce a software specification which is totally consistent, correct and complete – but only in terms of the information recorded in the first place. Be warned: total completeness is another myth.

3.4.4   Viewpoint analysis — an example

Assume that we have been asked to supply a digital controller for the system shown in Fig.3.17. How many viewpoints should be taken into account? There isn't a unique answer to this; it really depends on each particular case. One tendency is to think only in terms of inanimate objects; we frequently forget people and their interactions with the system. For this example we will describe the system as seen from the points of view of the operator and other major system items, Fig.3.18.

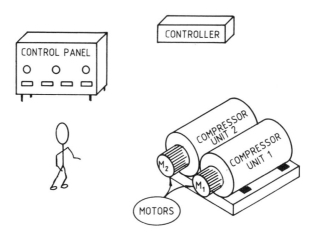

Fig.3.17 Specimen system

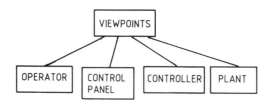

Fig.3.18 Viewpoint diagram for specimen system

Each viewpoint is described in terms of its inputs, actions (processing) and outputs, Fig.3.19. The appropriate information is usually recorded in tabular form, precise details depending on the particular analysis method used. In the case of CORE (Controlled Requirements Expression – chapter 10), the layout follows the pattern of Fig.3.20.

Here part descriptions are given for the operator and control panel viewpoints. The diagram, which is self-explanatory, highlights the important features of viewpoints and viewpoint description diagrams:

- Each viewpoint describes one or more system processing operations.
- Any particular processing operation takes place in one, and only one, viewpoint.
- Inputs and outputs must balance across the full set of diagrams.

There are two aspects of viewpoint analysis which cannot be automated. First, a set of viewpoints has to be established in the first place. Secondly, **all** relevant information needs to be recorded. It is perfectly possible to have a balance across the set of diagrams and yet have essential data missing.

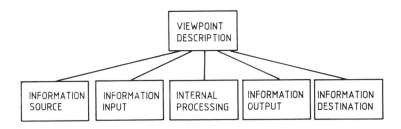

Fig.3.19 Viewpoint contents

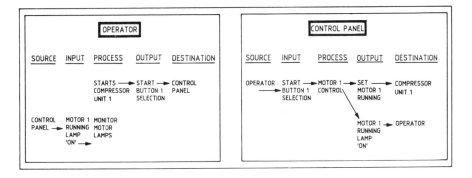

Fig.3.20 Viewpoint description diagrams

3.4.5   Analysis versus specification

Viewpoint analysis is an effective way of extracting, evaluating and collating information. The result should be a comprehensive description of the required system behaviour and its attributes. But two important features still need to be defined: what precisely happens within each process, and how do these relate in time (the system dynamic behaviour). To describe these we need to show three features:

- The data flow through a system.
- Detailed processing of this data.
- When such processing events occur.

One practical technique does this by combining data flow and events in a single description diagram, Fig.3.21. Note that here we aren't really concerned with absolute time, more the sequence of events. Diagrams like these can be formed for each viewpoint, being decomposed as necessary to show more detailed information. By recording this information in the same database as the viewpoint diagrams, consistency is maintained. Moreover, detailed descriptions can be recomposed to eliminate mistakes which may have occurred during decomposition.

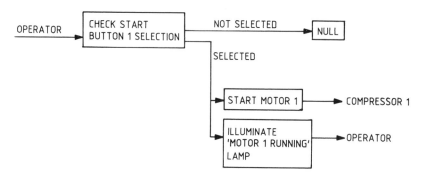

Fig.3.21 Combining data flow and events (control panel viewpoint)

These diagrams not only amplify information contained in the viewpoint descriptions; they also provide a bridge between requirements analysis and software specification. Our objective during software specification is to produce a definitive document which states what the system is required to do. Fundamentally each requirements specification document consists of three parts: functional, non-functional and development requirements, Fig.3.22. This model of the software requirements specification is based on that defined in STARTS (1987).

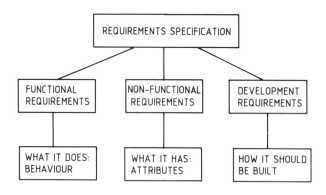

Fig.3.22 Software specification features

3.4.6 Functional, non-functional and development requirements specifications

Functional requirements specifications relate to system behaviour as shown in Fig.3.23. They describe system operation from three perspectives: what systems do, when they do it, and how they respond to deviations of normal behaviour. Note that they should not define **how** these requirements are to be satisfied.

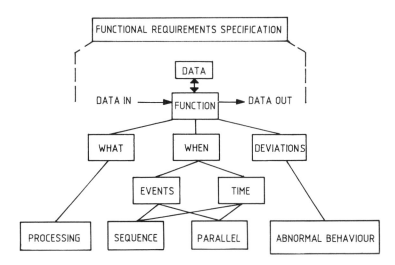

Fig.3.23 Aspects of functional requirements specifications

Observe that data input to the system, output from the system and that contained within the system itself forms part of the specification model.

The 'when' aspect expresses the dynamic behaviour of systems, both in terms of system events and real time. Events **may** be time dependent; but here the important point is their relationship to each other. For instance, it should not be possible to launch a missile until its hatch cover is removed. Time may be absolute, being defined in terms of the normal calendar time clock. Alternatively it may be a relative value, as in 'the low oil pressure alarm is to be inhibited for 40 seconds after the start switch is pressed'. It's also important that, when specifying dynamic behaviour, we distinguish between parallel actions and sequential ones. This can have a profound effect on resulting design decisions.

All real-time systems must be designed to cope with abnormal conditions to ensure safe operation. Where possible all significant deviations should be defined, together with appropriate exception-handling responses.

The information and diagrams produced previously form the basis for the software requirements specification document. These identify the various functions, the data flows, processing of data, dependencies and deviant behaviour. The major working diagrams are those which combine system data and events; viewpoint descriptions are less useful. These diagrams need to be augmented by text specifications to provide a full description of the function. There isn't a particular prescriptive format for these documents; only guidelines can be given. The following listing (Listing 3.1) is a very simplified high-level description of part of a flight control system.

```
**********************************************************************
FUNCTIONAL REQUIREMENT SPECIFICATION FOR MRCA AVIONICS:
SYSTEM: Flight Control.
SUB-SYSTEM: Autopilot.

1. Process: The autopilot, when in hard mode, is required to control
            altitude to 500 feet, plus or minus 10 feet, at airspeeds up
            to 500 knots.
2. Inputs:  Altitude, airspeed and groundspeed.
            Terrain-following radar.
            Angle of attack.
            Roll, pitch and yaw gyros.
            Stick demand.
3. Outputs: Aileron, rudder and elevator servo commands.
4. Major error: Loss of altitude or radar signals.
5. Exception response: Disengage autopilot normal mode, climb instantly.

**********************************************************************
```

Listing 3.1

Non-functional system requirements specifications are shown in Fig.3.24. These define:

- How well a function should be performed (performance).
- How the system connects to its environment (interfaces).
- What limitations are placed on the design (constraints).
- Anything which doesn't fit into these three groupings (others).

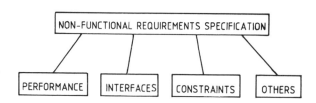

Fig.3.24 Non-functional requirements specification

It's impossible to define precisely what non-functional specifications should contain. Much depends on the particular system being assessed. However, guidance can be given. As an example, consider the system described by the functional specification of Listing 3.1. Its corresponding non-functional specification is given below (Listing 3.2). This, of course, is a highly simplified version; the real one would occupy many pages of text.

```
****************************************************************************
```
NON-FUNCTIONAL REQUIREMENT SPECIFICATION FOR MRCA AVIONICS:
SYSTEM: Flight Control.
SUB-SYSTEM: Autopilot.

1.PERFORMANCE:
   Computation: The control algorithm is of the form

$$Ka[(1+ST1)(1+ST2)]/[(1+ST3)(1+ST4)]$$

   Computation time: This must be achieved in 5 milliseconds.
   Computation accuracy: Calculations must be accurate to within 0.01%.
   Control loop update rates: 100 per second.
   Variation on loop sampling time: 1 millisecond from sample to sample.
   Response to loss of altitude signal: 100 microseconds maximum.
   Redundancy: Quad redundant processor system.
   System fault handling: Majority voting on processor outputs. Any
                          failure to be signalled to the crew.
   Mean Time Between Failures (MTBF) per control channel: 5000 hours.
   Reliability per control channel: 99.98%
   Mean Time To Repair (MTTR) per control channel: 1 hour.
   Storage capacity: 200 KBytes.

2. INTERFACES.
2.1 Interfaces - MMI.
      The pilots will be able to select hard, medium or soft rides via a
      touch screen facility on the head down display.
2.2 Interfaces - Plant.
   (a)Analogue input signals: These are derived from the following
      sources:
            Altitude, airspeed and grounaspeed.
            Terrain-following radar signal.
            Angle of attack.
            Roll, pitch and yaw gyros.
            Stick demand.
      All are digitised using a 12 bit analogue to digital converter
      having a conversion time of 10 microseconds.
   (b)Analogue output signals: These are fed to the following items:
            Aileron, rudder and elevator servo controllers.
      A 12 bit digital to analogue converter is used on the output of the
      controller.
   (c) Avionics data bus: All state information is to be fed out onto the
      aircraft Mil-Std 1553 data bus.
2.3 Interfaces - Software.
   The application software will be designed to interface to the VRTX32
   real time executive.

3. DESIGN CONSTRAINTS.
   Programming language: ADA.
   Operating system: VRTX32.
   Avionic's data bus communication protocols: Mil-Std 1553.
   Processor type: Motorola 68020.
   Maximum memory capacity (including expansion capability): 500 KBytes.
   Spare processor performance capacity on delivery: 50% min.
   Documentation: JSP188.

4. OTHER CONSTRAINTS.
   Maximum size: Half ATR case size.
   Maximum weight: 10 lb.
   Temperature range: -55 to +125 degrees centigrade.
   Servicing policy: Line replaceable unit.
   Test: Built in test to identify faults to unit level.

```
****************************************************************************
```

Listing 3.2

It can be seen here that there is overlap between sections. For instance, use of the VRTX executive is listed both as an interface requirement **and** as a design constraint. But this is necessary because it applies to both areas of design. Furthermore, it's not always easy to decide which category items fit into. The temperature range requirement is listed here as an 'other' constraint; but it could equally well be viewed as a design constraint.

Functional specifications are highly visible parts of any development. Therefore, no matter what analysis and specification technique is used, it's normally fairly easy to identify these factors. Non-functional specifications are equally important. Unfortunately, when using informal techniques, they can disappear in the detail. To minimize this problem – and that's all we can ever hope for – methods must be used which bring these factors formally into the design process. They then remain visible throughout the rest of the software life cycle.

The third component of software requirements specifications, development requirements, varies considerably from application to application. In the simplest situation the customer and supplier agree on:

- What is to be supplied.
- When it is to be supplied and installed.

At the other extreme requirements cover:

- The extent of supply.
- Delivery and installation.
- Formal acceptance testing.
- Project management structures and techniques.
- Formal progress reporting procedures.
- Configuration control systems.
- Design methods, methodologies and plans.
- Quality assurance.
- Reliability aspects.
- Legal, contractual and certification aspects.

One generalization can be made. As projects get larger the number of system requirements needing formal consideration increases. Even if the customer hasn't demanded such formality the supplier should impose it. Because without strict project management, formal rules, defined reporting procedures, proper recording techniques and configuration control, chaos is always likely to break out.

3.5   COMMUNICATION ASPECTS —THE ROLE OF PROTOTYPING

3.5.1   Prototyping — an introduction

In engineering a prototype is a pre-production version of a manufactured product such as a component, sub-assembly, system, etc. The purpose of building a prototype is to prove design and manufacturing aspects as early as possible – before resources are committed to full-scale production. A number of questions are evaluated during prototyping, including:

- Is the product actually feasible? In other words, are problems present which are fundamentally impossible to overcome?
- Are there unforeseen high-risk technical and cost aspects?
- Are the design and build correct? That is, has the correct product been built (validation), and has the product been built correctly (verification)?
- Can it be built in a manufacturing environment (as opposed to the hand-crafting methods of the prototyping phase)?
- Can it be built for the right price?

Once this phase is completed manufacture can commence with a very high level of confidence in the final product (even then this isn't guaranteed – witness the De Lorean car saga).

Normally prototypes are built to full scale. In some cases though, scaled down versions are cheaper and easier to produce. For instance, a three-eighths scale remotely controlled F15 aircraft research vehicle was used to evaluate digital flight control systems. But no matter which method is used, prototyping is carried out for one basic reason: to answer the questions set out above. Once this is done the prototype is usually consigned to the scrap-heap; it has served its purpose.

3.5.2   Software prototyping

Prototyping of software systems is, at this time, in its infancy (perhaps its omission from the software design cycle says more about the attitudes of software practitioners than pages of words). Fortunately though, software engineers are now beginning to understand that prototyping can bring real benefits to professional designs. Put in a nutshell, it helps us to produce the right job, on time, and within budget. It can be applied in a number of different ways – and at different times – in the software life cycle, Fig.3.25.

The delineation of areas is based upon those defined by Watkins (1988).

(a)   Exploratory prototyping
This is used as a tool in the development of the SOR to a point where it is acceptable to both parties. A particular version of this is animation prototyping. This involves the use of animated graphics to enhance communication between the customer and the supplier.

(b)   Solution prototyping
Here the system software requirements are prototyped, typically using a 4th generation language such as PROLOG. Frequently these prototyping tools produce executable code.

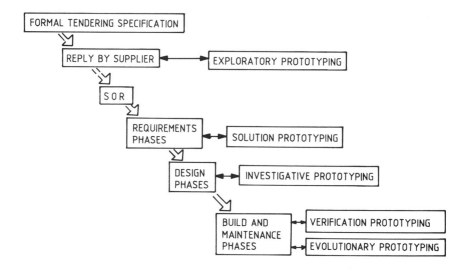

Fig.3.25 Prototyping within the software life cycle

(c) Investigative prototyping
This enables the designer to evaluate alternative software solutions at the design stage.

(d) Verification prototyping
This method is used to evaluate source code produced by using formal specification methods (chapter 7).

(e) Evolutionary prototyping
This describes the use of working prototypes to evaluate the effects of modifications and upgrades.

A number of points need to be made here concerning definitions, usage and prototype facilities.

First, definitions. The definitions given here are not necessarily generally accepted. This is especially true of evolutionary prototyping. For many workers, true evolutionary prototyping spans the whole life cycle.

Secondly, usage of the prototyping methods is not simple and clear-cut. For instance, investigative prototyping can be (and frequently is) implemented using tools designed for solution prototyping.

Thirdly, prototype facilities vary considerably. At one extreme are models designed for use in very specific parts of the software life cycle – and destined to be thrown away after use. At the other end of the scale are general purpose models from which actual production systems emerge.

This chapter is concerned with the 'front-end' section of the software development cycle, up to the start of the design phases. Two aspects of prototyping are relevant to this area: exploratory and solution methods. The following sections discuss these in more detail. For those generally interested in following up the topic consult Budde (1984) and Tanik and Yeh (1989).

3.5.3   Requirements prototyping

In this section the combination of exploratory and solution prototyping is, for brevity, defined as 'requirements prototyping'. There is, in fact, another reason for grouping them together. Basically they attempt to solve the same problems.

Central to requirements prototyping is the use of models ('prototypes') to demonstrate the essential features of the proposed system. Equally important is the provision of tools for constructing and manipulating these models. Requirements prototypes serve a number of purposes, the primary ones being to:

- Act as a reference point for supplier–customer communication.
- Allow both parties to increase their understanding of the proposed system.
- Allow both parties to appreciate properly the content and implications of the requirements documents.
- Highlight important qualities such as dynamic behaviour, response times, exception handling, etc.

Fig.3.26 describes the prototyping cycle as applied either to the tendering or the requirements phases – or both.

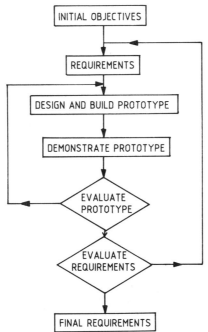

Fig.3.26 The prototyping cycle for requirements extraction

From some initial objectives a set of requirements is formed, expressed in a preliminary defining document. This, together with verbal and other sources of information, form guidelines for the construction of a prototype. Once the prototype is built it is demonstrated and evaluated, being modified until it satisfies the initial specification. At this point the requirements themselves can be evaluated using the prototype facilities. Problems found here normally result in changes to the requirements until they are acceptable to both parties. The outcome is a definitive requirements specification. In the first instance this forms the SOR; later it acts as the basis for the software specification (in practice, of course, events don't take place quite so neatly).

What are the limitations of prototypes? In other words, how do they differ from the final (production) version of the system? This isn't an easy question to answer. There aren't, at the present time, clear, defined and agreed guidelines. Prototypes vary from simple static text type models through to those which are virtually full simulations. As a general rule prototypes should behave like the real system but with reduced functionality. Differences occur because prototypes:

- May be required to illustrate only part of the final system.
- Might require the use of computer resources which aren't available in the target system (e.g. the model itself may require 500kByte of RAM space to run in, yet the target system may only have 128kByte available).
- Do not aim – or may be unable – to produce real-time responses.
- May not be powerful enough to demonstrate all operational functions.

All prototyping methods should be economical, fast and adaptable, for the reasons given below.

(a) Economical
Requirements prototyping is used right at the front end of the software development cycle. One possible conclusion of the analysis phase is that the proposed system is unattainable. Now, whether the project is abandoned at this stage or pursued in a modified form, the first lot of work is a write-off. Therefore costs must be kept to a minimum. This also implies a short time scale.

(b) Fast
Answers need to be produced quickly, especially prior to and during the tendering phases of the project.

(c) Adaptable
Development of prototypes is a continual – and not a once through – process. Thus it is essential that the model can be modified easily and quickly.

Unless these targets are attained three problems may be encountered:

- Slowness in responding to customer enquiries and requirements. This leads

to a lack of confidence by the customer in the supplier's abilities.
- Inflexible models. The consequence is that substantial effort is needed to modify and upgrade prototypes as time goes by.
- Excessive effort in developing prototypes in the first place. Prototyping is **not** an alternative to design.

Methods designed to satisfy the aims outlined above are categorized as 'rapid prototyping' – the process of building and evaluating quickly a set of prototypes.

3.5.4   Practical rapid prototyping of system requirements

Rapid prototyping has its origins in the development of interactive information systems (Mason and Carey, 1983). Three major factors were identified: the user interface, the modelling environment and an output support system, Fig.3.27.

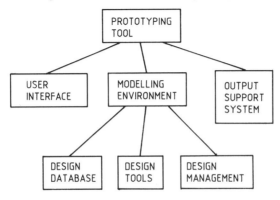

Fig.3.27 Elements of a prototyping tool

Such work showed that effective tools are needed if prototyping is to be an economical proposition. Without these it takes as much effort to develop a prototype as the production system itself. This perception lead to the development of computer aided rapid prototyping, also called fast prototyping. Central to this are a software design database, design tools specific to the prototyping method, and an overall design management sub-system. The function of the user interface is self-explanatory, but output support system features are tool specific. The output system is primarily concerned with demonstrating prototype operation and attributes. At its simplest level it produces fixed static descriptions in text form. At the other extreme it provides dynamic interaction features, representation of requirements in programming language form and debugging facilities (Luqi, 1989).

Requirements prototyping in real-time systems has two distinct aspects. The first describes user interaction with display systems – interactive information handling (IIH). The second relates to the interaction of a system with its external environment.

Interactive information handling is associated with human-computer inter-actions (HCI), usually involving screen displays. Here 'screen' prototyping is used to elicit user feedback on the 'feel' of the interface before its design is finalized. HCI operations rarely involve complex information processing or logic functions, the primary concern being the presentation of information. The purpose of screen prototyping is to ensure that operator responses are efficient, correct and timely. IIH in real-time systems is broadly similar to that in batch and on-line systems. These have features which are common to all applications, and which recur with great regularity. This includes menu formats, report generation and screen painters.

The same cannot be said for system-environment interactions. Tools designed to prototype these functions must support very diverse activities. At the present time this is a relatively new area of work. It would appear though that mimicking system actions (animation prototyping) is a powerful and meaningful way of demonstrating system behaviour (Cooling and Hughes, 1989).

The application of both screen and animation prototyping to real-time systems can be illustrated using the plant of Fig.3.28. This represents a chemical plant, designed to take in gas at atmospheric pressure and compress it into liquid form. This liquid is deposited, at high pressure, into a storage vessel. Two compressors are used, connected in parallel. A variety of valves are fitted which, together with the compressors, provide control of plant operation. It is required to equip this system with a processor-based controller having appropriate man–machine interfaces.

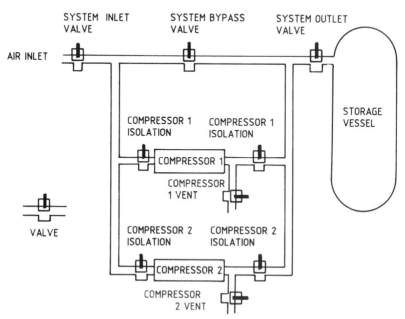

Fig.3.28 Plant schematic diagram

First let's see how screen prototyping fits into this. Based on information supplied by the customer a series of fixed sequence displays are designed and built. These computer display screens represent particular man–machine interactions or activities, Figs.3.29 and 3.30. The user interacts with these as if they were the final product, but with one major difference. The dialogue is preset. Thus the scenario is a fixed one, the user following a defined set of instructions. The system cannot, at this stage, be truly interactive. After all, the software required for these functions has not yet been written. Nevertheless the technique is a powerful one for resolving HCI requirements in real-time systems.

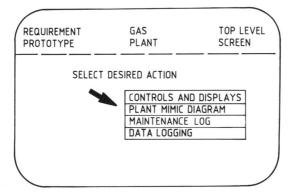

Fig.3.29 Main activity screen

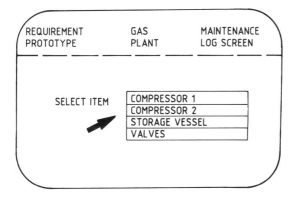

Fig.3.30 Maintenance log activity screen

Screen prototyping doesn't help very much in describing interactions between the plant and its environment (this also includes the operator). Instead, animating plant operation is highly effective as a learning and communication tool, Fig.3.31.

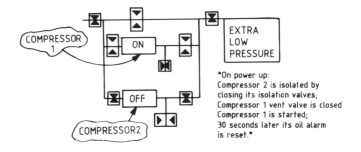

(a) POWER UP

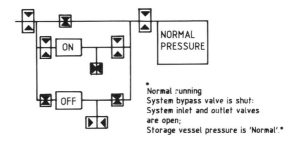

(b) NORMAL RUNNING

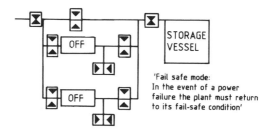

(c) FAIL SAFE

Fig.3.31 Animation prototype

Given here are particular frames from the animation, showing power-up, normal running and fail-safe conditions. Attached to each frame is the corresponding section from the SOR. In the initial stage of analysis each component is described in 'black box' terms; little internal detail is provided. Even so the model allows the user to single-step through various sequences and to interact with the display. As development progresses the model can be elaborated and refined. In particular, time constraints, component performance factors and safety features can be included. Thus the prototype is developed in an evolutionary manner, ultimately approaching the performance of a simulator.

Rapid prototyping is an effective and realistic requirements analysis method. But to be commercially practical three criteria must be satisfied. First, models must be produced quickly – ranging from a few days to a few weeks. Second, the model should represent the problem in terms of the customer's viewpoint. Third, both the customer and the supplier must be allowed to interact with the model.

3.6   FINAL COMMENTS

A number of requirements analysis methods and tools have been developed during the last two decades. But at the present time, there isn't any single generally accepted technique or tool. This is especially true in the real-time field. The situation is further complicated because some methods are specific to particular toolsets. Even more confusing are the claims made by proponents of the various methods. For those seriously interested in acquiring a requirements analysis tool the starting point should be the STARTS Guide (1987). After that it's a case of assessing possible candidates against the needs of real-time systems. Then, and only then, can informed decisions be made.

REFERENCES

Budde, R. *et al.* (1984), *Approaches to Prototyping*, Springer-Verlag, ISBN 3–540–13490–5.

Cooling, J.E. and Hughes, T.S. (1989), The emergence of rapid prototyping as a real-time software development tool, IEE second international conference on *Software Engineering for Real-time Systems*, Cirencester, UK, 18th–20th September.

DeMarco, T. (1978), *Structured Analysis and System Specification*, Yourdon Press, ISBN 0–917072–07–3.

Farnan, D.N. (1975), Reliable computer software – what it is and how to get it, project report, Defense Systems Management School, Fort Belvoir, Virginia, November.

Finkelstein, A. and Potts, C. (1985), FOREST – Evaluation of existing requirements extraction, strategies, Alvey project report R1, Imperial College of Science and Technology, Department of Computing, Queen's Gate, London.

Key, M. (1986), The reasons why software has a bad name, IFAC Conference, *Experience with the Management of Software Projects*, Heidelberg, FRG, pp97–102.

Luqi (1989), Software evolution through rapid prototyping, *IEEE Computer*, **Vol.22**, No.5, pp13–25, May.

Mason, R.E.A. and Carey, T.T. (1983), Prototyping interactive information systems, *Communications of the ACM*, **Vol.26**, No.5, pp347–354, May.

Sommerville, I. (1989), *Software Engineering*, 3rd Edition, Addison Wesley Publishing Co., Wokingham, UK, ISBN 0–201–17568–1.

STARTS Guide (1987), *The STARTS Guide – A Guide to Methods and Software Tools for the Construction of Large Real-time Systems*, NCC Publications, Manchester, UK, ISBN 0–85012–619–3.

Tanik, M.M. and Yeh, R.T. (1989), Rapid prototyping in software development, *IEEE Computer*, **Vol.22**, No.5, May.

Watkins, P. (1988), Investigation into improvements in software development centring on rapid prototyping, project report, Department of Electronic and Electrical Engineering, Loughborough University of Technology, April.

FURTHER READING

Gladden, G.R. (1982), Stop the life cycle, I want to get off, *ACM SIGSOFT Software Engineering Notes*, **Vol.7**, No.2, April, pp35–39.

McCracken, D.D. and Jackson, M.A. (1982), Life cycle concept considered harmful, *ACM SIGSOFT Software Engineering Notes*, **Vol.7**, No.2, April, pp29–32.

Swann, T. (1982), Requirements decomposition and other myths, AGARD: *Software for Avionics*, The Hague, September.

Chapter Four

Program design concepts

The effects produced by poor software – covered in chapter 2 – can't be dismissed lightly. Equipment damage, personal injury and deaths have resulted from mistakes in software. Even where such disasters are avoided software liabilities can financially cripple a company. Three factors are usually at work here: late delivery of the software, overrun on budget and massive installation/maintenance efforts. Therefore the primary goal of any software team is to eliminate the possibility of such events. To do this it must deliver dependable software, on time, within cost. These 'high-level' objectives can be attained only by using professional design methods. Such methods enable designers to achieve specific 'low-level' targets for quality code production. These features, already discussed in chapter 2, include:

- Formal and rigorous design methods.
- Properly documented software.
- Understandable designs.
- Robust and stable software
- Maintainable programs.
- Portable and re-usable software.

These are the goals of the software engineer. How well they are achieved depends considerably on both the tools and techniques used in the design process. Here we limit ourselves to techniques, the purpose of the chapter being to:

- Outline fundamental design strategies and design factors incorporated within these strategies.
- Describe how and why modular design is essential for the production of good software.
- Show the influence of structured programming on software design.
- Describe modern design methodologies, including functionally structured, data structured and object-oriented methods.

Chapters 5 and 6 extend this by showing how such methods are used to produce working design documents. Chapter 10 describes these in the context of specific design methodologies and computer-aided software engineering (CASE) tools.

4.1   DESIGN FUNDAMENTALS

4.1.1   The design and development process — an introduction

Design and development is the process of turning ideas (the specification) into reality (the product), Fig.4.1.

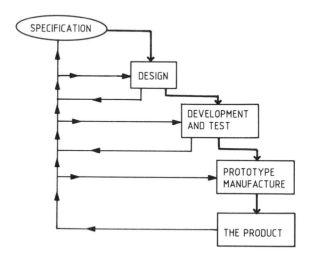

Fig.4.1 The design and development process

There are a number of distinct stages in this operation; each one can be analysed and described as a separate item. Here we'll concentrate on that identified as 'design'. But remember, in producing the product, they are highly interactive. The idea that design is a once-through activity, never to be repeated, belongs to the world of science fiction. Consequently any useful design method must be able to handle change easily, simply and efficiently.

The purpose of this section is to describe the design process in general conceptual terms. However, many people find that abstract descriptions of processes aren't especially helpful. So the approach used here takes a particular (fictional) auto-engineering design problem and shows alternative ways of solving it. It then generalizes from these specific ideas and methods to the more abstract design concepts.

Assume that the objective is to design a vehicle power-train system. The fuel source is paraffin, the final drive method being two road wheels. From this simplified specification the designer organizes his ideas, in the first case expressing the solution in very general terms. As with most forms of engineering this involves the use of diagrams (Fig.4.2). Here the design specification is translated into a number of feasible alternatives. The expanded descriptions are more detailed and refined, but still operate at the conceptual level. Now the designer can move – in stages – to the general design level (Fig.4.3). At

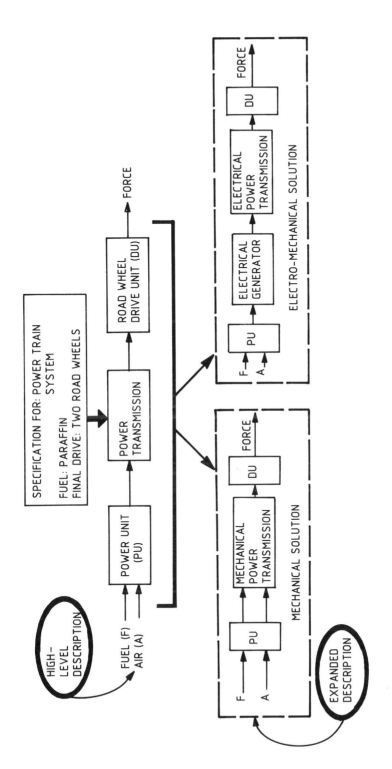

Fig.4.2 Specification translation – high-level description

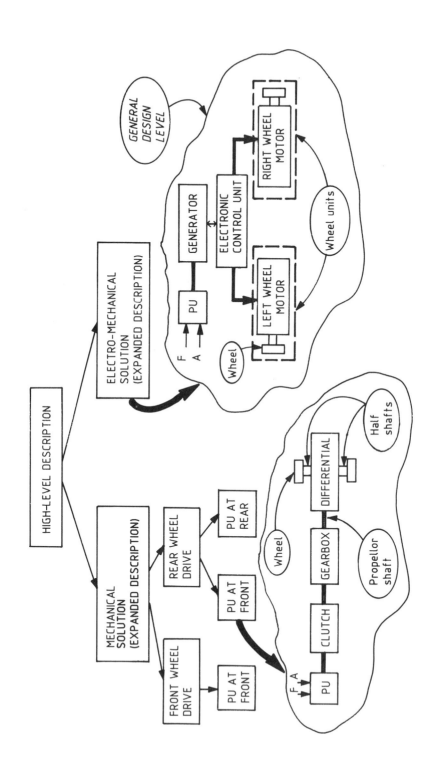

Fig.4.3 Translation to the general design level

this stage the 'best' solution is identified, and work proceeds into the detailed design phase (Fig.4.4).

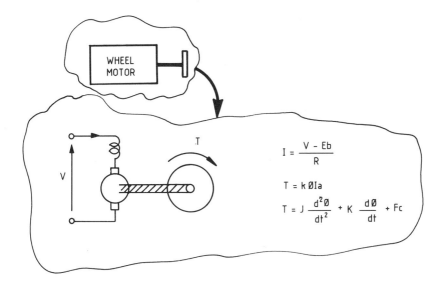

The equations shown in the figure:

$$I = \frac{V - Eb}{R}$$

$$T = k\,\emptyset\,Ia$$

$$T = J\frac{d^2\emptyset}{dt^2} + K\frac{d\emptyset}{dt} + Fc$$

Fig.4.4 Detailed design level

This approach should sound reasonable and logical. Good. But you may then well ask 'what's so special about this? Isn't it what we'd expect to happen?'. Yes, but because the approach is 'sensible' we tend not to see the profound design concepts inherent in the method. Let's look at it again, stage by stage.

First, there is translation from a specification to a conceptual solution. This is a creative activity which cannot be taught; it must be learned. Here there is no substitute for experience and knowledge. Moreover, even at this very abstract stage, the designer is guided by his knowledge of what is practicable. So, note point one: creativity and knowledge.

The second stage, expanding the basic ideas, is one which involves both design creativity and design technique. Expansion takes place in a controlled, organized and logical manner. Note point two: method and organization.

Observe here that two solutions have been generated (many others are possible). This highlights the fact that there isn't a unique answer to each problem. A good designer will try first to identify realistic alternatives and then assess their qualities. Here, for instance, the assessment factors involve cost, performance, technology level, manufacturing aspects, etc. Point three: identification and evaluation of design options.

It may seem surprising that it is easier to assess information when dealing with an abstract model. But what this does is allow us to ignore detail and concentrate on the big picture (the really important view). Point four: postponement of detailed design decisions for as long as possible.

When the descriptive model is expanded into something fairly specific the following factors can be tackled:

- Identification of functions and partitioning by subsystems.
- Identification of interfaces between subsystems.
- Evaluation of subsystem interaction.
- Identification of work-loading and allocation.
- Assessment of manpower requirements.

Point five: general design evaluation.

At this stage the basic feasibility of the project has been assured. Detailed design calculations can be carried out knowing, at least, that the right problem is being tackled. Point six: solve the right problem.

The process described here is one of working from a very general top-level view of the problem to a specific design solution. This approach is usually called 'top-down'. However, no real design proceeds in this way. The designer always guides the work towards feasible solutions (often unconsciously). That is, he uses knowledge relating to the bottom end of the design process, a 'bottom-up' method. Added to this is a further complicating factor. Frequently the designer identifies high-risk areas early on in the design exercise (in the example here for instance, the use of electrical power transmission may raise special technical difficulties). Such problems are likely to be tackled early (and in some detail), a 'middle-out' design approach.

Gathering all these facts, recommendations and ideas together enables us to define the rules of workable design techniques:

- Use method and organization in the design process.
- First define the problem solution in general concepts.
- Identify and evaluate all sensible design options.
- Postpone detailed design decisions for as long as possible.
- Identify system functions.
- Partition the overall system into manageable subsystems.
- Identify interfaces between subsystems.
- Evaluate subsystem interaction.
- Solve the right problem.
- Base the design method on a top-down approach augmented by bottom-up and middle-out actions.
- Always review and, where necessary, re-do designs (iterate).
- Be prepared to throw away awkward, complex or redundant design parts (no matter how attached to them you become).

By using these rules we've introduced order and logic into system design, that is, structure. Now, you'll see the words 'structured design' in every textbook on software engineering. Some computer scientists actually believe that this general methodology was invented by the software community. In fact all good engineering design is structured; the Egyptians practised it thousands of years ago when they built the Pyramids.

4.1.2   Fundamental design strategies

Currently three distinct methodologies are used for software design:

- Functional structuring.
- Object structuring.
- Data structuring.

In reality there is a fourth approach, defined by Tom DeMarco as the 'Mugwump School' (Hansen, 1986). It is practised by 'people who believe design is for cissies and that the structure of the system should be whatever occurs to the coder while seated at the terminal'. This has no place in a professional environment; yet all too often real-time software is designed in this way.

These three design methods aren't restricted to software systems; they apply to engineering in general. Therefore, to explain the concepts and principles involved, the engineering design of a vehicle system is described; later the ideas will be discussed in terms of software design.

The task in question is the design of a vehicle anti-skid braking system. Its purpose is to eliminate vehicle skidding by preventing lock-up of the wheels. The control system measures the speed of each wheel, calculates acceleration/deceleration values, and, using this data, detects the onset of wheel lock-up. Should lock-up occur then command signals back-off the braking effect. Speed sensors and brake actuators (hydraulic servo units) are fitted as appropriate.

First consider describing the system and its design using a functionally-structured method (Fig.4.5). Here the system structure is expressed in terms of the functional interaction of the different parts. In this case four functions are defined:

- Measure wheel speed.
- Store measured data.
- Calculate vehicle conditions.
- Output commands to brake units.

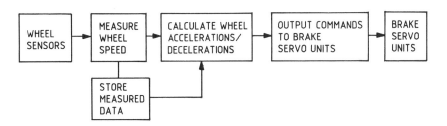

Fig.4.5 Functional view of the anti-skid system

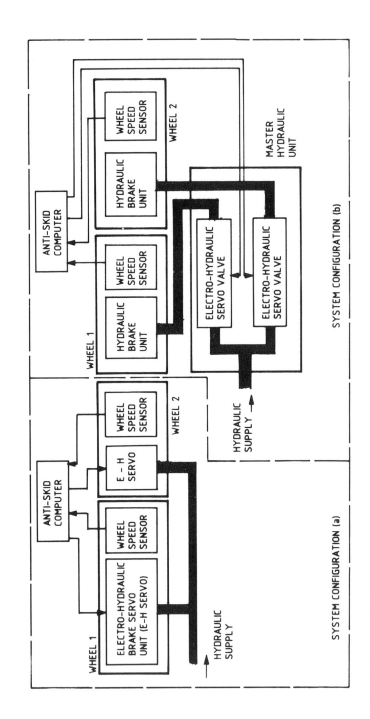

Fig.4.6 Anti-skid braking system

Using this functional description we **could** implement the system shown in Fig.4.6(a). Equally well we could adopt the method of Fig.4.6(b). In contrast, the object-structured method describes the system as a collection of objects (Fig.4.7), not functions.

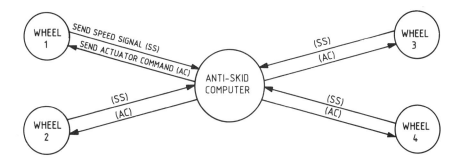

Fig.4.7 Object-structured view of the anti-skid system

Communication between objects is carried out using messages, the ones shown here being 'send speed signal' and 'send actuator command'. Object internal actions aren't shown (at this level) in order to hide the 'how' from the 'what'. By using this technique objects can be treated as separate but co-operating entities. This profoundly changes how we view the problem and institute design solutions. Remember that when using a functional approach, speed measurement, computation and actuator control are all linked together. But with object structuring they are quite clearly decoupled. This may not seem especially significant – until we change the system. Suppose now that each wheel is to be monitored for tyre pressure, this being linked into a diagnostic computer. Changing the object-structured design to reflect this modification is fairly simple, Fig.4.8.

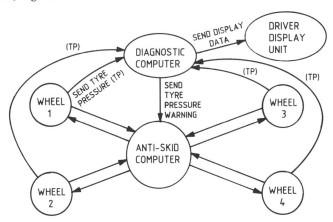

Fig.4.8 Modified object-structured diagram

By contrast the corresponding functionally-structured design would require a major re-build. However, this example isn't meant to imply that object structuring is better or easier than functional structuring. It's just a different way of looking at the same problem.

The final method is that of data structuring. It is based on the concept that systems are:

- Data driven.
- Shaped by their data structures.

Fig.4.9 shows the general aspects of this technique.

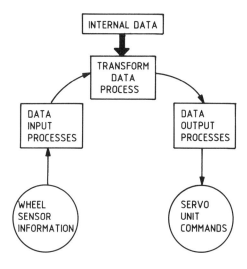

Fig.4.9 A data-structured view

'Data input processes' collect data from the vehicle system, manipulate them as appropriate and pass them onto the transformation process. This process implements the functional operations to be carried out on the data. The 'data output processes' extract information from the transformation process for use by the real world. The suggested design path is:

data structure → process structure → implementation

More will be said later concerning this topic when software design processes are described.

4.1.3   Design strategies — a comment

Each method described above illustrates one specific way of tackling a design and development problem. But these aren't mutually exclusive; using one doesn't preclude use of the others. Each provides a different view of the problem. In practice most solutions use a combination of the methods, picking them as appropriate. Some design methodologies are composites of these, which, at first, can be quite confusing.

Both functional and object structuring fit well into conventional design organizations, data structuring less so. It would appear that data-driven methods don't provide the right type of support for engineering design.

4.1.4   How to generate abysmal software — the good kludge guide

There are at least three ways to develop software: unplanned, apparently planned and properly designed. The first is practised by those who don't believe in software design. But, surprisingly, this is also true of the second group. Only it doesn't seem like it at the time. Such people produce plans; and don't use them at the coding stage. Documentation produced for the software is often done **after** coding. It may look impressive; whether it really describes what the code does is another matter.

Lee Harrisberger, in his *Engineermanship, a Philosophy of Design* (1966), describes the production of a 'kludge'. In essence this is a product that, no matter what you do, is always going to be a mess. Producing code without designing the software in the first place results in a kludge. For those who consider design rules to be an infringement on their creativity and individuality, the following good kludge guide is offered. Moreover the rest of the chapter can be skipped.

- Don't plan.
- Don't introduce structure or order into the software.
- Begin coding straight away.
- Be clever.
- Be obscure.
- Don't use standard methods – invent new ones.
- Insist that the source code listing is sufficient to document the software – and use cryptic and meaningless comments.
- Never revise the design.
- Make the software unportable.
- Sacrifice all to code efficiency.

The real reason for giving this guide is that it neatly and concisely highlights why so much software is abysmal. Simply put, good design methods are the direct opposite of these.

4.2   THE ELEMENTS OF MODULAR DESIGN

4.2.1   Introduction

At this stage the overall concepts of structured design should be clear (if they aren't, go back and re-read the sections above). We can now put them in the context of software design methodologies. But before doing so the more important elements and building blocks of the design process need to be explained. Some of these we've met already within the framework of general design procedures. Now their functions as software design elements are examined.

4.2.2   Modules and modularization

It can be seen that a basic feature of 'good' design is the partitioning of systems into smaller chunks. The primary reason is to reduce the total problem into one of manageable proportions (the 'head full of information' limit). In software terms this process is called 'modularization', the elements resulting from this being 'modules'. It is a basic requirement that modules should be fairly simple, thus enabling us to:

- Understand their purpose and structure.
- Verify and validate their correctness.
- Appreciate their interaction with other modules.
- Assess their effect on the overall software structure and operation.

But precisely what is a module? Many definitions are possible; here it is considered to be 'a software task which has a well-defined function and well-defined interfaces to other program elements'. Clearly, a module can be defined using functional structuring or object structuring or a combination of the two. How it's implemented is – at this stage – not important. Before doing that, the designer must answer one major question: precisely how should a system be modularized?

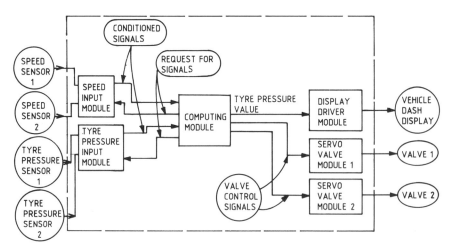

Fig.4.10 Modularization – solution 1

There isn't a unique solution to this; much depends on the particular application (Parnas, 1972). Even then, significantly different approaches can be used. Consider, for instance, writing software to implement the anti-skid braking and tyre-pressure monitoring systems. One solution is shown in Fig.4.10 (for simplicity only two wheels are automated). Note the similarity between this and Fig.4.5. This reinforces the fact that software design is just one stream within the total range of design techniques.

An alternative solution is that of Fig.4.11. This might be the one which maps the software onto the hardware in a more logical manner. Then again, it might not. It depends on the decisions which were made when designing the modules (Fig.4.12). These determine the resulting module structure, organization and performance. But how can we decide whether the modularization we've arrived at is a good one or not? The answer (in part, at least) lies in the properties of modules known as coupling and cohesion (Yourdon and Constantine, 1979).

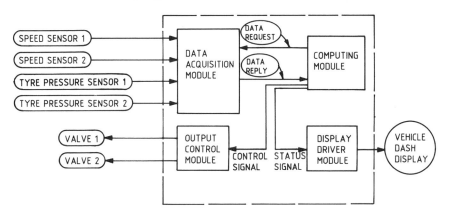

Fig.4.11 Modularization – solution 2

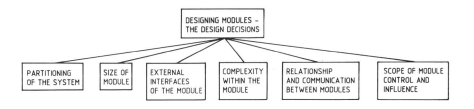

Fig.4.12 Modules – design decisions

4.2.3 Coupling — a measure of module independence

Modules cannot exist in isolation. Each one is designed to perform part of the total system function; therefore they must communicate with each other. Now, experience has shown that the amount of interaction between modules has a significant effect on software quality. Where modules are well defined, having clear functions and simple interfaces, levels of interaction are low. In other words, modules are relatively independent. Such designs are usually easy to understand; they are also reliable and maintainable when put into service. Moreover, the software exhibits a high degree of stability; changes within a single module don't 'ripple through' the program.

In aiming for low interaction we need to distinguish between information volume and information complexity. Transferring a large amount of data between modules may be a fairly simple task – if we're dealing with simple data types. For instance, moving an array of 500 elements is both straightforward and easy to comprehend. Yet a module which transfers five different data items may be much more difficult to understand – because it has a complex interface, as in:

WriteReal (Integrate(Square,a,b,Simpson,Intervals), 15);

where Integrate and Square are both function procedures. Consequently, reducing information **complexity** is a primary design aim. But this isn't the only factor which affects module interaction. Information **type** and **communication** methods also strongly influence system behaviour. Thus when evaluating the degree of module independence we need to take all three into account. This is done using a software measure called 'coupling'. Module coupling occurs in a number of ways, as follows:

- Content coupling.
- Common coupling.
- Stamp coupling.
- Data coupling by reference.
- Data coupling by value.

These are discussed in detail later.

When modules communicate, the information content may take various forms, Fig.4.13. In (a), module A sends data to B, just about the simplest contact method (typified by the conditioned speed signals of Fig.4.10).

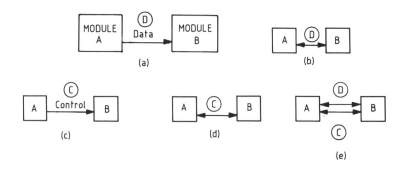

Fig.4.13 Communication between modules

Naturally enough data transfer can be a two-way process, (b). Modules also need to be able to control actions within other modules, leading to the use of control signals, Fig.4.13(c) ('flags', 'control couples'). Again looking at Fig.4.10, the 'request for signal' can be regarded as a control couple. This increases the interaction between modules; what happens in one depends on decisions made in the other. Control coupling can also be a two-way affair, (d), while the most general case involves two-way data and control couples, (e).

Note that no assumptions have been made about the relationship between modules. They may, for instance, have equal standing in the system. Alternatively there may be a hierarchical structure, involving calling and called modules (Fig.4.14).

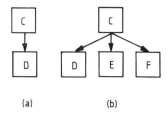

(a)   (b)

Fig.4.14 Hierarchical module structure

Two simple examples are shown here. In the first, C invokes D to perform some task; in the second, C first invokes D, then E, and finally F. These invoked modules are activated only by command of the calling module. Operations like these can be implemented quite easily in software, especially when using procedurized high-level languages. However, when modules have the same rank their activation is quite different; fundamentally it is a system (usually a real-time executive, chapter 9) function. Be warned: much published work on structured design implicitly assumes that modular designs are always hierarchical.

Many early texts on this topic were written from the DP point of view. In such designs control couples can be minimized (even more radically, in 1979 Yourdon considered them to be 'non-essential'). But for embedded software they are a natural and commonplace requirement, being essential for event signalling. So although they increase the coupling between modules, they can't be dispensed with. The rule is, use them with care and thought. And, with hierarchical modularization, control flags should only be transferred at a single level. If they pass through a number of levels there is a marked increase in coupling between modules.

Now let's turn to **communication connection** methods, using the output control module of Fig.4.11 as an example. There are two quite distinct methods for transferring information into the module (Fig.4.15).

Using the 'normal' (sometimes called 'minimal') method, all information transfer is done via a controlled interface. Assume, for instance, that the computing module wishes to update the valve position command. Information is transferred into the output control module via its interface; setting up the command value is performed by code within the module. This gives secure, reliable and testable module operation. However, if the valve position command information can be loaded directly from outside the module, these benefits are lost. This is called a 'pathological' connection (yes, I know it's a crazy word but that's computer science for you).

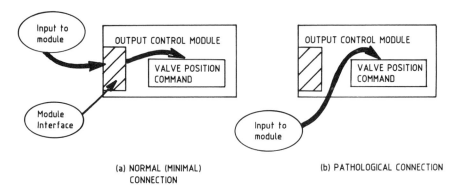

(a) NORMAL (MINIMAL) CONNECTION   (b) PATHOLOGICAL CONNECTION

Fig.4.15 Module connection methods

Information complexity and type are highly visible items; hence they are readily controlled. By contrast, **module connection** methods can be quite difficult to manage. There are many ways (deliberately or accidentally) to increase coupling between modules through poor choice of connectivity. Let's begin with the worst possible situation, commonly met in assembly language programming. This, called 'content coupling' (Stevens *et al.*, 1974), is shown in Fig.4.16.

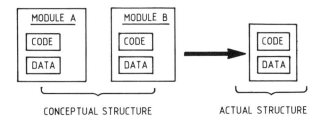

CONCEPTUAL STRUCTURE   ACTUAL STRUCTURE

Fig.4.16 Content coupling

Our concept is one of separate modules, each having their own code and data areas. In reality all items can be accessed from anywhere within the program because there isn't a mechanism to prevent this (it depends entirely on the discipline and professionalism of the programmer). Therefore module A can, at any time, make a pathological connection into B (and vice versa).

But there is a more subtle (and very undesirable) feature here. Because the code written for A is visible in B, it can be used by B. So, thinks the programmer, if there are identical functions in A **and** B, why write the code twice? Do it once only and use it in both modules. The result? A saving on memory space (usually insignificant) – and instant tight coupling. Code sharing should **never** be done unless there are very good reasons for it (discussed later under 'functional decomposition').

Improvements can be made by limiting the amount of code and data which can be accessed globally (Fig.4.17). Here each module has its own private code and data areas. A global data area is used for the sharing of common information, while some code is available for general use. This structure is frequently met in high-level languages, particularly the older ones such as Coral66. Modules are built using program segments; this serves to keep code and data private. Shared resources are normally provided via some form of 'common' attribute of the language.

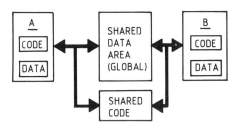

Fig.4.17 Common resource sharing (common coupling)

Limiting resource sharing significantly improves (that is, loosens or weakens) coupling between modules. It is, though, intrinsically unsafe. All global data areas are accessible by all modules; therefore they can also be modified by all modules. Better coupling is attained by defining a specific data structure for holding shared data, then passing pointers to this structure between modules (Fig.4.18). For this to work properly both modules must know how the data area is structured. Moreover, the information within each module must be consistent.

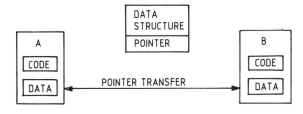

Fig.4.18 Data structure coupling (stamp coupling)

Data structure coupling (called 'stamp coupling') is useful for handling file information. Larger real-time systems frequently use comprehensive file storage systems, including duplicated on-line data bases. However, mass storage is rarely incorporated in smaller embedded systems. Here stamp coupling is most likely to be used for the design of real-time executives or operating systems.

In all real-time designs a primary concern is the handling of program data, this being located in normal RAM store. To transfer such information between modules we can use either direct or indirect data coupling. With direct transfer, Fig.4.19, the sending module passes the **value** of the data to the receiving module.

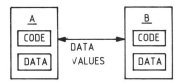

Fig.4.19 Data coupling – by value

This is a highly secure method – data values can be modified by only one module at a time, the current holder. In many instances transmitted items are copies of the originals. As these originals are held in the sending module the recipient cannot change their state. There may not seem any particular advantage in this – until the receiving module corrupts the data. At least then we can 'roll-back' the program to the point where the data was good, a technique sometimes used in critical systems.

It isn't possible to use direct data transfer for all applications, two particular commonplace examples illustrating this. Consider first where the data includes relatively large arrays of floating point numbers, each one occupying 8 bytes of RAM space. Making copies of these structures would soon exhaust the data store space of a normal computer. Another situation also negates the use of the direct transfer method. This occurs when the receiver module isn't able to directly pass data back to the original sender – a regular requirement when using hierarchical structuring. To cope with these situations the **address** of the data (not the data itself) is passed between modules (Fig.4.20). Thus the receiving module accesses the data using the address information – access by reference.

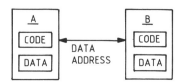

Fig.4.20 Data coupling – by reference

Coupling by reference is much more secure than stamp coupling. This security is enhanced by using modern languages which ensure consistency of data structures amongst program modules. It is, though, less secure than coupling by value (for obvious reasons). Taking all factors into account we can draw up a table which shows their influence on module coupling (Table 4.1).

In conclusion, the basic aim of the designer is to produce program modules that are as independent as possible – achieved by having low coupling.

Table 4.1 Factors affecting module coupling

System parameter Module coupling	Information complexity	Information type	Module connection method	Coupling technique
HIGH (poor)	Complicated/ Obscure	Control	Pathological	Content Common Stamp
LOW (good)	Simple/ Clear	Data	Normal	Data (ref) Data (value)

4.2.4   Cohesion — a measure of module binding

An ideal module has a single entry and a single exit point (Fig.4.21a). One way to achieve this simple structure is to keep module function and operation very simple. Now, any complete system is made up of a number of modules, interconnected to perform the required function (Fig.4.21b). So far, so good – for a very small design. But adding even a few more modules (Fig.4.21c) makes the connecting link structure fairly complex. As a result it becomes difficult to understand **system** functions and operations. Link complexity can be reduced when the modular structure is hierarchical – but it still remains difficult to grasp system details.

Here is a classic two-way pull situation. Improving factor 1 (module simplicity) degrades factor 2 (system complexity). Is there an easy answer to this problem? Unfortunately, no. The 'right' balance between the number of modules in a system and the size/function of these modules is subjective.

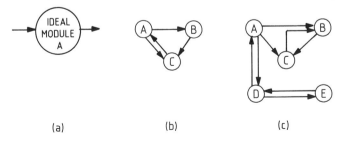

(a)   (b)   (c)

Fig.4.21 Module interconnection complexity

We can reduce system complexity by grouping elementary operations together, these becoming the **elements** of a single module (Fig.4.22). Where elements of a module are very closely related, most module activity is internal. Elements don't need, or want, to 'talk' to other modules. Consequently such designs have low module coupling. The parameter which defines how strongly elements are inter-related is called 'cohesion' (the 'glue' factor). High cohesion results from strong relationships. This leads not only to good designs; it also produces maintainable software.

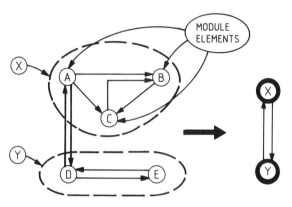

Fig.4.22 Complexity reduction

It's one thing to say that a high glue factor is desirable; it's quite another thing to implement it. What the designer needs, when modularizing his system, is some **measure** of cohesion. One such measure was proposed by Yourdon and Constantine, the seven-level model of Fig.4.23.

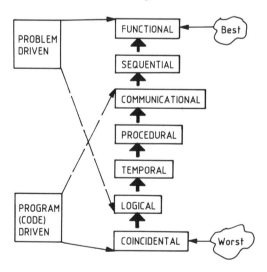

Fig.4.23 The seven-level cohesion model

In reality this is not a discrete scale; it's impossible to draw a clear line between levels. Moreover, these aren't mutually exclusive qualities. For instance, a module may have both sequential and temporal cohesion.

Cohesion can be approached from two points of view, the problem (system) or the solution (program). The results are quite different, as discussed below.

(a) Coincidental cohesion

If the elements of a module are found to be unrelated, then we have zero cohesion. Such modules usually come about because 'somewhere had to be found for the code'. There are, though, underlying reasons for this: inferior design, weak design co-ordination or pressure to produce operational software. It can be difficult to minimize module coupling in such designs.

Another common reason for ending up with minimal cohesion is demonstrated by the flowchart problem of Fig.4.24.

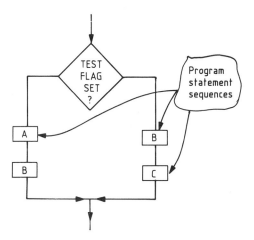

Fig.4.24

During program design the programmer realizes that instruction sequence B occurs twice. To improve code efficiency he produces a module for B, the individual statements forming the elements of this module. In practice, this method is simple to apply during the initial design stage. Later though, when modifications are made, difficulties arise. It may be, for instance, that the left path B has to be changed, but not the right one. The result? We'll probably have to create an extra (new) module, thus disturbing the original structure of the system.

(b) Logical cohesion

Let's assume that our programmer is writing code for the task shown in Fig.4.11. Further assume that a system requirement calls for each input signal to be filtered. Ergo, he forms a 'filter' module to perform this function. Into this he inserts the code for each channel filter (the elements), these being related by their logical functioning (logical cohesion).

Now, the code could be written so that each time the module is activated all input signals are filtered. But this might not be necessary (or desirable); some inputs may need servicing more frequently than others. The solution is to process selected signals only, by using a general module activating call accompanied by a selector tag. The tag identifies which inputs are to be filtered. Furthermore, it is commonplace to use a single body of code to perform the program function. Unfortunately, the result is that it then becomes difficult to modify any individual filter function without affecting the others.

These problems are inherent in modules which house logically related elements. The reason is simple; such modules do not carry out a single function only. 'Filter' isn't a single action. It is, in fact, a collection of separate functions grouped together for our convenience.

In the example here the makeup of the 'filter' module was driven by system requirements. Quite frequently such designs make good sense in embedded systems. The resulting modules often exhibit much better cohesion than groupings derived from program code functions. However, when used without care it promotes tight coupling, leading especially to maintenance problems.

(c) Temporal (time) cohesion

When elements of a module are related by time then we have 'temporal cohesion', i.e. time is the glue. A frequently-quoted example is that of an initialization routine to set up the hardware of a processor system. All such set-up operations have to take place within a particular period of time. Therefore it makes good sense to group these together in one module – then execute them all at once. But, once again, care and common sense must be used in the program design. When temporal grouping is used, unrelated parts of the system may be located within the resulting module. This, like logical grouping, may well lead to maintenance problems.

(d) Procedural cohesion

Module elements have procedural cohesion when each one is part of a well-defined operation – the procedure. 'The common procedural unit may be the iteration (loop), decision process, or a linear sequence of steps' (Yourdon). All elements of a procedure **must** be present if it's to perform its desired function. Therefore the binding of elements is good. Procedural cohesion usually results in low coupling – but then again it may not. It hinges very much on how the procedure was devised in the first place. Where, for instance, it performs a clearly defined mathematical operation (say computing the sine of an angle), cohesion and coupling are good. But frequently procedures are used to implement sub-tasks of larger tasks. The resulting module coupling depends very much on the initial partitioning of the overall system.

(e) Communicational cohesion

A module has communicational cohesion when its elements act on common data. The actions performed on the data generate the connecting links between the elements, typical instances being shown in Fig.4.25.

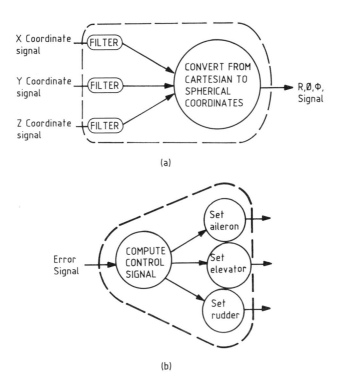

Fig.4.25 Communicational cohesion

(f) Sequential cohesion

Here the elements are organized as a sequence of operations, Fig.4.26. Observe that the output from one element acts as the input to the next one. Sequential structures can be formed starting from the code point of view (a flowchart approach). But much better function groupings occur when designs are tackled from a system point of view. Any module designed in this way may contain only one function. On the other hand it may hold either part of a particular function or a number of related functions. It fits in naturally with the data flow approach to designing software structures (chapter 10).

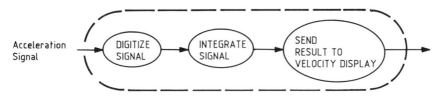

Fig.4.26 Sequential cohesion

(g)   Functional cohesion

In general terms a functional module is one that performs a single function. Such structures have the highest level of cohesion because all elements are essential to the operation of the module; none is redundant.

Thus the concept of functional binding seems clear enough – until we try to define it. One definition could be that, for functional cohesion, each element in the module is an essential part of that module. From an abstract point of view this excludes all other forms of cohesion. Therefore each element must perform a single function. Is this recursive, I ask myself? Yourdon and Constantine (1979) give a precise but negative form of definition. That is, 'functional cohesion is whatever is **not** sequential, communicational, . . . etc.'. Even they admit this isn't very helpful, by saying that 'any truly adequate definition of function is a structural defect in the theory through which camels and Mack trucks could readily pass'. And, when taking a system point of view, designers often disagree on what makes up a single function.

There's no doubt that good modular designs have high module cohesiveness. And high-strength modules have far fewer faults than low-strength ones (Card *et al.*, 1986). How then does a designer arrive at a 'good' final structure? One approach is to produce an initial design, assess it using the rules given above, refine it, re-assess it – and so on. But it's stretching imagination (and credibility) to think that, in a commercial environment, such practices exist. Moreover, it isn't a case of using a simple design template for cohesion; many modules exhibit a number of cohesion qualities. For instance, a plant sequence controller may have a performance specification which reads (in part):

> At time = T+10
> Shut Nitrogen and Hydrogen valves
> Open vent valve
> Run purge motor

Thus the items are time related. The cohesion is quite strong because all activities must be done in this particular time slot. At the same time there is a strong functional relationship between these operations – from a system point of view. This module has an extremely high glue strength.

Sensibly, then, the only workable design methods are those which **inherently** produce high cohesiveness. Can we define such methods? The answer lies in Fig.4.23. Observe: module structures derived from the system (problem) point of view have the highest glue factor. In other words, if we start in the right way, we'll end up with the right results.

4.2.5   Size and complexity

What is the ideal size for a module? One general – but not very helpful – rule can be laid down: don't make it too large. As a result, the amount of information given at any one time is limited. This enables the reader to see the module code as a whole, making it easier for him to absorb and understand it. Smaller modules usually have very clearly defined (and usually simple) functions. Unfortunately, when using small modules, it then becomes difficult to absorb the overall functioning of the system. So, ultimately, the minimum size of a module is determined by our ability to digest information.

One figure frequently quoted is to limit program size to between 30 and 50 executable statements (Jensen and Tonies, 1979). The number of lines of source code corresponding to this depends on the programming language and environment. But, using a high-level language, one would expect to see a listing of (roughly) between 60 and 100 lines. This equates to two pages of source code per program module.

Using the number of statements as a guide to module size is really only a rough and ready guide. A second factor is the complexity of the language constructs used in the module. Compare, for instance, a program consisting of only sequential statements with one using highly nested combinations of iteration and selection operations. Obviously it's going to take much more mental effort to understand the second one – even if both have the same print-out length. Much work has been done to develop models of software complexity – software metrics. A number of different rules have been developed (Martin and McClure, 1985; Bache and Tinker, 1988).

One technique is based on counting the number of operators and operands in the program code. Furthermore, it takes into account the number of distinct items as well as the totals. Program complexity is deduced from a count value computed using these values. This method gives a better guide than a simple count of instructions; more complex instructions give a higher count value.

A second method uses a count of the number of independent paths through a program as a measure of complexity (McCabe's cyclomatic number). This approach has its roots in graph theory (McCabe, 1976). How well it works in practice is a contentious issue, suggestions being made that it's merely a mathematician's plaything.

Extensions to this work have been done by McClure (1978) and Oviedo (1980), both taking data (program variable) references into account.

Unfortunately, after many years of research, we still haven't any simple (or for that matter, complex) watertight rule for measuring program complexity. Even worse, some studies have produced results which run directly against the given wisdom. Card *et al.* (1986), in their paper, found that there was no significant relationship between module size and fault rate. They also reported on two other studies which concluded that smaller modules were more fault prone (but then pointed out how the results were significantly affected by the analysis methods used).

It seems that any pronouncement on module size is likely to be challenged. Moreover, a distinction must be made between library modules and functional modules (discussed later). But personal experience has shown that limiting module size to only a few pages of print-out is a good rule. It seems to produce little benefit in the initial design stage; error rates are relatively unaffected. The difference shows later on, though. Such code is quickly comprehensible, making updating and modification work a relatively easy task (especially if you didn't write the code in the first place). Limiting size has another advantage. It is easier to perform static analysis of the code during the software test phase (chapter 12).

4.2.6   Some general comments on modules

(a)   Why modularize programs?

- The 'divide and conquer' approach produces programs which are easy to manage, understand and test.
- Program development can be done on an incremental basis ('a bit at a time').
- Errors are easier to track down and correct.
- Modifications are usually localized, so maintaining high program stability.
- Portability can be increased by burying machine-specific features within designated modules. Thus, when moving to other target systems, only these modules need changing.
- Libraries of useful functions can be built up (especially true of complex maths functions), so leading to software re-use.
- It is easier to attack the problems of slow code and memory inefficiency when using modular construction (the 'code optimization' requirement).
- In a large system, development times can be pruned by using a team of designers working in parallel. Although various work-sharing methods could be used, allocating work on a module basis has two particular advantages. First, it enables programmers to work independently; second, it simplifies integration of the resulting code.

(b)   What are the ideal characteristics of 'good' modules?

- Each module has a clearly-defined task.
- There is a one-to-one relationship between system function and module function – functional cohesion.
- There isn't a need to see the internals of a module to understand its function.
- Modules can be combined to form 'super' modules – without regard to their internal implementation details.
- It is possible to test a module in isolation from other modules.
- Module functional connections are defined by their functional relationships with other modules.
- Module control connections are defined by their code. Each module should have a single program entry point and a corresponding single exit point (though see 'exceptions').
- Data connections are made with the lowest form of coupling – parameter-passing mechanisms.

(c) **What are the disadvantages of modularization?**

- Much greater effort has to be put in at the initial design stages.
- Much greater project management is required (even if, in a small job, it's self-management).
- Much more time is spent designing (as opposed to coding). Thus productivity, measured in a very narrow way over a limited part of the job, decreases.
- Program run times usually lengthen.
- More memory is required (most noticeably RAM).

4.3   PROGRAM CONTROL STRUCTURES —THE INFLUENCE OF STRUCTURED PROGRAMMING

4.3.1   Introductory comments

The first real step away from undisciplined program methods was made in the late '60s by a group of academics. Their proposals, summarized as *Structured Programming (SP)*, were typified in a 1969 article by Edsgar Dijkstra (1969). SP is a methodology used for translating module descriptions and specifications into program source code. Its primary objective is to reduce software complexity, so:

- Reducing the number of mistakes made in the first place.
- Reducing the time and effort taken to correct such mistakes.
- Improving overall reliability, correctness and safety.

As defined by Wirth (1974) SP 'is the formulation of programs as hierarchical, nested structures of statements and objects of computation'. Over the years its original ideas were modified. Nowadays we generally consider the basic rules of SP to be that:

- Programs are designed in a top-down manner.
- Programs are constructed as hierarchical modules.
- The program control structures are limited.
- Program correctness can be proved.

Until recently, structured design and structured programming were regarded as being synonymous. However, this link has been weakened as design structures may now be either functional or object oriented. Nonetheless, in both cases, the rules concerning control structures and program correctness still apply. These are the items which go right to the heart of good programming.

4.3.2   Fundamental control structures

Is it possible to define a minimum set of program control structures from which **any** program can be built? And why should we want to do this in the first place?

Much of the heat generated by arguments concerning the first question results from ignorance of the reasons behind the second one. The primary reason for restricting control structures is so that we can prove that programs are correct. Consider, for example, the program operations described in Fig.4.27.

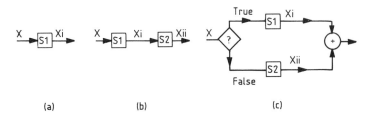

(a)   (b)   (c)

Fig.4.27 Simple transformation actions

In (a) the variable X is operated on by the program statement S1 to give Xi. Now, provided we can define the range of values taken on by X (called a pre-condition), then we can define those of Xi (post-condition). This can be considered to be an elementary step; we're dealing with a single statement which produces a single transformation. For Fig.4.27(a), suppose that

TRANSFORMATION S1: $Xi := X/2$;
PRE-CONDITION: $0 \leqslant Xi \leqslant 10$
Then POST-CONDITION is $0 \leqslant Xi \leqslant 5$

If the statement S1 (as actually implemented in code) generates a result which violates this assertion, then clearly the program is incorrect.

Fig.4.27(b) is again quite straightforward, as is (c) (although proving its correctness is rather more difficult). But what about the case of Fig.4.28?

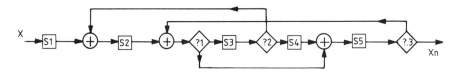

Fig.4.28 Complex transformation action

Here the effects produced by individual statements are easy to check out. Unfortunately, as their interaction is quite complex, this isn't a great deal of help. Trying to prove the relationship between X and Xn is a fairly daunting task. Yet flow structures like these can easily be generated, especially when programming at a low level (such as assembly language operation). Frankly, with such designs, it is highly unlikely that their correctness is ever verified because:

• They're too complex to analyse in the time available.

- It would cost too much to prove it.
- Programmers just wouldn't do it because of the tedium of the job.

The groundwork in tackling this problem was done by G. Jacopini (Bohm and Jacopini, 1966) and further refined by others, notably Wirth, Dijkstra and Hoare. Jacopini showed that only three basic flow control structures were needed to form any program: sequence, selection and iteration (Fig.4.29).

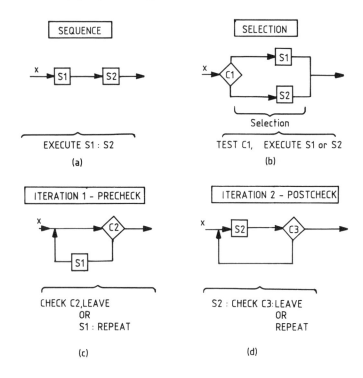

Fig.4.29 Basic control structures of structured programming

Note that the two iteration structures can always be implemented using either the pre-check or post-check operation; thus only one is needed (Fig.4.30).

These basic forms were later augmented by variations on the multiple select operation, the 'Else-If' and 'Case' (see programming languages, chapter 8).

A second (very important) point is that each structure has one entry point and one exit point. From these simple beginnings any program can be built up. Moreover, when using such building blocks, the program always consists of the basic control structures (Fig.4.31) – no matter what level it's looked at. Therefore, given a program formed like this, we can first prove the correctness of the individual building blocks. Then, by extending this to larger groupings, the proving process encompasses larger and larger program sections. Ultimately it takes in the complete program.

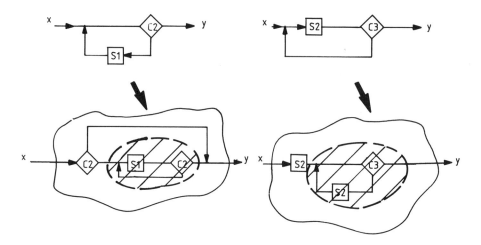

Fig.4.30 Equivalence of iteration structures

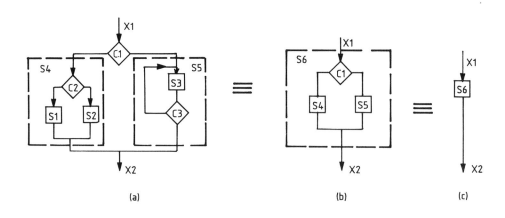

Fig.4.31 Composition of a structured program

In informal (non-mathematical) terms, program correctness is checked as follows:

(a)   Sequential operation

- Are all statements listed in correct order?
- Are these executed **once** only?
- Are sequence groups executed from a single entry to a single exit point?
- Do the statements represent the solution to the problem?
- Does the order of execution produce the required result?

(b)   Iteration operation

- Are the controlled statements executed at least once (post-check)?
- Can control pass through the operation without ever executing the controlled statements (pre-checks)?
- Is iteration guaranteed to finish (that is, are the loop termination conditions correct)?

- Is the correct number of iterations carried out?
- Is the control variable altered within the loop itself?
- What is the state of program variables on exit from an iteration?

(c)   Selection operation

- Are all alternative courses of action explicitly taken into account (including answers that don't fit the question)?
- Are the alternative statements constructed using the basic structures of SP?
- Have the questions relating to sequential operations (and, where appropriate, iteration) been considered?

That's fine. But, you may well argue, few programmers are actually ever going to carry out a correctness check on their code. It's enough effort to produce it in the first place. Does this diminish the value of the control structures of structured programming? The answer, emphatically, is **no**. Programs built using these rules are much more likely to be reliable, robust and trustworthy.

Modern high-level languages directly support these aims, in many cases building in extra controls. For instance, several languages prevent statements within a loop changing the loop control variable. Consequently, when good design practices are combined with high-level language programming, the result should be quality software.

4.3.3   Uncontrolled branching of control — the great GOTO debate

Most languages enable a programmer to branch without constraint using a 'go to' statement (the destination being either a line number or label). In assembly-level programming this is done using a 'jump' instruction. As this construct is not allowed in SP it became a controversial issue, fuelled by Dijkstra's famous letter 'Go To statement considered harmful' (1968). More heat than light was generated in the resulting arguments, most combatants losing sight of the underlying arguments behind this conclusion.

Is the GOTO statement by itself a problem? No, of course not. When used with care and attention, particularly when confined by conditional expressions, there aren't any particular difficulties. The problems come about because of the 'creative' aspects of GOTO programming. Consider the program fragment shown in Fig.4.32.

Here the resulting control flow is perfectly well controlled and structured, even though the GOTO is used. Now look at that in Fig.4.33. Here the use of the GOTOs is controlled – but not very well. The result is a complex interactive control flow structure – produced from only a few lines of code. What then is the likely outcome if program jumps are made without any form of control?

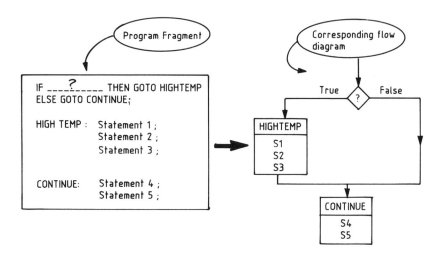

Fig.4.32 Well-controlled use of the GOTO statement

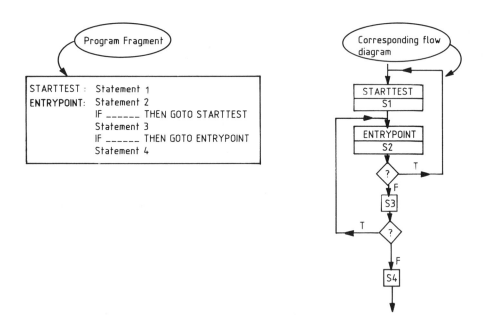

Fig.4.33 Poorly-controlled GOTO statements

It is clear that the GOTO statement provides a means for writing poor, unprovable programs. What Dijkstra observed was that where the GOTO was used extensively, programs were complex – and difficult to verify. Generally, good programs contained few GOTOs (note, though, that the absence of GOTOs doesn't necessarily mean that a program is a good one).

Is it possible to eliminate the GOTO statement (or its equivalent) from real-time programming? In theory it is possible to write any program without having unconditional transfers of control. But this involves a time (and complexity) overhead which may cause problems for time-critical applications. For example, suppose that during program execution an exception occurs which requires prompt attention. Further, the only way to handle this is to branch instantly to the exception handler. But that requires an unconditional transfer of control. So in reality, we can't throw away the GOTO or its equivalent; but it should be used **only** in very exceptional conditions.

4.4   FUNCTIONAL STRUCTURING OF SOFTWARE DESIGNS

4.4.1   Background

Program structures can be derived in many ways, each one having its supporters and critics. But how does one make sense of the various claims and counter-claims? Well, the real test of any method is to see how well it works in practice. Judged against this, techniques based on functional structuring of programs rate highly. Currently these are some of the most popular design methods for real-time applications.

'Functional structuring' is here used as a general characteristic (generic) term, covering a number of design methodologies. It belongs firmly in the Yourdon-Constantine-Myers-Meiler-Ward-Mellor-DeMarco school of design, its premise being that a program takes its shape from the functions carried out by the system. The overall design approach (Fig.4.34) is based on many of the ideas and concepts discussed earlier in this chapter.

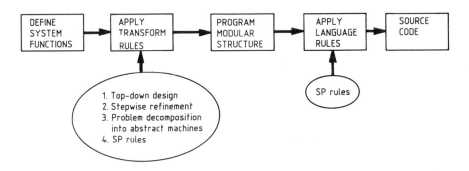

Fig.4.34 Functional structured design

First, system functions are defined. Then, from these, the modular structure of the program is devised using a set of 'transform' rules. These use a top-down, stepwise refinement decomposition method, resulting in a set of abstract machines. Structured programming is an inherent (and sometimes implicit) part of this process. Once the program structure has been obtained the program source code can be written. And once again the rules of SP are applied, in this case to the flow control constructs.

System functions can be defined using one of two methods. In the first the designer uses an 'informal' style, based on his own experience. Alternatively he may choose to use a prescribed technique. Functions, for instance, may be described in terms of system data flow, data transformations, and connections between transformations (see chapters 5 and 6). Here, though, we aren't particularly concerned with how we derive system functions. The important point is how we devise program structures to implement these functions.

4.4.2   Problem decomposition using abstract machines

Programs devised using functional structuring are based on the concept of abstract machines organized in layers (Fig.4.35). Taking a simple view, an abstract machine corresponds to a module. In (a), computing machine M1 invokes machine M2 to perform a specific task. When the task is complete, control is returned to M1, together with relevant data and status information. In (b), M1 invokes both M2 and M3. Unfortunately there isn't any indication as to whether M2 runs before M3 or vice versa. Here, to avoid confusion, all sequences run from left to right (thus, M2, then M3). In (c) M1 invokes M2, thus transferring program control to this machine. M2 in turn activates M4 and M5; on completion of their tasks it returns control to M1, which then starts up M3.

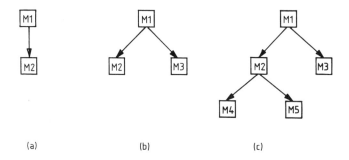

(a)   (b)   (c)

Fig.4.35 The layered abstract machine concept

This is shown in more concrete terms in Fig.4.36 when used as part of the anti-skid system of Fig.4.5.

When using abstract ('virtual') machines it is important to focus on the service they provide, not how they do it. Ideally it is best to completely ignore the 'how' until fine details have to be worked out. This may seem a pretty abstract point, removed from the reality of program design. If so, look at how we regularly use abstract machines at the program level – without even realizing it (Fig.4.37).

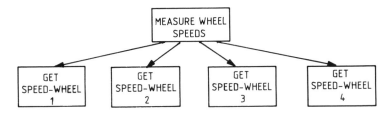

Fig.4.36 Abstract machines – task level

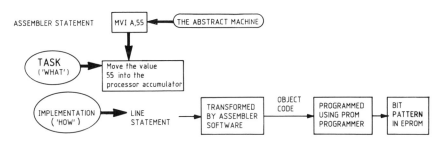

Fig.4.37 Abstract machines – program level

Here a line statement in assembly language can be considered to be an abstract machine. We invoke it to perform a particular task, completely ignoring how it's translated into code or how it works at the processor level. Moreover, we assume that the operation always works correctly when the code is installed in the target computer. If this isn't an example of abstract operations, what is?

The process of building up the complete program structure is one of hierarchical decomposition, Fig.4.38. Note that in this example both M2 and M3 invoke the same machine (module), M5. In other words, a low-level module is shared by a number of higher-level ones. Now this is undesirable as it can lead to complex and unforeseen interaction between modules. Ideally, hierarchical decomposition should result in a pure tree structure, Fig.4.39. In this case a module at any level can be invoked directly by only one higher-level module; sharing is banned. Thus higher-level modules have sole control over the modules they call. Further, the branches of the tree are fully decoupled from each other (data coupling is needed to achieve this). The final result is a highly controllable, visible and stable structure.

A tree structure, taken to its logical conclusion, results in each and every module having its own code. This **could** be done but it would be very inefficient (and perhaps costly). Because, within all computer systems there are 'building brick' functions which are used repeatedly (e.g. standard maths functions, terminal handling, real-world interfacing). The idea of writing separate code every time we use one of these functions is unrealistic. The sensible way to implement them is to use standard procedures (subroutines), calling them as required in the program.

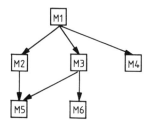

Fig.4.38 Hierarchical decomposition – general form

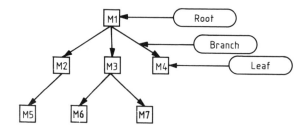

Fig.4.39 Hierarchical decomposition – pure tree structure

Now this presents us with the need to handle a second form of problem decomposition, based around the building bricks. Traditionally it has been called 'functional decomposition' (which is confusing); for convenience the term 'service decomposition' is used here. When such decomposition is used the pure tree structure degenerates into the more general hierarchical structure. Therefore it is vital that modules designed as program building bricks must be fully tested and totally predictable in operation. Where appropriate, formal correctness testing should be carried out. Once this is done such service modules may be used as single objects ('primitives') in the program structure. But even so the programmer must always be aware of the effects of service decomposition. Sloppy use of this destroys the inbuilt qualities of functionally decomposed programs. Hence the design and use of service modules must be rigorously controlled. Where possible they should be placed in a library, with access to the source code being a privileged operation.

When designing any system we need to identify the main program first and then (later) the service sub-programs. The main program is designed as described earlier, but **must** have a pure tree structure. Service sub-programs are produced to carry out common tasks defined by service modules. Modules within the main program may invoke service modules, but these service modules don't appear explicitly in the structure. Also, they can be invoked by modules at **any** level in the pure tree structure of the main program.

4.4.3   Example implementation

Let's tackle the task of implementing the anti-skid braking system of Fig.4.5. There isn't a unique answer to this (or any other) problem; one possible solution is shown in Fig.4.40. For simplicity only part of the design is given. This is pretty-well self-explanatory, the partitioning used leading automatically to low coupling and high cohesion. Many diagramming methods are available to describe program structures obtained using hierarchical decomposition (see chapters 5 and 6); these shouldn't be confused with the underlying principles of the method.

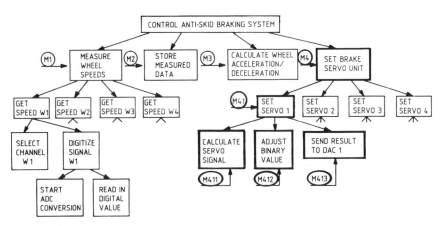

Fig.4.40 Functional structure of the anti-skid braking system (part)

From this information the program source code can be produced, typified (in part) by that in Fig.4.41. Observe that at the highest level – machines M1 to M4 – simplicity is the keynote. Each machine is implemented using a parameterless procedure. At the next level down the procedures become more complex. Note also that the 'SetServo1' machine (M41) communicates with the ones below it via parameters. Consequently machines M411, M412, and M413 use only local parameters in their computation. Also, it's impossible for them to communicate with each other; they haven't the means to do this. Consequently, these modules affect only a very small, localized part of the total program; they are said to have localized scope of reference.

Tree structuring of designs makes it especially easy to develop programs in

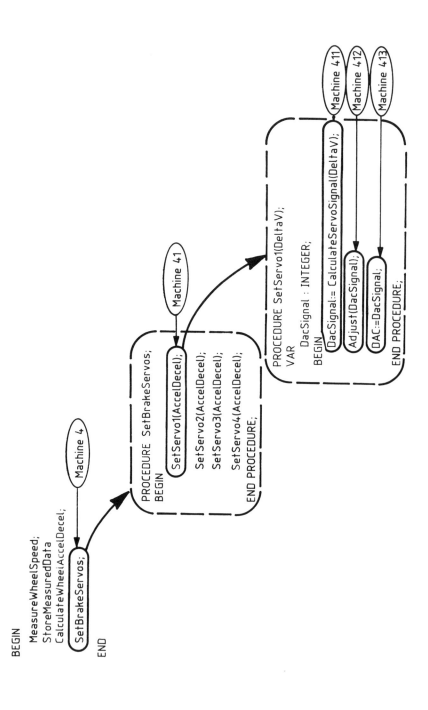

Fig.4.41 Program structure for Fig.4.40 (part)

an incremental way. For instance, assume that hierarchical decomposition has been carried out on the braking system problem. Fig.4.40 has been produced, and coding now begins. Using incremental methods, machines 1 to 4 would be coded first – a fairly simple (but not trivial) action. Now the modules stemming from M1 can be implemented, while all other second level modules are coded as dummy stubs. Frequently these contain simple text messages, printing up 'module not yet implemented' or something similar. Once the first set of modules is coded and working, the next set can be tackled, then the next set, and so on until programming is finished. In my experience this is the quickest, easiest and least frustrating way to develop reliable software. But it really does require coupling and cohesion to be right for it to work effectively.

4.5   OBJECT-STRUCTURED (ORIENTED) DESIGN

4.5.1   Object-oriented design — what and why?

It has already been shown in section 4.1 that designs may be structured as sets of interconnected objects. In the example given (Fig.4.7) the computing objects were clearly linked with physical items. Generally, though, objects don't have such a clear-cut relationship. Mostly they are abstract items which represent computing processes within the system. In formal terms an object, as far as object-oriented design (OOD) is concerned, may be defined as:

'A machine which has a number of defined operational states and a defined means to access and change these states'.

A change of state is achieved by passing a message into an object, as shown conceptually in Fig.4.42(a). So, in simple terms, an object-structured program executes as a set of interacting machines (Fig.4.42b), communicating using messages.

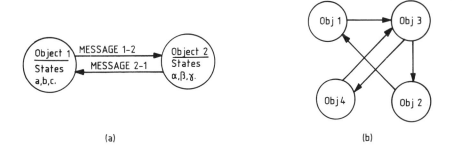

(a)   (b)

Fig.4.42 Fundamental concept of object-oriented design

At this point a word of caution must be given. The topic of OOD is relatively new. Various design methodologies have and are being proposed (Booch, 1987; Plessman, 1988). And it isn't always clear whether authors are dealing with object-oriented programming, OOP (Anderson, 1988) or object-oriented design (Sommerville, 1989). Sommerville makes the point that OOP implementations may be language dependent. Most examples in the literature are usually based on Smalltalk (Goldberg, 1983) or, more recently, C++ (Drake, 1989). The view taken here is the same as Sommerville's; OOD is a way of design and does not depend on specific language features. Furthermore, OOD features are here assessed as a means of producing software for real-time systems.

Why use an object-oriented approach to software design? Because, for many real-world applications, software objects map quite naturally onto system models. Remember, the computer is seen as merely another component in the overall system. It, and its processing activities, form part of a totally integrated activity (some software designs give the impression that the important activities take place only within the computer, the outside world being a minor irritating side-issue). Moreover, in the real world, many events occur simultaneously (concurrently). This concurrency can be shown simply and clearly using OOD. In contrast, functional structuring is geared towards a sequential view of life. One consequence of this is that we constantly find ourselves redefining our problem to suit the design method.

There are a number of major steps involved in producing an object-structured design, as follows:

(a)   Identify objects and their features.
(b)   Identify relationships and communication links between objects.
(c)   Define the interface of each object.
(d)   Implement the objects.

4.5.2   Object-oriented design — the identification process

From a program point of view an object must have specific qualities. It should, for instance, be:

• Able to represent system functions properly.
• Easy to build.
• Simple to integrate into the overall system.
• Amenable to testing and debugging as a separate unit.
• Straightforward to maintain.

This looks very much like the specification for a module. In fact, at the source code level, it may be impossible to distinguish a module from an equivalent object (to a dedicated object-oriented programmer this statement is heretical). Therefore the ideas of cohesion, coupling, abstraction and data hiding all apply.

How does one go about identifying and implementing objects? Well, consider again the system requirements of the anti-skid braking system. What would an OOD look like here? One possible solution is shown in Fig.4.43, using 'entity' abstraction (the abstraction terms used here are based on those of HOOD, 1989).

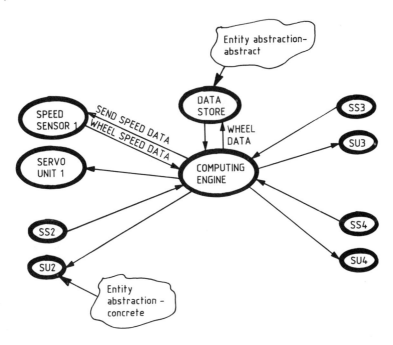

Fig.4.43 OOD of the anti-skid braking system (1)

Entity abstraction results when we first clearly define the problem structure and then map objects closely onto this. Two sub-groups result, concrete and abstract. The speed sensor object is a concrete entity as it represents a physical device. The data store is much more conceptual in nature, thus forming an abstract object. Clear distinctions aren't always possible. For instance, is the computing engine a concrete or an abstract object?

An alternative OOD solution to the braking system problem is shown in Fig.4.44. Here a different structure is formed, involving both entity and action abstractions. Entity abstraction results in 'things'; action abstraction produces objects which have 'operation' properties. In this case the operations are those of signal processing.

Another possible implementation, Fig.4.45, introduces the concept of the virtual machine abstraction. A virtual machine groups together a set of operations. As defined in HOOD these operations are all used by some superior level of control; generally this doesn't have to be the case. The virtual machine can be a very powerful construct, especially when tied in with the use of object class (see later).

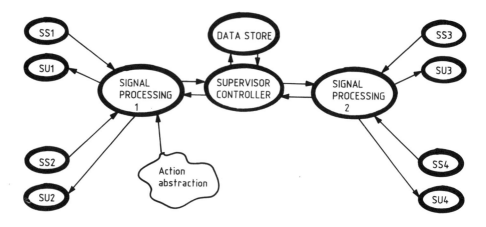

Fig.4.44 OOD of the anti-skid braking system (2)

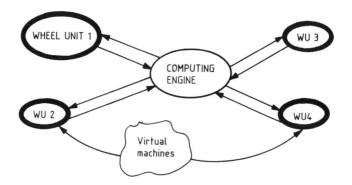

Fig.4.45 Virtual machine abstraction

Entity abstraction leads to good object structures, action abstraction being inferior to it. Virtual machines may or may not be good implementations; it depends on the design approach. The weakest objects are those formed by grouping sets of operations together because 'they have to go somewhere' – logistic abstraction. Not surprisingly, this results in coincidental cohesion.

OOD provides us with a way of implementing top-down design and problem decomposition, the 'parent/child' structure (Fig.4.46). Virtual machines may be built in this way; in practice it depends on how the object interfaces are constructed.

At this point we are in a position to describe fully all objects and their features (although with a top-down design this may be done in an incremental way). For instance:

OBJECT: Speed sensor (SS).
ABSTRACTION TYPE: Entity.
FUNCTION: Provide wheel speed data in binary form.
OPERATION PERFORMED: Sample speed transducer.
OPERATION DEMANDED: Send speed data.

The 'operation performed' can be viewed as a response to a system requirement. In contrast, 'operation demanded' is a response to an input from some other object. At this level of design there must be correspondence between the two operations. After all, it doesn't make sense to do something which isn't needed. And obviously, one can't demand an item which doesn't exist.

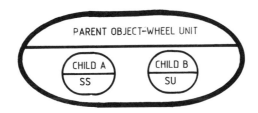

Fig.4.46 Object decomposition – parent/child structure

4.5.3   Relationships and communication between objects

The first (identification) stage of design defines the broad relationships between objects and the messages sent between them. The second stage firms up these items, specifying them precisely and totally. It also identifies passive and active objects, and where appropriate, shows interrupt and exception features.

Assume an object demands an action by another object (Fig.4.47), transfers control to this object, and the demand is immediately actioned. On completion of the demanded action, control is returned to the calling object. In this case the receiving object is said to be a 'passive' one. Where action is demanded but control is not transferred, the object is an 'active' one. With such arrangements the receiving object may or may not react instantly; it depends on its current situation (Fig.4.48).

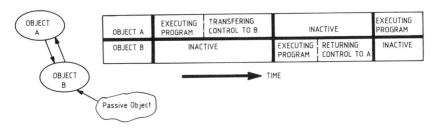

Fig.4.47 Passive object behaviour

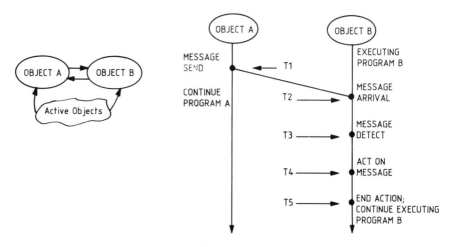

Fig.4.48 Active object behaviour

Interrupt sources ('system objects') should be shown so that they stand out from normal objects (Fig.4.49). In all cases the reasons for generating such interrupts should be made clear. Conceptually, an interrupt-driven object is an active one. In all cases, if the receiving object cannot perform its task, it must raise an exception signal.

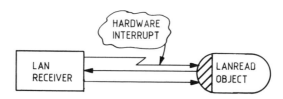

Fig.4.49 Interrupt-driven object

Communication between objects is done using either data and/or commands. Where passive objects are used there is an inbuilt hierarchy in the structure, a form of 'client/server' relationship. Communication then takes place using a call/return protocol. Active objects, though, are regarded as independent items operating as concurrent communicating processes. The techniques used to implement communication between such processes is described in section 9.6.

At a system level the difference between active and passive objects may not seem significant. They are, in fact, profoundly different. When designs use active objects they need the support of a real-time operating system (or at least a real-time executive). And, as the number of active objects increases, the performance demanded of the executive also rises. This loading can be reduced by using passive objects wherever possible. Generally it is acceptable to decompose a major object into a set of subordinate passive objects. It is also possible to implement designs so that one, and only one, object ever executes at any one time. This can be achieved by using, for instance, the co-routine construct of Modula-2.

A final – important – point is that passive objects can be built using standard procedures and functions. Thus the source code can be written using a standard declarative language such as Pascal or C.

4.5.4   Object interfaces

One of the primary aims in object-oriented design is to hide as much information as possible. It's a variant on the 'need to know' principle; what you don't know about can't hurt you. We do this by separating an object into two parts: the visible and hidden sections (Fig.4.50).

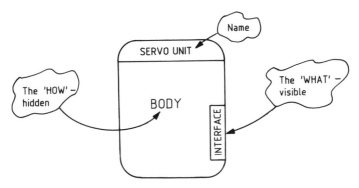

Fig.4.50 Global view of an object

The visible section (the interface) describes what the object does, the resources it needs to do it, and the services it provides. In the outside object world only the interface details can be seen. The body itself implements the required functions of the object. How these are achieved is hidden within the body, being of no concern to the user. In fact, it is imperative that internal operations cannot be accessed directly by external objects.

Because objects may act as both providers and users the interface can be split into two sections, Fig.4.51.

The import interface describes items taken into the object, while the export interface covers the opposite requirement. Unfortunately (and confusingly) there are two ways of looking at this problem when deciding on object relationships. One particular form of notation used to eliminate ambiguity is shown in Fig.4.52. If object X depends on provided resources in Y for its operation, then a line is drawn **from** X to Y (clearly, when using active objects, Y may also depend on X). But there isn't a true standardized method. Moreover, diagramming methods – chapter 6 – should take into account the way language features affect the interface construction (examples of this are given by Booch).

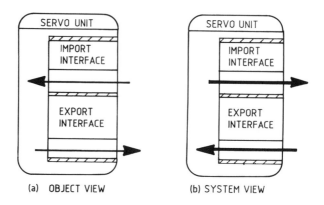

(a)   OBJECT VIEW   (b) SYSTEM VIEW

Fig.4.51 Import and export interfaces – alternative views

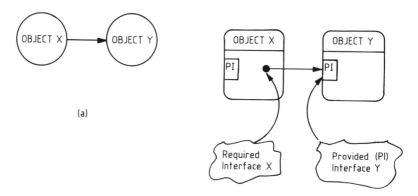

Fig.4.52 Representation of system relationships

It is important to appreciate that the interface doesn't get actively involved in program activities. In fact, executable code isn't usually produced as a result of compiling the interface section. Its primary function is to set up a static relationship between objects, setting constraints on object provisions and requirements. If this isn't clear, consider the following analogy. A military airfield houses a number of sensitive installations (the provided facilities). Only holders of security passes can access and use these facilities. The issue of these passes is carried out by the security office (the interface function). Thus, by defining the type and content of such passes, control is exercised over internal/external relationships. But the security office isn't itself actively involved when such interactions take place (executable code).

4.5.5   Implementing objects

Assume that we have the task of implementing the servo unit object of Fig.4.43, this now having a slightly modified function. In addition to setting the servo valve position it must also transmit positional information back to the computing object. Informally its features may be described as follows:

OBJECT: Servo unit (SU).
ABSTRACTION TYPE: Entity – Active.
FUNCTION: Control of wheel-braking effort.
OPERATION PERFORMED: 1. Modulate hydraulic servo valve (HSV) position.
                                               2. Measure HSV position.
OPERATION DEMANDED: 1. Set HSV valve position.
                                               2. Send HSV position data.

Because it's an active object a real-time executive must form part of the system design. Here the executive provides signalling commands needed for use with the concurrent processes SendDownChannel and GetFromChannel. For the object to carry out its function it **requires** that it be supplied with acceleration/deceleration information from the computing module. It must also set up a channel to this module (AccelDecelChannel). In turn it must **provide** the servo valve position data.

How is this implemented in source code? Both the interface and the body must be constructed, their form and content depending on the programming language. Listing 4.1 shows one possible solution, this being based loosely on the library module structure of Modula-2. The line statements (procedures) within the implementation module may be formed as a collection of child objects of an object-oriented design. Alternatively, they may be designed using the layered abstract machine method of functional structuring.

The interface module ComputingEngine must have appropriate import/ export activities which match the export/import ones of the servo unit module (Listing 4.2).

4.5.6   Object-oriented programming — introductory aspects

This section introduces, in general terms, a number of concepts and terminology used in OOP. At the present time the subject is still in a state of change, having had little exposure to embedded applications. Consequently it's still not clear how significant this programming methodology will be to the real-time designer. Detailed aspects of the topic are beyond the scope of this text; for further information consult the reference list.

Object-oriented programming is founded on the use of sets of objects which communicate by sending messages to each other (Fig.4.53).

In our work many objects are very much alike, allowing us to form classes of objects. We can, for example, have classes of sensor objects and actuator objects, Fig.4.54. Moreover, these classes may be broken down into a collection of subordinate classes or subclasses. In turn the subclasses may themselves be composed of lower-level subclasses. Of course any bottom level subclass can

```
****************************************************************************

INTERFACE MODULE ServoUnit;

IMPORT FROM
RealTimeExecutive - SendDownChannel, GetFromChannel;
ComputingEngine - AccelDecelChannel, AccelDecel;

EXPORT
ServoValve1PositionChannel, ServoValve1Position;

END INTERFACE MODULE ServoUnit.

****************************************************************************
****************************************************************************

IMPLEMENTATION MODULE ServoUnit;

VAR
    DacSignal, ServoValve1Position :INTEGER;

BEGIN

LOOP
    GetFromChannel (AccelDecelChannel, AccelDecel);
    DacSignal:=CalculateServoSignal(AccelDecel);
    Adjust(DacSignal);
    ServoValve1Position:=UpdateDac(DacSignal);
    SendDownChannel(ServoValve1PositionChannel, ServoValve1Position);
END LOOP;

END IMPLEMENTATION MODULE ServoUnit.

****************************************************************************
```

Listing 4.1 Source code for servo unit object (part)

```
****************************************************************************

INTERFACE MODULE ComputingEngine;

IMPORT FROM
RealTimeExecutive - SendDownChannel, GetFromChannel;
ServoUnit1 - ServoValve1PositionChannel, ServoValve1Position;
ServoUnit2 - ServoValve2PositionChannel, ServoValve2Position;
ServoUnit3 - ServoValve3PositionChannel, ServoValve3Position;
ServoUnit4 - ServoValve4PositionChannel, ServoValve4Position;

EXPORT
AccelDecelChannel, AccelDecel;

END INTERFACE MODULE ComputingEngine.

****************************************************************************
```

Listing 4.2 Computing engine object – interface module code (part)

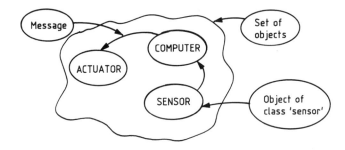

Fig.4.53 Objects – sets and classes

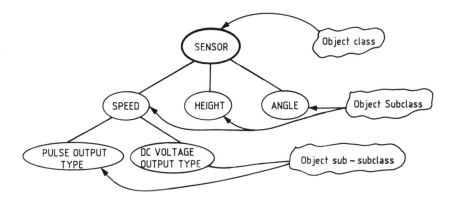

Fig.4.54 Objects – subclasses and sub-subclasses

be regarded as a class of objects (it just depends on our view of things). In that case higher levels are referred to as 'super-classes'. Note here that we aren't decomposing objects in program terms; it's merely a class-cataloguing exercise.

At each class level we define various properties of the class. Any subclasses derived from a parent class may acquire these properties, this being known as 'inheritance'. The inherited features may, if desired, be modified by the subclass.

At some stage we come down to specific objects (either actual or virtual). Each particular object is defined to be an 'instance' of the object class, as shown in Fig.4.55.

The variables associated with a class instance are called 'instance variables', Fig.4.56. Those defined at the higher (class) level are designated as 'class variables'. Instance variables are usually held in private data stores while class variables are made public to all instances. Creating a new instance of a class is known as 'instantiation'.

When a message request is passed to an object the resulting action is known as a 'method'. Methods can be invoked at class and instance levels, Figs 4.57

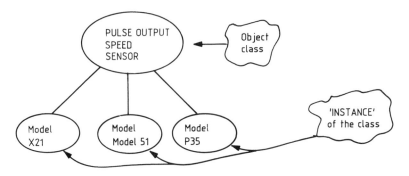

Fig.4.55 Instances of a class

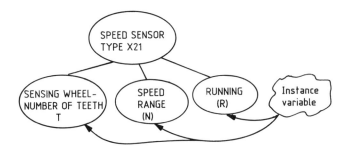

Fig.4.56 Instance variables

and 4.58. In Fig.4.57 the method 'NEW' creates a new instance of class 'PulseSensor'. Then, as shown in Fig.4.58, messages are sent to the instance to set up the instance variables. Other features specific to OOP (but not discussed here) include 'encapsulation', 'genericity' and 'persistence'.

One of the most important aspects discussed here is the idea of object classes. This allows us to form virtual objects, these being composed of both software and hardware. The speed sensor object, for instance, could be structured like

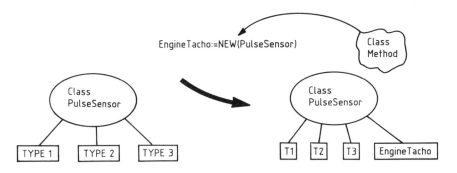

Fig.4.57 Example of a class method

this. Using this approach we can build up a library of speed sensor objects, one for each type of sensor. But the object interface doesn't change, so allowing us to replace object instances with minimal effort. This is one large step along the road to achieving the goal of truly re-usable software components.

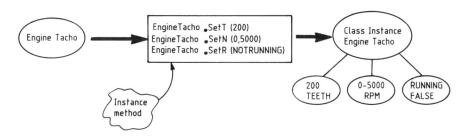

Fig.4.58 Example of an instance method

4.6   DATA STRUCTURED DESIGN

What is the fundamental purpose of data structured design? Put simply, it is the derivation of a program structure from the structure of the data manipulated by this program. The major implications (not always noticed) are that:

- The system is driven by the data flow into and out of it.
- The task of handling such data is a primary function.
- Time and event dependencies are relatively unimportant.
- Concurrent communicating tasks are less important design issues.

What are data structured designs best suited to? A brief scan through Kirk Hansen's book *Data Structured Program Design* (1986) soon gives the answer: the DP field.

In data processing the handling of large volumes of data is the essence of the problem. Here we have to:

- Store data properly, safely and efficiently.
- Retrieve this quickly and easily.
- Add to and delete from as required.
- Establish relational information concerning this data.

The actual manipulations carried out on the data are often quite trivial (in functional/mathematical terms). Much more effort is spent on getting the file-handling part of the problem right.

It has to be concluded that a pure data structured approach is not suitable for embedded systems design. However, it has been included within the method of Jackson System Design (JSD, chapter 10) which has been used successfully on the Spearfish Torpedo project (Cameron, 1988).

4.7   BUILDING THE SOFTWARE — ALTERNATIVE TECHNIQUES

Assume that we've reached a point where we've produced a design solution to our problem. Now the structure and its details can be translated into program code. This can be tackled in one of three ways, defined here as monolithic, modular and independent. The concepts behind these methods can be explained fairly easily by using the analogy of designing and building a kit car.

The monolithic approach is illustrated in Fig.4.59. Work begins by producing an all-embracing design plan, i.e. the problem is considered as being a single design task. Once the design is complete the car can be built to the plan's specifications and instructions.

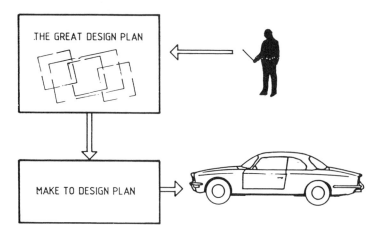

Fig.4.59 Monolithic design and make

Method 2 (Fig.4.60) tackles the problem in a different way at the design stage. An overall design plan is produced together with individual designs for major subsystems such as chassis, wheels, etc. The design can be carried out either by one individual, as in method 1, or a number of designers can work on the job simultaneously. Finally the various subsystem designs are integrated to produce a manufacturing work-plan. Manufacture takes place as in method 1.

Note a significant difference between these two methods. In the first, as the design is monolithic, all system information is implicitly available at all times. However, in the second ('modular') method, this may not necessarily be the case. Some information just doesn't need sharing; it's private or 'local' to that particular design activity. Clearly some information does have to be made generally available, otherwise there's no guarantee that the items will fit together correctly. Question: how are these details made known throughout the design team? Simply by explicitly defining design data which is to be made available to all parties, so-called 'global' information.

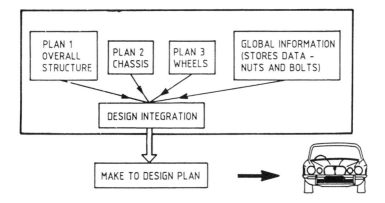

Fig.4.60 Modular design

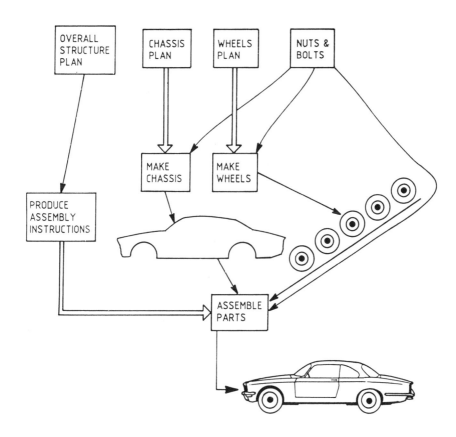

Fig.4.61 Independent design and build

In the third design method the concept of splitting the total task into a number of ('independent') sub-tasks is taken one stage further. Not only is the design compartmentalized; the same ideas are applied to manufacturing as well (Fig.4.61). Only at the final stage of production do all parts come together, in what is fundamentally an assembly operation. At this point only the interfacing details of the subsystems are important (assuming, of course, that the design itself is satisfactory).

Note also that the final assembly is essentially divorced from the detailed design process. This means that we can develop optional designs and choose the most appropriate one at assembly stage (compare this with selecting either a 1.3- or 1.6-litre engine in a standard production car).

The most flexible and powerful method of the three is the independent approach. This is relatively easy to organize using functional or object structuring, or both. However, implementing it is another matter. Much depends on the programming language selected for the design (chapter 8) and the way in which it is used.

4.8   A LAST COMMENT

Functional and object-oriented designs should not be seen as mutually exclusive techniques. Both have strong and weak points and, in many instances, are complementary. Functional structuring fits naturally into object-oriented designs as a way of forming the structure **within** the object. It's also been the experience from Matra Space (see HOOD) that, on large projects, a hierarchically-structured object-oriented design approach works well. But no matter what methods are used, the fundamentals of good design always apply, including:

- Problem abstraction.
- Problem structuring.
- Modularization.
- Stepwise refinement.
- Hierarchical and service decomposition.
- Decoupling.
- Cohesion.
- Information hiding.
- Control structure correctness.

REFERENCES

Anderson, B. (1988), Object-oriented programming, *Microprocessors and Microsystems*, **Vol.12**, No.8, October, pp433–442.

Bache, R. and Tinker, R. (1988), A rigorous approach to metrication: a field trial using Kindra, Second IEE/BCS Conference, *Software Engineering 88*, University of Liverpool, 11–15 July, Conference publication No.290, pp28–32.

Bohm, C. and Jacopini, G. (1966), Flow diagrams, Turing machines and languages with only two formation rules, *Communications of the ACM*, **Vol.9**, No.5, pp366–371, May.

Booch, G. (1987), *Software Engineering with ADA*, 2nd Ed, Benjamin/Cummmings Publishing Company Inc., California, ISBN 0–8053–0604–8.

Cameron, J.R. and Butcher, J.M. (1988), The use of JSD on the Spearfish system, IEE/BCS Conference, *Software Engineering 88*, University of Liverpool, 11–15 July, IEE publication.

Card, D.N., Church, V.E. and Agresti, W.W. (1986), An empirical study of software design practices, *IEEE Transactions on Software Engineering*, **Vol.SE-12**, No.2, February, pp264–271.

Dijkstra, E.W. (1968), Go To statement considered harmful, *Communications of the ACM*, **Vol.11**, No.3, pp147–148, March.

Dijkstra, E.W. (1969), Structured programming, in *Software Engineering Techniques* (Eds J.N. Buxton and B. Randell), NATO Science Committee, Rome, pp88–93.

Drake, R. (1989), Object-oriented programming and C++, *MDS Real-time Software Engineering Conference*, Wembley, UK, February, pp A/5/1–A/5/5.

Goldberg, A. and Robson, D. (1983), *Smalltalk-80. The Language and its Implementation*, Addison-Wesley, Reading, Mass., USA.

Hansen, K. (1986), *Data Structured Program Design*, Prentice-Hall, Englewood Cliffs, New Jersey, ISBN 0–13–196841–6.

Harrisberger, L. (1966), *Engineermanship, a Philosophy of Design*, Brooks/Cole Engineering Division, Monterey, California, ISBN 0–8185–0441–2.

HOOD – Hierarchical Object Oriented Design (1989), *HOOD Manual*, prepared by CISI Ingénierie, CRI A/S and Matra Espace for the European Space Agency, Issue 3 September 1989.

Jensen, R.W. and Tonies, C.C. (1979), *Software Engineering*, Prentice-Hall Inc., New Jersey, ISBN 0–13–822148–0.

McCabe, T. (1976), A complexity measure, *IEEE Transactions on Software Engineering*, **SE-2**, No.4, December, pp308–320.

McClure, C. (1978), *Reducing COBOL Complexity through Structured Programming*, Van Nostrand Reinhold, New York.

Martin, J. and McClure, C. (1985), *Structured Techniques for Computing*, Prentice-Hall Inc., New Jersey, ISBN 0–13–855180–4.

Oviedo, E.I. (1980), Control flow, data flow and program complexity, *Proceedings 4th COMPSAC*, Las Alaminitos, California, IEEE Press.

Parnas, D.L. (1972), On the criteria to be used in decomposing systems into modules, *Communications of the ACM*, **Vol.15**, No.12, December, pp1053–1058.

Plessman, K.W. and Tassakos, L. (1988), Concurrent, object-oriented program design in real-time systems, *Microprocessing and Microprogramming*, **No.24**, pp257–265.

Sommerville, I. (1989), *Software Engineering*, 3rd Ed., Addison-Wesley, ISBN 0–201–17568–1.

Stevens, W., Myers, G. and Constantine, L. (1974), Structured design, *IBM Systems Journal*, **Vol.13**, No.2, pp115–139.

Wirth, N. (1974), On the composition of well-structured programs, *Computing Surveys*, **Vol.6**, No.4, December, pp247–259.

Yourdon, E. and Constantine, L.L. (1979), *Structured Design – Fundamentals of a Discipline of Computer Program and Systems Design*, Prentice-Hall, Englewood Cliffs, New Jersey, ISBN 0–13–854471–9.

FURTHER READING

Meyrowitz, N. (ed.) (1989), *Object-oriented Programming: systems, languages and applications*, OOPSLA '89 Conference Proceedings, ACM Press, Addison-Wesley Publishers, Wokingham, Berkshire, UK.

Peterson, G. E. (1987), *Tutorial–object Oriented Computing*, Vol. 1: concepts, IEEE Computer Society Press, ISBN 0–8186–0821–8.

Chapter Five

Diagramming – an introduction

In the early days of computers, diagramming didn't figure as an important topic in the design process. Further, the only pictorial method used was that of the flow chart. At that time there was little distinction between programming and design (nor, for that matter, between programmers and designers). The design and development process usually went something as follows:

- Programmers thought about the problem to be solved.
- They wrote lines of code to solve it.
- The code was tested and modified until it was correct (or appeared to be so).
- This source code was released as the system documentation.

Sometimes, in a token gesture to appease senior management (or the customer), a system flow chart was produced. Whether it represented what went on in the program is another matter.

In the last 15 years a revolution has taken place concerning the use of diagramming for software. Practically all modern software tools use diagrams as an integral part of the design and development process. The driving force for this has come from commerce and industry, not academia. Underlying this has been the need to produce reliable software which is delivered on time at the right price. Although these changes have their roots in large system developments they are making a major impact in the microprocessor field. We are also seeing the arrival of tools specifically produced for use in embedded systems.

This chapter sets out to:

- Show why diagrams are used as part of the modern software toolset.
- Describe, in general terms, what they achieve.
- Define the requirements and attributes of software diagrams.

5.1   DIAGRAMS — WHY?

5.1.1   Introduction

Why do we use diagrams? Not 'why do we use software diagrams?', but why do we use diagrams at all? We couldn't imagine civil, mechanical or electrical engineers working without diagrams. And, at a much simpler level, try putting together self-assembly furniture using only written instructions (no pictures).

This takes us into the area of psychology. Our experiences show us that pictures must convey information in a different way from words: and in a way which is clearer and easier to understand. T.R.G. Green (1982) describes this in terms of temporal processes, dealing with many aspects of the problem, including:

- Recognition – is the process familiar?
- Modularity – what chunks can the description be broken into?
- Tractability – how can a modification be made?
- Sequence – in what order do the events happen?
- Circumstance – if such-and-such happens, what does it mean?'

So, assuming that pictures really do help us, where can we sensibly use them in the software world? There are four main areas in which diagramming methods can be applied (Fig.5.1).

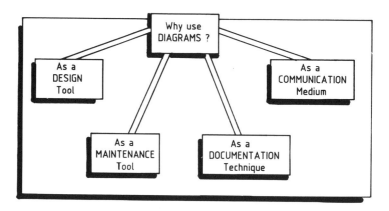

Fig.5.1 The role of diagrams in software development

In the following sections these are discussed in general terms; specific techniques are covered in chapter 6. But note that here we are mainly concerned with the **effects** produced by using diagrams, not **how** they are used in detail.

5.1.2   Diagrams as a design tool

Consider an electronic engineer carrying out circuit design. One of the first things he does is to sketch the circuit diagram (Fig.5.2).

Very quickly this is followed up by a series of calculations to verify the performance of the design. It **would** be possible to describe the design using words only. In one sense this is how computer-aided design tools for printed circuit board layout works. Yet no engineer would adopt such an approach at the initial design stage. Why not?

Fig.5.2 Initial design

First, the exercise of producing the diagram requires an explicit action. Implicit relationships cannot exist. Thus, even to draw a diagram requires a clear understanding of the problem. But when we just think about designs we often carry implicit information in our minds.

Next, if we work to an agreed set of drawing rules we introduce formality and design rigour into the process (Fig.5.3). This means that it is possible for others to review, assess and discuss the design. It also eliminates ambiguity and ambivalence. For instance, in Fig.5.3, a dot indicates a connection; but why is one arrangement satisfactory and the other not so? Because in one format there is no confusion between crossing lines and connecting lines should the draftsman omit a dot.

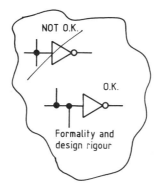

Fig.5.3 Drawing rules

Finally, the design as a whole can be reviewed and analysed, and the performance assessed. At this stage many incorrect or illogical design features come to light (Fig.5.4). These can be corrected at a very early stage, saving time, effort and money (and embarrassment for the designer).

All of this is directly applicable to software. After all, at this stage of the design we are still working with concepts and ideas, so it should work for software as well as hardware.

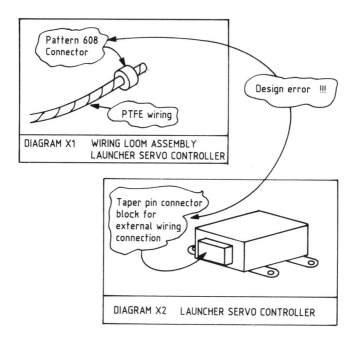

Fig.5.4 Design review

5.1.3   Diagrams for design documentation

Diagrams are a powerful means of documenting the design task (preferable to a mass of source code listings). But a moment's thought shows that a single type of drawing is very unlikely to meet all our needs. Two groups of diagrams are needed (Fig.5.5). The first gives us a high-level view of the problem, showing what we've set out to do. The second, low-level one, concentrates on how we're going about solving the design problem. Each one is oriented towards a different aspect of the same problem. For any particular system, high-level diagrams:

- Are task oriented.
- Show the overall system structure together with its major sub-systems.
- Describe the overall functioning of the design.
- Show the interaction of the system with its environment.
- Describe the functions and interactions of the various sub-systems.

Low-level diagrams:

- Are solution oriented.
- Concentrate on detail.
- Emphasize system internal information.

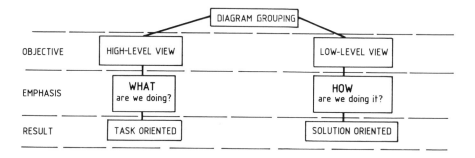

Fig.5.5 Diagrams for documentation

Consider the attributes of such diagrams when applied, at a functional block level, to a mythical weapon control system (Fig.5.6).

The high-level view concentrates on the overall task; its object is to ensure that we tackle the right problem. We can see from this figure how the main building blocks of the system fit together. Questions like 'Is the launcher compatible with the servo controller? Will the servo be powerful enough? Should we use hydraulics instead of electrics?' are considered at this level. In contrast, the low-level diagram tells us how the design task has been solved. It gives much information about the system internals, together with the interaction of such internals. It deals with questions like 'What's the best type of power amplifier? Is the processor fast enough? Should the analogue signals be bipolar or unipolar?'

Good high-level diagrams are simple and clear, bringing out the essential major features of a system. Using these it is relatively easy to see the effects on system behaviour when making modifications. On the other hand, low-level diagrams tend to be cluttered and complex. This is inherent in their nature; it isn't a criticism of such drawings. But, although their structure helps us to answer the question 'are we doing the job correctly?' they aren't very good when we ask 'are we doing the right job?'.

These ideas can be directly translated to software engineering. We gain all the benefits outlined above by using pictures in the design process. What it also shows is that whatever diagramming method is used, it must be able to give both high- and low-level views.

5.1.4 Diagrams for maintenance

Post-design maintenance is done for two reasons; either to correct faults or to upgrade equipments. Ideally, this would be done by the original designers. But, in reality, once some years have passed, few of the original designers are still around. So, software maintenance is usually carried out by workers who:

• Weren't involved in the development in the first place.

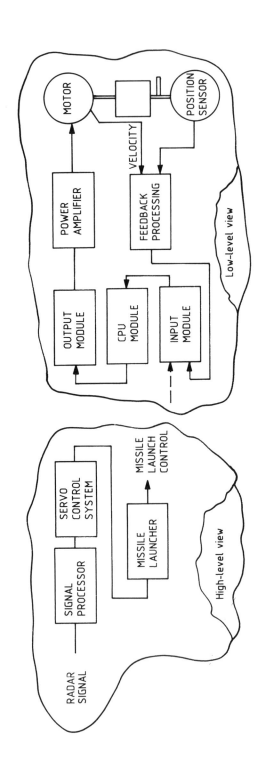

Fig.5.6 High-level vs low-level views

- Have only a limited understanding of the overall task.
- Have to learn a lot very quickly to perform even small design changes.
- Wouldn't have written the code like that in any case.

It is not surprising that maintenance is unpopular. It may be an obscure and difficult job but somebody has to do it. And the better the original documentation the easier it can be. Therefore, design information must support the maintenance process by being complete, correct, clear and consistent (Fig.5.7). System documentation needs to give both an overview as well as detailed information. It is very easy to be swamped by an excess of paper, typified by many technical manuals. As an example of such overkill, Rothon (1979) reported that 'the recent specification for the software for an American fighter plane occupied more than 26 thick volumes of text. It is hardly surprising that developers faced with such bulky documentation are unable to perceive the nature of the software . . .'. By using overview information it is much easier to see the overall picture. For instance, questions such as 'where and how can changes be made? What are the knock-on effects of these on the complete program?' can be much more easily answered. However, we still need detailed information, relating specifically to the source code itself. Once again there is a clear need for a two-level documentation system.

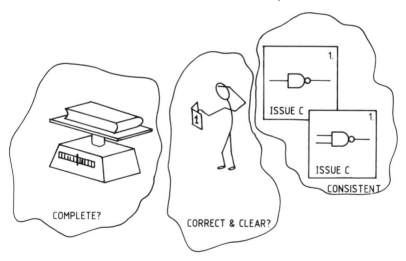

Fig.5.7 Document requirements

5.1.5   Diagrams for communication

It's already been shown that written and spoken words can be ambiguous, ambivalent or even totally confusing. We've also seen that by using sketches, pictures, etc., many such problems are eliminated. Therefore, design diagrams can be used to help communications between members of the software and system project teams.

Who are likely to be the main users of such diagrams? They are: the system users (or procurement agency), the system designers and the post-design support group (maintainers). Fig.5.8 shows the general lines of communication between these groups. It also shows at which periods of the design these take place.

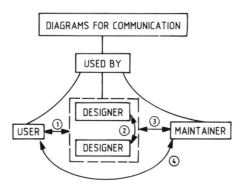

DIALOGUE	MAIN USE
①	During tendering, design and system acceptance.
②	During the design phase
③	On completion of design
④	Post-design service phase

Fig.5.8 Communication aspects of diagrams

What questions do diagrams aim to answer? Consider first the user–designer interaction, Table 5.1.

Table 5.1 User–designer dialogue

User	Designer
Does **he** understand what I want?	Has the job been properly specified in the first place?
Am I getting what I want?	Am I doing the right job?
How is the job going?	How is the job going?

Let's now turn to designer–designer communication. Even in a small job involving only one designer there are still 'chiefs' to be talked to (Table 5.2). Ideally, such discussions should be clear, understandable and not open to individual interpretation. Pictures can help considerably in such cases.

Table 5.2 Designer–designer interaction

Chief Designer	Designer
This is the overall plan.	I understand the task.
This is how the job is split up.	Here is the detailed design response.
These are **your** responsibilities.	
This is the development plan.	Here is a progress document.
These are the time scales.	
These are the task interfaces.	Here is a record of the design
I want a record of progress	

In the post-design phase the requirements of the user tend to reduce in quantity. Unfortunately for the maintainer, these requirements are usually highly demanding ones (Table 5.3).

Table 5.3 User–maintainer interaction

User	Maintainer
Fix my problem (now!).	Can this problem even be fixed?
How much to fix my problem?	
What happens if .....?	How does the system really work?
Modify my system.	
How much for the modification?	Can it be modified successfully?
How long?	How long, how much?

5.2   THE ESSENTIALS OF SOFTWARE DIAGRAMS

5.2.1   Fundamentals

What is the fundamental purpose of software design diagrams? In a very simple way they can be seen as a way to bridge the gap between what is wanted (the problem) and what is provided (the solution), Fig.5.9.

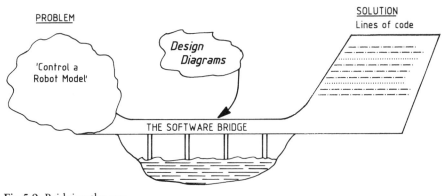

Fig.5.9 Bridging the gap

In fact, the total design process can be viewed as a two-stage activity (Fig.5.10). The diagram sits in the middle of this, serving two groups of people. From the point of view of problem translation, diagrams **must** meet the needs of the user. That is, the design approach must be stated in terms of the problem not its solution; they must be easy for the user to understand. In most cases he won't be a software engineer, so there's not much point in sending him a pile of computer print-outs. Finally, it must be easy to produce and modify such diagrams to encourage their use in the translation stage.

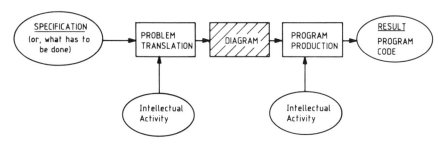

Fig.5.10 The two-stage design process

The information shown by the diagram is then used as an input to the program production process. But unless diagramming methods support program design techniques (e.g. top-down design), programmers won't find them very helpful. In such cases all that happens is that yet another translation stage is used in the design process. It is also essential that the diagramming method relates strongly to modern design structures, e.g. the sequence, selection and iteration actions of structured programming. Ideally the diagram constructs should mirror those of modern programming languages.

5.2.2   Basic qualities

Consider the assembly instruction diagram of Fig.5.11. This has taken time and money to produce; yet the furniture manufacturer considers this a worthwhile investment. This isn't done through a sense of altruism, it's just good business practice. It conveys considerable information to the user in a simple, direct way. But it succeeds in this only if it has specific basic qualities (Fig.5.12). Let's look at each point in turn, putting it in terms of software production.

(a)   Small
Here, small means an A3 or A4 size diagram. One major reason for limiting diagram size is to avoid overloading the reader with information. Good pictorial methods use a top-down method in presenting such information, as in Fig.5.13.

There are, however, some mundane grounds for keeping to these sizes. In the first case they can be produced easily on low-cost plotters and printers.

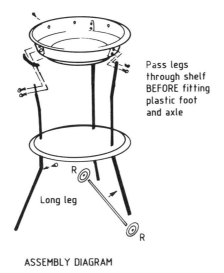

ASSEMBLY DIAGRAM

Fig.5.11 Kit assembly diagram

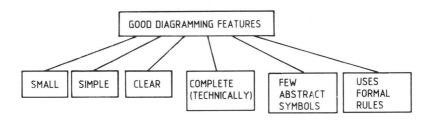

Fig.5.12 Diagrams – desirable features

Moreover, these are usually widely available; there's no need to invest in expensive flat-bed plotters. Second, such diagrams usually form part of a main design document; thus it must be easy to integrate these with the rest of the documentation. Large diagrams cause problems here.

(b) Simple and clear

Diagrams are supposed to help our understanding, not act as intellectual puzzles. When diagrams are simple and clear they are quickly understood and assimilated. This may seem a statement of the obvious, yet many diagrams break these rules. The resulting consequences may be disastrous. Some years ago a military transport plane crashed on take-off, killing 50 passengers. The fault was caused by the reverse fitting of a non-return fuel control valve. But the factor which led to this was a poor, ambiguous fitting diagram which didn't show clearly the flow direction through the valve.

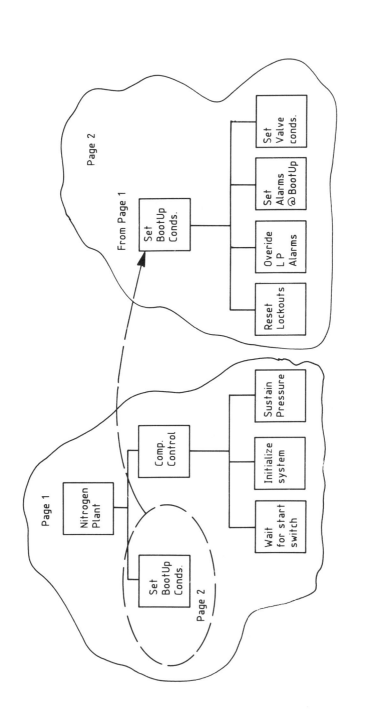

Fig.5.13 A top-down diagramming method

An example of a diagram which breaks all the rules is given in Fig.5.14 (Green, 1982, reproduced by permission).

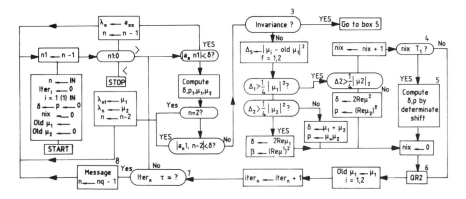

Fig.5.14 A confusing diagram

(c) Complete
This means that information should not be missing from the diagram. Now this shouldn't be confused with the use of extra pictures to show all the facts. That, for software documentation, is the rule rather than the exception. What it does mean is that omissions of data which leave the information incomplete are taboo.

(d) Few abstract symbols
It is impossible to construct software design diagrams without using abstract symbols, Fig.5.15 (O'Sullivan, 1986). Unfortunately, abstract symbols can be a problem in themselves, especially if complex constructs are used. In such cases it may be quite difficult to see what message the picture is trying to convey. So the fewer symbols used the better. And keep them simple.

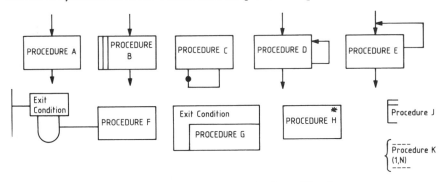

Each of the procedures above has been selected from a different diagramming methodology. They all say the same thing, that the procedures they contain may all be performed more than once.

Fig.5.15 Example of abstract symbols

(e)   Uses formal rules

All notation used in diagramming should be done in accordance with a set of rules. These rules should be defined, clear and consistent. Without this we can never be sure that we understand what the diagrams mean.

5.2.3   Basic types

No single diagram type can meet all the needs of the software designer. Many different types have been proposed in recent years, and many have fallen by the wayside. Only those which are genuinely useful have survived the test of time.

In this section the need for, use of and information content of the most widely-used diagrams are introduced. Let's assume that we have the job of implementing a computer-based machinery test system, Fig.5.16.

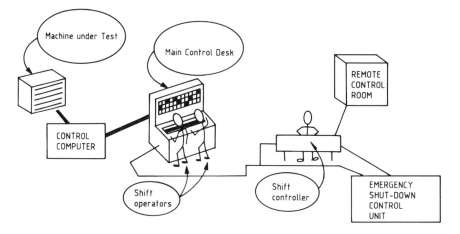

Fig.5.16 Hypothetical machinery test system

Here a piece of machinery is put through its paces on a test-bed. The machine has its own control computer, but its performance is also monitored remotely. This remote operation, the 'main control task', involves both manual- and computer-based systems. Manual functions are carried out by two shift operators and a shift controller. Each shift operator looks after a specific task while the controller oversees both. Further, he can override the actions of the individual operators. The plant includes an emergency shut-down control unit; this can be activated by any of the human operators. All test information is gathered and stored on hard disk in a remote control room. Data is transferred from local data stores to the remote one as determined by the shift controller. Fine. So far we've described what the plant function is. But what diagrams should we produce for the software design?

In tackling this problem the first question concerns **what** a system is supposed to do (the analysis). To help answer this we need to show the total system, its parts, and how they interrelate with the software system. A diagram used for this purpose is called a context diagram (Fig.5.17). Note, by the way, that the notation used here hasn't any special significance.

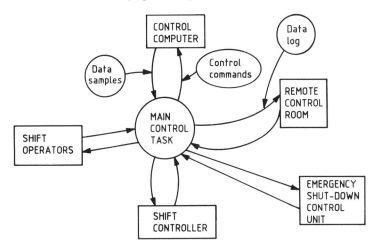

Fig.5.17 Context diagram

Each line connects two items, the attached text describing the flow of information between these items (the diagram has been deliberately simplified to keep it clear). The context diagram, in conjunction with the statement of requirements, aims to answer the **what** question. It will, though, only give part of the answer. In many situations, especially large systems, the relationship between items is important (and often complex). These items (or objects) which have data values associated with them are defined to be 'entities'; their associations are shown in entity relationship diagrams (ERD), Fig.5.18.

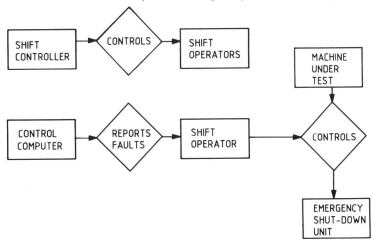

Fig.5.18 Entity relationship diagram

What we've done so far is to show what the software system must respond to. At this point we need to consider **how** it should react to its external environment. This is depicted in terms of:

• Data flow into, through, and out of the system.
• Data storage within the system.
• Data transformation by processes within the system.

Such information is given on a data flow diagram (DFD), Fig.5.19.

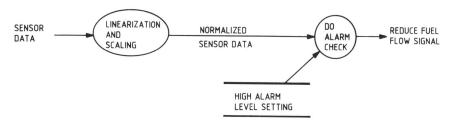

Fig.5.19 Data flow diagram

A diagram which is very similar in concept to the DFD is the process structure chart (Fig.5.20). This is used where the design is best described as a set of parallel activities (or, rather formally, communicating concurrent processes). Its basic functions are to describe system data flow, data stores, and intertask communication and synchronization.

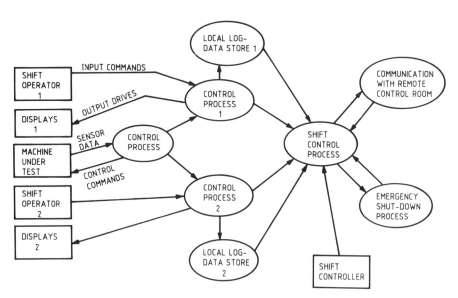

Fig.5.20 Process structure chart

At this stage we can move on to look at the **how** of system design. Both the DFD and the process structure chart are used as part of this function. In practice we would use expanded ('levelled') versions of these diagrams.

Although there is now considerable information at hand we still haven't really described just how the processes work. This is needed to generate both the overall program structure and the detailed program behaviour. Diagrams used to show program structure and behaviour are here lumped together under the generic title of 'program structure diagrams' (PSD). They are used as input information for the production of source code. Two forms are used, diagrams and structured text (Fig.5.21).

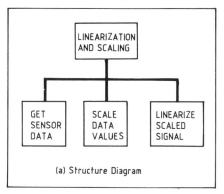

Fig.5.21 Program structure description diagrams

DFDs show what data moves around the system, how it is modified, what is stored, etc. What they don't show is when things happen and the effects of such changes. In other words, what we have in front of us is static, not dynamic, information. Frequently it is very difficult to write programs without taking into account system dynamic behaviour. In simple applications (e.g. a single closed loop digital controller) we can probably remember exactly how the system behaves at all times; we just carry the information in our head. In more complex arrangements (such as a local area network controller) this would be impossible; we have to resort to written descriptions. These must show all the possible discrete and finite states of the system; that is, events and event dependencies. The most common form of event-dependent diagram is the state transition diagram (STD), Fig.5.22. All possible states are shown in the diagram together with the reasons for changes of state.

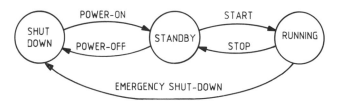

Fig.5.22 State transition diagram

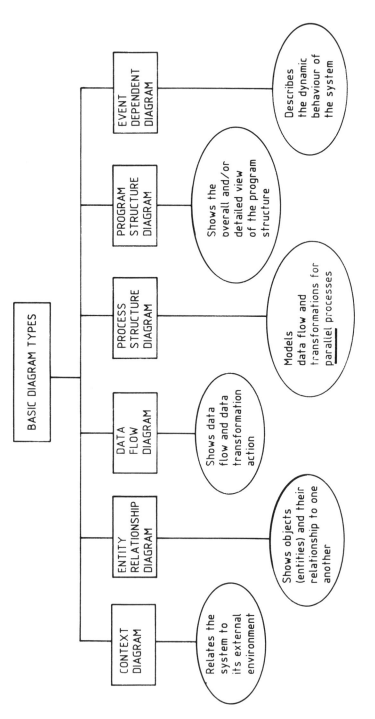

Fig.5.23 Basic diagram types

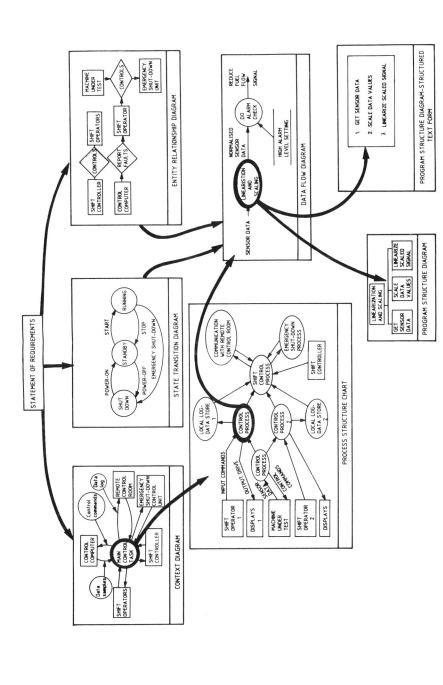

Fig.5.24 The relationship of software diagrams

5.3   PRACTICAL DIAGRAMMING TECHNIQUES — A GENERAL COMMENT

From the previous section we've seen that there is a basic set of diagram types (Fig.5.23). Their general relationship with each other is shown in Fig.5.24.

It is important to realize that, in any particular job, not all types may be necessary. It depends very much on the size and complexity of the task in hand. And the situation may be further complicated by diagramming techniques which are integral parts of specific design methods. Frequently these look quite different, yet they all relate to the basic set described here.

REFERENCES

Green, T.R.G. (1982), Pictures of programs and other processes, or how to do things with lines, *Behaviour and Information Technology*, **Vol.1**, No.1, pp3–36.

Martin, J. and McClure, C. (1985), *Diagramming Techniques for Analysts and Programmers*, Prentice-Hall, Inc., Englewood Cliffs, New Jersey 07632, USA, ISBN 0–13–208794–4.

O'Sullivan, V.J. (1986), The use of diagrams in the software development process, *Master's Thesis in Information Technology*, Department of Electronic and Electrical Engineering, Loughborough University.

Rothon, N.M. (1979), 'Design Structure Diagrams: a new standard in flow diagrams', *Computer Bulletin*, **Series 2**, No.19, pp4–6.

Chapter Six

Diagramming methodologies in software design

Chapter 5 laid the groundwork for the use of diagrams as a software design tool. In general it described the basic ideas of the subject in a fairly abstract way. These now need to be related to practical design methods. In this chapter the work is extended, using a specimen example to illustrate:

- Precisely how diagrams are used.
- How these fit in with established design methodologies.
- What information they contain.
- How diagrams are produced.

6.1   INTRODUCTION

It is easy to confuse diagramming methods and design methods. This happens because some diagramming methods form an integral part of specific design processes. One can end up believing that design and diagramming are inseparable. This isn't so. Diagramming methods **can** be used without adopting the associated design principles.

The following sections show, in a fair amount of detail, how these methods are used. Their inclusion within specific design processes is also shown. To do this, a fairly simple gas turbine control system, Fig.6.1, is used as a specimen example.

The objectives are to show that:

- Different techniques have been developed to solve the same problem.
- Many techniques differ in detail but are based upon the same structural concepts.
- Some diagramming techniques can be used only in one application area.
- Other techniques can be used in more than one diagram type.
- Some techniques combine the basic types described in chapter 5 into new (hybrid) types.
- Extensions and modifications of the basic types are needed in certain real-time applications.

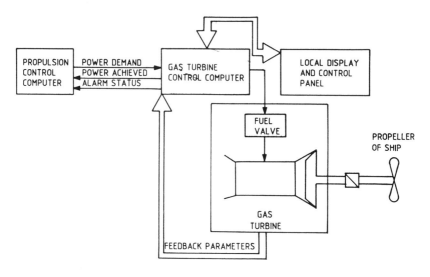

(a) OVERALL SYSTEM

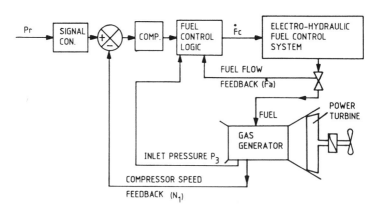

(b)   CONTROL LOOP

Fig.6.1 Specimen embedded system – gas turbine control

6.2 CONTEXT AND ENTITY RELATIONSHIP DIAGRAMS

These are taken together as they relate specifically to the system analysis phase, not the design phase.

The purpose of the context diagram has already been described; now what about its form? One widely-used structure is that of the Yourdon method (Yourdon, 1978), Fig.6.2.

The software system to be implemented is shown as a single circle. This represents the overall, top-level view of the complete process handled by the software. It interfaces to the outside world using the signals ('data') shown on the diagram. Thus the context diagram can be regarded as a very high-level data flow diagram. However, it is important that it shows the relationship of the software with its environment, not the details of the task itself.

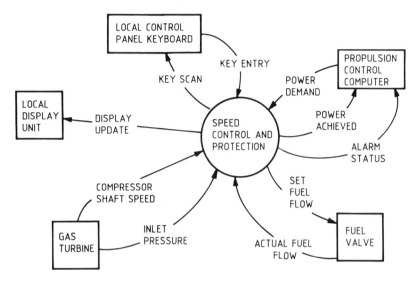

Fig.6.2 Context diagram – gas turbine system

This would be used in concert with the system operational description contained in the SOR document. Definitions concerning system behaviour, signal levels, required response rates, etc. are held here. Using these the designer aims to obtain a description of the system which is complete, correct and unambiguous. Such descriptions are augmented by diagrams which show relationships and dependencies between system objects ('entities'), Fig.6.3.

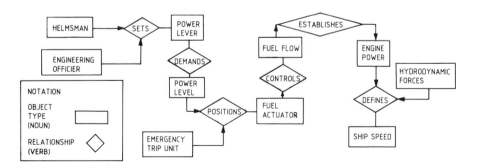

Fig.6.3 Entity relationship diagram

6.3   DATA FLOW DIAGRAMS

Data flow diagrams (DFDs) show processes and the flow of data among these processes (Fig.6.4).

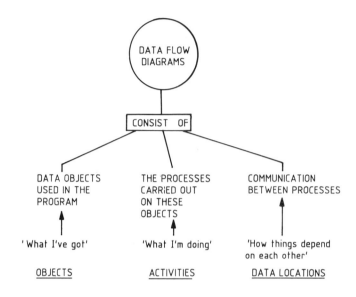

Fig.6.4 Content of data flow diagrams

In some DFD diagramming methods the control communication between processes may also be shown. DFDs can be used in both the analysis and the design phase of the project. For analysis, its main role is to show the functional processes and the transactions which take place between these. At the lower (more detailed) levels it is used as a design tool (Fig.6.5).

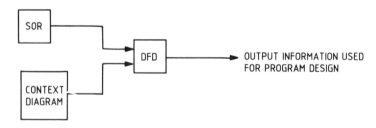

Fig.6.5 The DFD as a design tool

The notation and layout of DFDs varies considerably; those shown in Fig.6.6 are based on MASCOT (1983, 1987), Yourdon (1978) and Gane and Sarson (1977). Thus part of the total DFD for the gas turbine system could be drawn as in Fig.6.7. When more detail is needed, individual processes are expanded or 'levelled' (the meaning of this term is buried in the mists of time). For example, Fig.6.8 gives the levelled version of process 'Compute Required Fuelling'.

ITEM　　　NOTATION	YOURDON	GANE and SARSON	MASCOT
FLOW OF DATA	→	→	⊣►⊢ ⊣►⊢
PROCESS	Process Description	IDENT No. / Process Description / Physical Location (option)	Process Description
DATA STORE	═══	Identification	▲ ▼
EXTERNAL DEVICES	Name	Name	Name

Fig.6.6 Notation used on DFDs

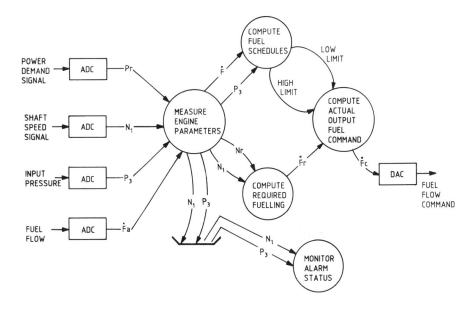

Fig.6.7 DFD example – gas turbine system

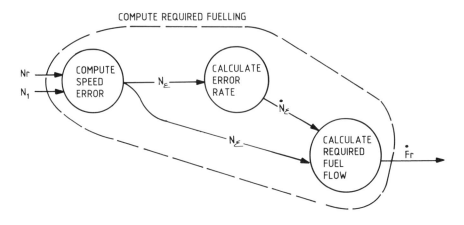

COMPUTE REQUIRED FUELLING

Fig.6.8 Levelled DFD (part)

6.4   PROCESS STRUCTURE DIAGRAMS

The process structure diagram is, at heart, a data flow diagram. However, its intent is quite different. It is specifically designed for use with parallel processing structures. In such designs the overall task is modelled as a series of co-operating parallel sub-tasks or processes. This may be supported in hardware using multiple processors, using for instance, one processor per sub-task. This is a true concurrent multitasking configuration (usually called multiprocessing). Alternatively, all tasks may be run on just one processor as a time-shared quasi-concurrent operation. For convenience, this is referred to here as 'multitasking'. In large systems a combination of multiprocessing and multitasking may well be used.

Additional information is carried in process structure diagrams (compared with DFDs) to describe how processes interact and communicate. Such tasks are the responsibility of the system executive, chapter 9. Examples of process structure diagrams are given in chapter 10.

6.5   PROGRAM STRUCTURE DIAGRAMS

6.5.1   Overview

Program structure diagrams have essentially one function. They provide the link between the problem specification and the production of source code. To do this they should meet some basic requirements, Fig.6.9.

But not all program design methods operate in the same way. Each approach shows program constructs in its own particular fashion. As a result, many diagramming notations have been developed. And they all tackle the requirements outlined in Fig.6.9 in different ways.

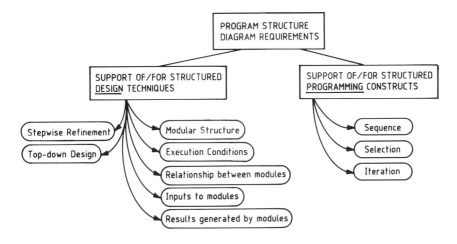

Fig.6.9 Requirements of program structure diagrams

The topic can be very confusing initially. This fogginess is due partly to the use of very similar names for different techniques. It is further compounded by the way in which these are used. Sometimes a particular name defines a quite specific diagramming technique. In other cases a name is used as a blanket cover for a number of similar techniques (i.e. a generic grouping). Diagramming methods described in this section have been selected using two rules:

- Are they used for the program (code) design process?
- Are they generally used by the software community?

6.5.2 Top-to-bottom decomposition — basic form, Jackson and Yourdon diagrams

Structured programs are designed as a layered set of operations (Fig.6.10), following the concepts of top-down design. At the top there is a single root module or root operation. This is decomposed using a tree structure to interconnect lower-level operations. The philosophy behind these diagram constructs is covered in the section on design techniques; here we are concerned only with what the diagrams show.

Fig.6.10, although it uses 'home-grown' notation, should be fairly simple to follow and use. Note, though, that it doesn't explicitly show **when** an action is turned into code. Two different notations, Jackson (1975) and Yourdon (Yourdon and Constantine, 1978) use the same top-down design approach. However, they handle the design task in quite different ways.

(a) Jackson structure diagrams

Jackson diagrams can be used to show both program and data structures (this can cause some confusion at first). On the other hand they don't do both simultaneously; separate diagrams are used. Here we are concerned specifically with their use for describing program behaviour.

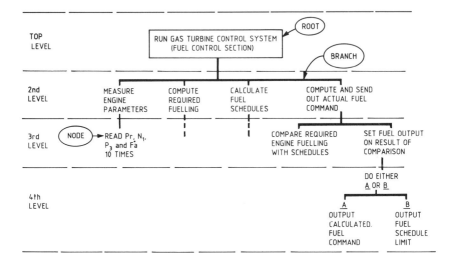

Fig.6.10 Top-to-bottom decomposition – basic structure

Jackson diagrams show three operations: sequence, selection and iteration (Fig.6.11).

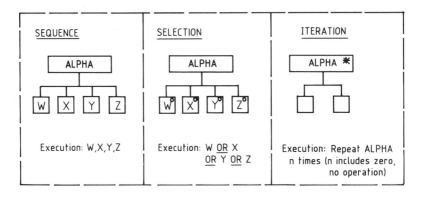

Fig.6.11 Jackson structure diagrams – basic constructs

In this example the SEQUENCE construct shows that ALPHA is composed of W, X, Y, Z; they are executed in the order shown. Next, ALPHA involves a choice, that is, SELECTION. Thus, either W or X or Y or Z is executed; these choices are mutually exclusive. The diagram, in its basic form, doesn't show the test condition for the selection action.

Finally we come to ITERATION. This construct defines that ALPHA is a repeated operation. But it doesn't indicate how many iterations are involved; condition information must be shown separately. Iteration here includes the case where we don't execute ALPHA at all, the zero loop. Further, observe that we can't tell which are pre-check loops and which are post-check ones. Also, the exit conditions aren't built into the diagram structure. The Jackson diagram corresponding to Fig.6.10 is shown in Fig.6.12.

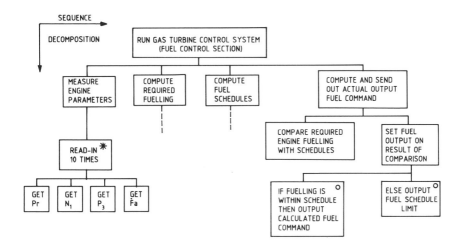

Fig.6.12 Jackson structure diagram – gas turbine example

One fundamental point concerns code generation. In the Jackson method, code is produced which directly relates to the bottom-most nodes (also called 'terminal points' or 'elementary components'). Code is **never** produced for higher-level operations. Looked at in another way, a high-level component is the 'sum' of its lower-level parts; it doesn't have an independent existence.

(b)   Yourdon structure diagrams
Yourdon structure diagrams, usually called 'structure charts', are based on those devised by Yourdon and Constantine (1978). At first sight they are (apparently) very similar to Jackson diagrams. In fact, their information content is quite different in many ways.

The fundamental building blocks of Yourdon structure charts are mainly rectangular boxes. These are interconnected using data and control flow arrows (Fig.6.13).

Each box describes a process, known as a module. Where a process (A) needs to be split into a number of parts (step-wise refinement) it is broken down into lower-level processes (B, C). Lowest-level modules are known as 'leafs'. The structure diagram shows this hierarchical relationship between the modules. Arrowed lines are used to show the connection between modules. In Yourdon design each module is implemented as source code; it consists of a sequence of program instructions having a single entry and single exit point.

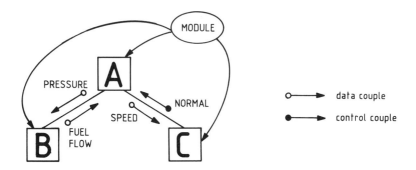

Fig.6.13 Yourdon structure diagram – basic layout and components

The arrowed line connection does more than just show the connection between modules. It also specifies that, at execution time, control passes from the higher-level (or 'parent') module to the lower-level, 'child' module. That is, the first module calls the second one. In doing so it may well pass information to it; at the end it may receive data back. This flow of information is called a 'data couple.' In many cases the response required from the called or 'invoked' module is not data, but information to be used for control of the program. The module, for instance, might have to evaluate if the speed of a unit is in the normal range. The reply would be a simple YES/NO, which can't really be considered to be data. It is, in fact, defined to be a control couple or 'flag'. Note that a called module always returns control to the calling module. Additional components used in Yourdon diagramming are shown in Fig.6.14.

Where any particular module can be called by more than one higher level module it is called a common module (the use of common modules changes

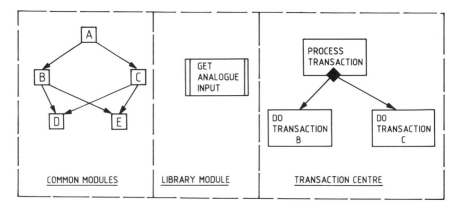

Fig.6.14 Yourdon diagram – additional components

tree-structured diagrams to mesh ones). Library modules are those which carry out predefined tasks; in fact they are the building blocks in service (functional) decomposition. Normally one would expect a library module to be a leaf.

Note that this diagram does **not** show sequence, selection and iteration control structures. The ordering of blocks does not define the sequence of module execution. Selection can be implemented using a transaction centre, the black diamond symbol of Fig.6.14 (the centre, by the way, is the diamond, not the module). A transaction centre is used where different types of operations may be needed and each type requires a different module to process it. The Yourdon diagram for the example gas turbine control system is shown in Fig.6.15.

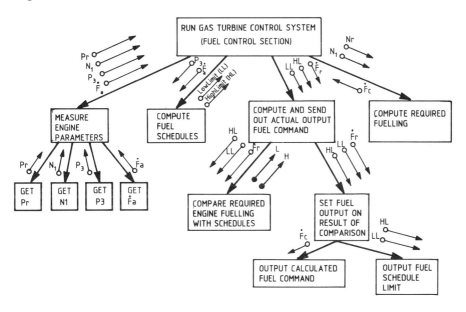

Fig.6.15 Yourdon structure diagram (chart) – gas turbine example

The modules have been organized as shown to reinforce the point that the diagram does not give sequence information. One claimed advantage for Yourdon diagramming is that it shows the control and data coupling in a system. But even in this simple example, the diagram becomes cluttered and difficult to read when the couples are put in. An advantage?

Jackson and Yourdon diagrams are very good at providing the higher-level views of the program. Also, they can be (and are) used quite successfully down to the code generation stage. Translation from the diagram to code is straightforward when a good high-level language is used. It is not so easy when programming complex constructs in assembly language. Experience has shown that these often need to be described using a notation which is highly detailed.

6.5.3   Left-to-right decomposition — general form, Warnier-Orr and Action diagrams

In its simplest form, left-to-right decomposition is merely top-to-bottom turned through 90 degrees (Fig.6.16). Such diagrams have the advantage of being easy to print out using standard narrow-carriage printers. The earliest methods pre-date the word processor era; hence they were designed to be implemented using teletypes or typewriters.

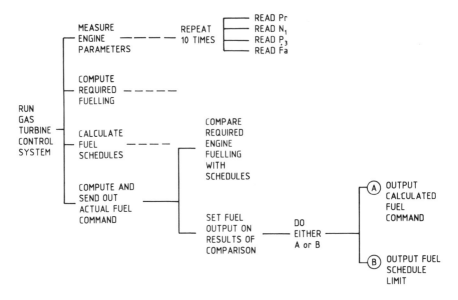

Fig.6.16 Left-to-right decomposition – basic structure

(a)   Warnier-Orr diagrams

This method, designed by Jean-Dominique Warnier and Ken Orr, has been around since the early 1970s (Warnier, 1981). It uses text in an organized, hierarchical fashion to show program structure. The constructs are shown in Fig.6.17. Here the sequence function name is ALPHA, the sequence consisting of the components W, X, Y, Z. Execution takes place in that order, being defined by the top-to-bottom order on the diagram. Any individual component can be further expanded like this until the lowest level of detail is arrived at.

Selection between components is shown by using the exclusive OR symbol. If a function may or may not be executed then we write '(0,1)' below the function name. The method can also show how to select more than one function from a given choice, i.e. an n from m selection, n < m.

Iteration is shown by writing the number of executions below the function name. Where the item may not be executed at all this requires a pre-check loop; this is defined by having a lower iteration bound of zero. Thus, in such cases, the notation below the bracket would be (0,n), showing lower and upper bounds.

Both WHILE DO (pre-check loop) and REPEAT UNTIL (post-check loop) can be shown in this notation. The corresponding exit conditions are written as footnotes and matched to their position using markers, typically as ?1, ?2, ?3 etc. Exactly the same method can be used to denote selection conditions.

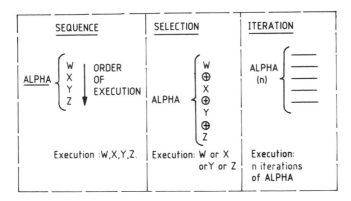

Fig.6.17 Warnier-Orr diagrams – basic constructs

The gas turbine program, in Warnier-Orr form, is shown in Fig.6.18. A major feature of these diagrams is that they can show both high-level and low-level (detailed) views of the program.

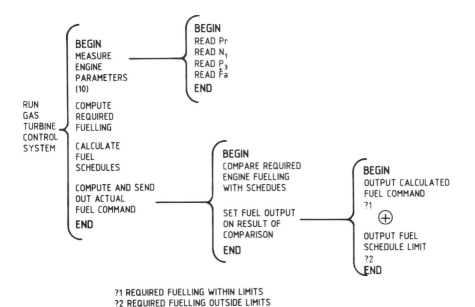

Fig.6.18 Warnier-Orr diagram – gas turbine example

(b)   Action diagrams

Action diagrams were designed by James Martin for use at all levels of program operation. As a result they are comprehensive and, in some cases, quite detailed. Therefore only the major features are described here.

The basic component of the action diagram is the bracket, Fig.6.19. This can be as long as needed for the job in hand. The operations to be carried out are listed within the bracket, being executed in the order shown. Decomposition takes place from left to right to show hierarchical structures; nested brackets are used for this. The various single and multiple selection operations are shown in Fig.6.20.

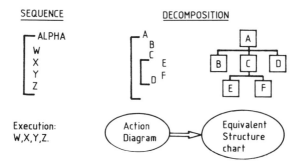

Fig.6.19   Action diagram – sequence and decomposition

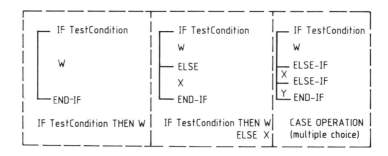

Fig.6.20   Action diagrams – selection

Such selection operations are enclosed in brackets. The control words used here (e.g. IF, ELSIF) are not defined by the diagramming method. Iteration operations are also enclosed in brackets, as in Fig.6.21, these having a double line at the top.

When applied to the gas turbine problem, action symbols give the diagram shown in Fig.6.22. Action diagrams have a number of very useful features.

They:

- Can show both high- and low-level views of the problem.
- Are quick and easy to draw, both manually and in automated form.
- Are easy to print using normal width printers.

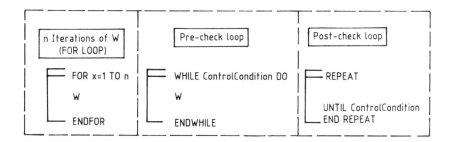

Fig.6.21 Action diagrams – iteration

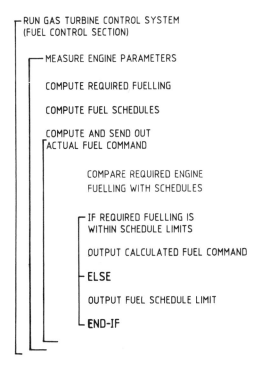

Fig.6.22 Action diagram – gas turbine example

6.5.4   Low-level structures — flow charts, Nassi-Shneiderman diagrams and Design Structure diagrams

Here we have diagrams which are only one step away from the source code. They don't normally use hierarchical decomposition, being meant to represent closely the way programs are written. Flow charts were certainly one of the first methods of showing programs in picture form. Unfortunately, they don't support structured design methods; as such they shouldn't be part of the modern designer's toolkit. Both Green (1982) and Martin (Martin and McClure, 1985) give very convincing reasons for this. No more will therefore be said on the subject. Instead we'll concentrate on its replacements, Nassi-Shneiderman and Design Structure diagrams.

(a)   Nassi-Shneiderman (N-S) diagrams
One of the earliest methods proposed to replace flowcharting was that of Nassi and Shneiderman (1973). Their diagrams are built around the idea of program structures that:

- Have one entry and one exit point.
- Use the basic control constructs of sequence, selection and iteration.

A program module is shown as a rectangular box. Within this, the sequence operation is shown as a set of 'boxes' arranged vertically (Fig.6.23). Selection is shown by using a two-part box (Fig.6.24). Test conditions and results are described using the top section; subsequent actions are shown in the lower one. For a two-way selection, the top part is split into three sections or triangles. The middle triangle holds the selection test condition. The others show the flow direction taken for YES ('True') or NO ('False') results from the test question. The bottom box is split to show the two resulting processes. Where multiple choices have to be made the diagramming method can also show this.

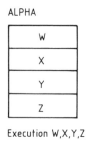

Execution W,X,Y,Z

Fig.6.23 Nassi-Shneiderman diagram – sequence

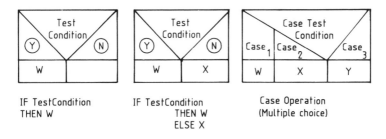

Fig.6.24 Nassi-Shneiderman diagram – selection

Iteration using FOR, WHILE DO (pre-check) and REPEAT UNTIL (post-check) loops are shown in a simple and straightforward way (Fig.6.25). Any individual box can be subdivided showing levels of selection and iteration. Note that if a sequential action is subdivided, then the individual parts are shown, not the parent. Thus, using this technique, hierarchical decomposition is quite different from the ones looked at earlier. Stepwise refinement is achieved by taking individual subfunctions and drawing them on another N-S chart (Fig.6.26). In practice, if N-S diagrams are used, they should be limited in size to a page of print-out. Consequently, in any real job, stepwise refinement would have to be used.

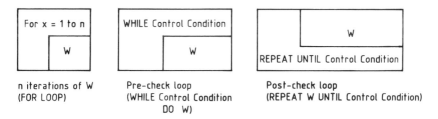

Fig.6.25 Nassi-Shneiderman diagram – iteration

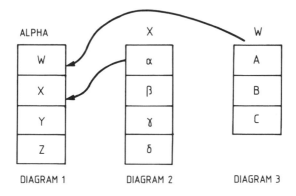

Fig.6.26 Stepwise refinement using N-S diagrams

A major criticism of N-S diagrams was that, while they are easy to read, drawing them can be quite difficult. You have to have a good feel for the size of your outer box in the first place. And, with a lot of subdivision, the innermost boxes are very small and are difficult to read. Nowadays, using automated tools, this is much less of a problem. Fig.6.27 shows the standard example pictured using N-S methods.

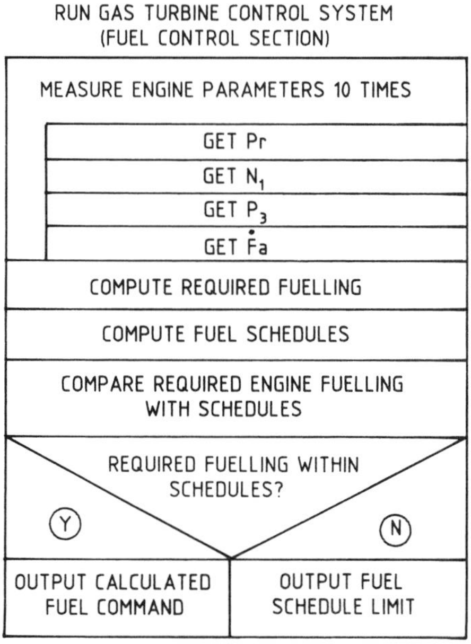

```
              RUN GAS TURBINE CONTROL SYSTEM
                  (FUEL CONTROL SECTION)
    ┌────────────────────────────────────────────────┐
    │ MEASURE ENGINE PARAMETERS 10 TIMES              │
    │    ┌──────────────────────────────────────────┐ │
    │    │              GET Pr                       │ │
    │    ├──────────────────────────────────────────┤ │
    │    │              GET N₁                       │ │
    │    ├──────────────────────────────────────────┤ │
    │    │              GET P₃                       │ │
    │    ├──────────────────────────────────────────┤ │
    │    │              GET Fa                       │ │
    │    └──────────────────────────────────────────┘ │
    ├────────────────────────────────────────────────┤
    │         COMPUTE REQUIRED FUELLING               │
    ├────────────────────────────────────────────────┤
    │         COMPUTE FUEL SCHEDULES                  │
    ├────────────────────────────────────────────────┤
    │   COMPARE REQUIRED ENGINE FUELLING              │
    │            WITH SCHEDULES                        │
    ├────────────────────────────────────────────────┤
    │\       REQUIRED FUELLING WITHIN               / │
    │  \           SCHEDULES?                     /    │
    │ (Y)\                                  /  (N)     │
    ├───────────────────────┬────────────────────────┤
    │ OUTPUT CALCULATED     │    OUTPUT FUEL          │
    │ FUEL COMMAND          │    SCHEDULE LIMIT       │
    └───────────────────────┴────────────────────────┘
```

Fig.6.27 Nassi-Shneiderman diagram – gas turbine example

(b)   Design structure diagrams (DSD)

These were designed in the late seventies by N.M. Rothon as a structured replacement for flow charts (Rothon, 1979). They are designed to give a very close link between diagrams and code, the aim being to generate structured code. Conversely, given structured code, a DSD can be constructed quickly. To achieve this they are built around the three constructs of sequence (Fig.6.28), selection (Fig.6.29) and iteration (Fig.6.30). Execution sequence runs from top to bottom, bounded by BEGIN and END identifiers. At any connecting point ('node') on the main flow line program control branches out to the box connected on the branch line. When the task designated in the box is finished, control 'falls back' to the node; it then continues down to the next branch point.

Where a selection occurs, the test condition is shown connected to a decision-point diamond symbol. Control flow reaches the diamond and checks the test condition. If this is true then, in the IF-THEN construct, control flows horizontally to the right; otherwise it falls back. All other conditions can be easily deduced from the diagram, showing just how clear this notation is.

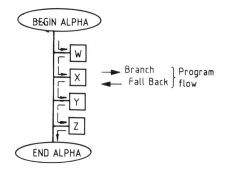

Execution : W,X,Y,Z.

Fig.6.28 Design structure diagram (Rothon) – sequence

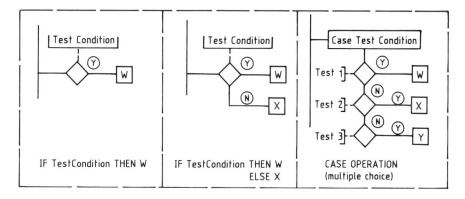

Fig.6.29 DSD – selection

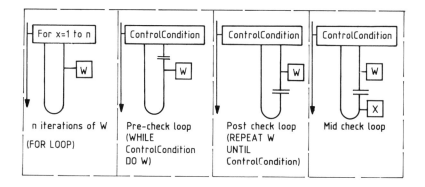

Fig.6.30 DSD – iteration

All types of iteration constructs are supported. In each case the control condition is written on the branch. Check points within the loop are shown as parallel, horizontal lines. These can be inserted at any point, as in the case of a mid-check loop. This is sometimes frowned on as 'not really being a structured arrangement'. Unfortunately, real-life tasks often need just such a construct.

DSDs also allow us to show exceptional exit conditions, something missing from most other methods. Yet exception handling is a fundamental aspect of embedded systems programming. Given below is the gas turbine program example in DSD form (Fig.6.31).

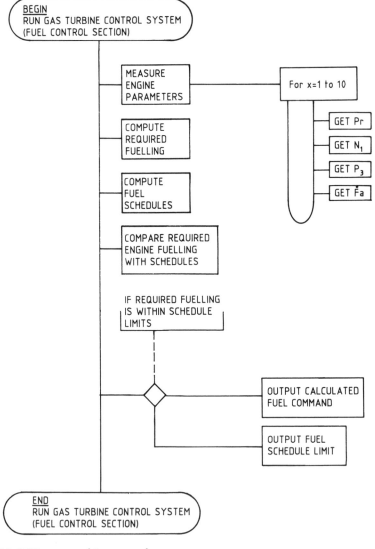

Fig.6.31 DSD – gas turbine example

The design structure diagram does not show hierarchical decomposition. Although selection and iterations can be expanded, this is an expansion, not a decomposition. DSDs are therefore not a good way of showing a high level view of the program. They do, though, give an extremely good, clear and constructive insight into the detail of the program. It is highly recommended that they be used in place of flow charts. The justification for this should be obvious from Fig.6.32 which shows a flow chart and a DSD solution to the same problem.

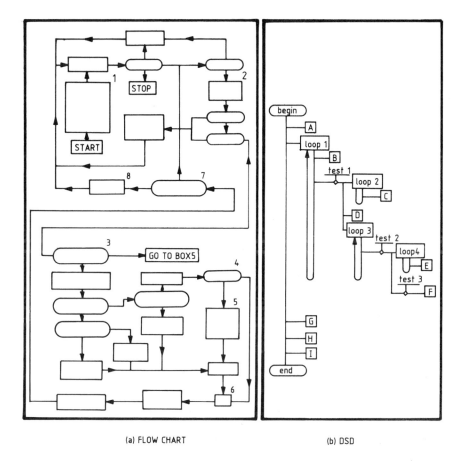

(a) FLOW CHART   (b) DSD

Fig.6.32 DSDs vs flow charting

6.6   EVENT-DEPENDENT DIAGRAMS

6.6.1   Overview and use of modified data flow diagrams

In real-time systems we continuously face the problem of making decisions based on:

- The present state of the system.
- The previous state of the system.
- Timing information.

Supporters of the data-driven design approach attempt to explain these in terms of data-triggered actions. This would seem to be stretching semantics to their limits. Suffice it to say that event-driven operations couldn't be shown using the original notation of DFDs.

One method in widespread use for showing event-dependency is the Yourdon real-time extension to data flow diagrams (Ward and Mellor, 1985). On this, events may be generated by external signals or by processes within the software system. Such event flows are handled by a new process type, the 'control transformation' process. This is included in the data flow diagram (Fig.6.33). Control transformations react to inputs, producing outputs which can start or stop data transformations. On this diagram events are shown as a form of data flow, but using dotted lines. Control transformation processes are shown as dotted circles.

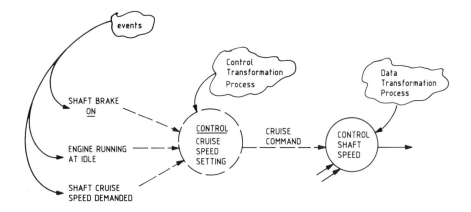

Fig.6.33 Real-time data flow diagram

It is recommended by Post (1986) that 'unless it should warrant data flow diagram expansion (consisting exclusively of control transformations), a control transformation is expanded upon using a state transition diagram . . .'. So, we can regard the STD as an expanded form of the real-time data flow diagram.

6.6.2   State transition diagrams

A finite-state machine (FSM) is a device for modelling the behaviour of a system in time. Specifically it represents this behaviour as a set of discrete, mutually exclusive and finite states. Events cause the system to change state; these changes are assumed to take place instantly. Events can occur both synchronously and asynchronously. The behaviour of finite state machines is shown using state transition diagrams. The basic reason for using STDs is so that we can draw up complex processes, evaluate all system states, and check for errors, failures and exception conditions. A simple example is given in Fig.6.34. Here the states are shown as boxes, the events being the arrowed lines connecting the states.

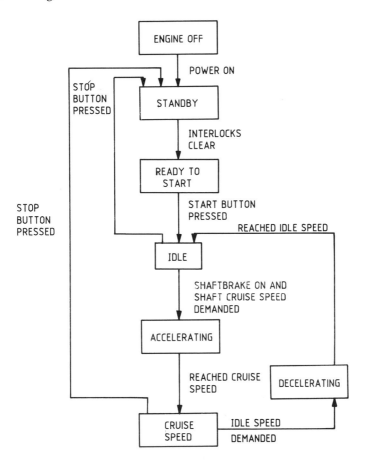

Fig.6.34 State transition diagram (part)

6.6.3   Petri nets

Petri nets (Peterson, 1981) are directed graphs, used for the modelling of time-dependent behaviour. In software design they are applied mainly to multiprocessing and multitasking systems. Using these, the states of concurrent processes and the transitions between states can be shown. The graph symbols of the Petri net (Fig.6.35) consist of:

- Nodes (states and transitions).
- Connections between nodes (edges or arcs).
- Tokens.

States (also called 'places') represent conditions; transitions depict events. Tokens are used to define the model conditions at any particular instant in time.

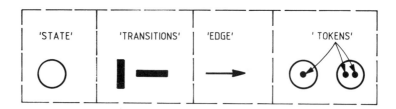

Fig.6.35 Petri net symbols

Edges are only allowed to connect state to transition symbols and vice versa. Connection of like symbols is not allowed. Note that, unlike earlier state transition diagram examples, states are not necessarily mutually exclusive. Remember, we're dealing with concurrent or quasi-concurrent processes.

Transitions between states take place on the 'firing' of a transition bar (Fig.6.36). The bar can fire only when it is enabled to do so; this is the function of the token. Each input state to a transition must have at least one token present for the transition to be enabled. However, the tokens themselves do not fire the transition. Firing occurs when:

- The transition is enabled (asychronous operation).
- The transition is enabled **and** the timing signals become valid (synchronous operation).

The transition, in firing, removes one token from each input state and deposits one token at each output. In Fig.6.36a, for instance, transition E1 could represent 'start of message transmission to network'. A token in state S1 indicates that an item is available for transmission; one in S2 shows that the channel is transmitting an item. This could be extended as in Fig.6.36b where a token in S2 represents the 'data channel clear' condition. Hence a data item can be transmitted only when the data is available and the channel is clear.

By using Petri nets it becomes relatively easy to examine complex interactions in concurrent systems, Figs.6.37, 6.38 (Elzer, 1988). In Fig.6.37, the token residing in state (or 'place') Sc ensures that either S2 or S5 is entered, but not both. When either one is fired up, the token is removed from Sc; thus the other is barred out. On exit from the active state a token is deposited once more in Sc.

Fig.6.38 shows how deadlock situations can happen. Once this occurs the whole system is locked up as the input state conditions prevent any further firings.

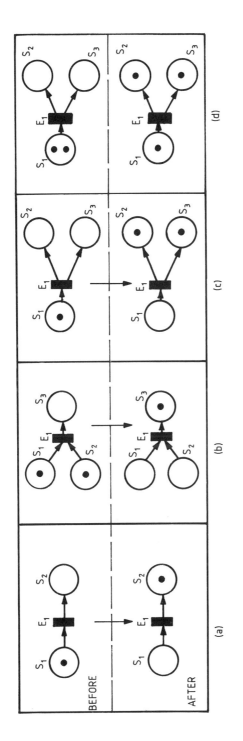

Fig.6.36 Firing of a transition

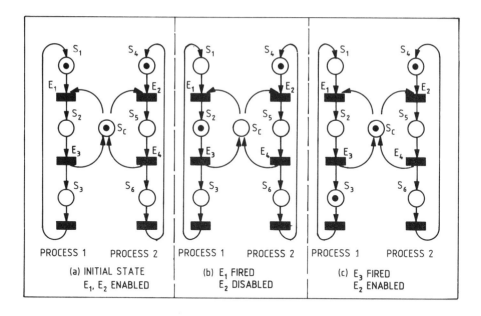

Fig.6.37 Critical section with mutual exclusion

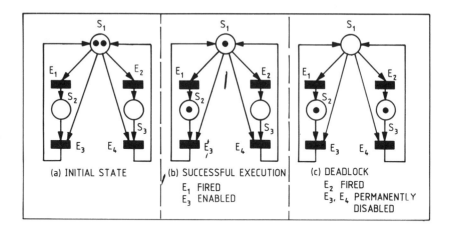

Fig.6.38 Deadlock example

6.7   STRUCTURED TEXT

Structured text is designed to express program operation using either structured English or Pseudocode (these words are often used interchangeably). It describes program operations using the fundamental control structures of structured programming – thus bringing formality to the process. These descriptions are extended – and made more understandable – by defining program objects and decision-making operations using everyday language.

There isn't a single definitive method in general use. Techniques range from structured but casual English notation to rigorously-defined layout methods. Whichever is used, the following rules should be followed if they are going to be of any use:

- They must be easy to understand.
- They should use a hierarchical structure.
- This structure should be obvious from the text layout.
- The structures of sequence, selection and iteration must be supported.
- Keywords should be used to identify these structures.
- Keywords should be used to identify logic operations.
- Comments to be inserted in the source code should be clearly marked.

An example is shown in Fig.6.39.

```
RUN GAS TURBINE CONTROL SYSTEM
(FUEL CONTROL SECTION)

        SEQUENCE  (1)                              ┌─────────────────────┐
                                                   │ UNDERLINED WORDS    │
                                                   │ ARE KEYWORDS        │
    MEASURE ENGINE PARAMETERS                      └─────────────────────┘
                ITERATION (1) - 10 TIMES
                GET Pr
                GET N1
                GET P3
                GET Fa

                END ITERATION (1)

    COMPUTE REQUIRED FUELLING

    CALCULATE FUEL SCHEDULES

    COMPUTE AND SEND OUT ACTUAL OUTPUT FUEL COMMAND
                SEQUENCE (2)
                COMPARE REQUIRED ENGINE FUELLING WITH SCHEDULES
                SET-FUEL OUTPUT ON RESULTS OF COMPARISON

                        SELECTION  (1)

                        IF FUELLING IS WITHIN SCHEDULE THEN
                            OUTPUT CALCULATED FUEL COMMAND
                        ELSE

                          OUTPUT FUEL SCHEDULE LIMIT
                        END IF

                        END SELECTION  (1)

                END SEQUENCE  (2)

        END SEQUENCE  (1)
```

Fig.6.39 Structured text – gas turbine example

6.8   DATA STRUCTURE DIAGRAMS

Data structure diagrams play a relatively small part in embedded systems design. Probably the extremes of use are, at one end, data bases (essential) and at the other, very small embedded units (not used). Here we will limit ourselves to data structures which can be shown in hierarchical form. These are the ones most likely to be met in practice; further, they use existing diagramming concepts and practices.

In the following example the contents and structure of a disk file are shown using Jackson (Fig.6.40) and Warnier-Orr (Fig.6.41) methods. A fuller description of data structure diagrams is given by Martin and McClure.

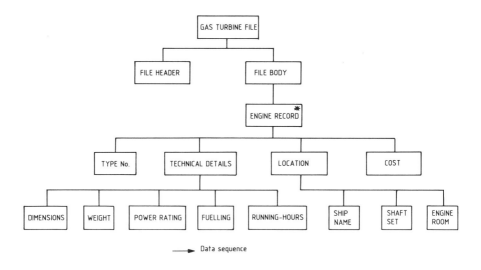

Fig.6.40 Data structure using Jackson diagramming

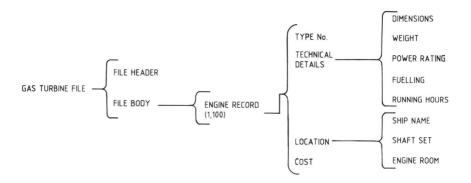

Fig.6.41 Data structure using Warnier-Orr diagramming

6.9   PRODUCING DIAGRAMS

If diagramming is really such a powerful technique, why have so few designers used diagramming methods? Lack of exposure to the techniques, lack of experience, cynicism and conservatism are all well-known reasons. But one particular aspect deserves special attention – the time, cost and effort involved in producing drawings manually. One senior engineering manager put it as follows: 'It is a fact of life that including the cost of such diagrams at the contract tendering stage would price us out of the job. However, when we get the job we can't do the diagrams because we haven't allowed for the cost. It doesn't matter that they would help us considerably in the design, installation, commissioning and post-design phases. Either we have to absorb the costs of such problems, or, more hopefully, get the customer to cough up'. Fortunately things are changing rapidly (Fig.6.42) as more and more computer-based tools come onto the market. A comparison of these methods is given in Fig.6.43.

It is highly recommended that, for high-quality software, an automated design package is used.

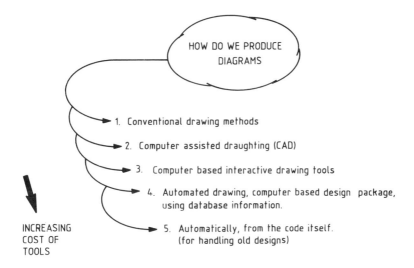

Fig.6.42 Methods of diagram production

6.10 A LAST COMMENT

Diagrams form just one part of the total software design package. But for professional work they are an essential ingredient. In this they have much in common with electronic, electrical, mechanical and civil engineering disciplines. The printed details may be different but the reasons for using diagrams are the same. Moreover, like traditional engineering, it's not surprising that different diagrams are needed for different purposes. But that's not to say that we always

	CONVENTIONAL	CAD	INTERACTIVE DESIGN TOOLS	AUTOMATED DRAWING
TIME	Slow process	Much faster	Faster still	Fastest
EFFORT	Significant and tedious	Significant but more satisfying	Total effort reduced – A direct design activity	Least effort – no separation of drawing, and design activities
CHANGES	Difficult and time consuming to modify diagrams	Easier to make changes- but still time consuming	Much easier and faster to make changes	Much easier and faster to make changes
GENERAL COMMENT	Disliked by designers	Quite acceptable by designers	A design tool in its own right Can be the source data for automatic generation of code	A design tool in its own right Can be the source data for automatic generation of code.

Fig.6.43 Comparison of diagram production methods

have to produce the full range for every design. Different jobs require different solutions. Where tasks are small and relatively simple, few diagrams are needed; large designs are quite a different matter. It is a case of using commonsense and good judgement.

Irrespective of the number and type of diagrams produced, an integrated approach should be used. That is, all information used in the design should reside in a common database. This has many advantages. First, it ensures total consistency in all diagrams. Second, errors and omissions are very quickly identified. Third, it provides a simple means of controlling document status, issues, amendments (i.e. configuration control).

As a final comment, it is desirable that such design tools should be part of a general Computer-Aided Software Engineering (CASE) toolset.

REFERENCES

Elzer, P. (1988), Course notes – Software engineering techniques for real-time control systems, Institute for Industrial Information Technology, University of Wales, Swansea, July.

Gane, C. and Sarson, T. (1977), *Structured Systems Analysis: Tools and Techniques*, IST Inc., New York.

Green, T.R.G. (1982), Pictures of programs and other processes, or how to do things with lines, *Behaviour and Information Technology*, 1982, **Vol.1**, No.1, pp3–36.

Jackson, M.A. (1975), *Principles of Program Design*, Academic Press Inc., New York.

Martin, J. and McClure, C. (1985), *Diagramming Techniques for Analysts and Programmers*, Prentice-Hall, Inc., Englewood Cliffs, New Jersey 07632, USA, ISBN 0–13–208794–4.

MASCOT (1983), *The Official Handbook of MASCOT, MASCOT II*, Issue 2, Issued by the Joint IECCA (Inter Establishment Committee on Computer Applications) and MUF (MASCOT Users Forum) Committee on MASCOT (JIMCOM).

MASCOT (1987), *The Official Handbook of MASCOT, Version 3.1*, Issue 1, Issued by JIMCOM, June.

Nassi, I. and Shneiderman, B. (1973), Flowchart techniques for structured programming, *ACM SIGPLAN Notices*, **Vol.18**, August, pp12–26.

Peterson, J.L. (1981), *Petri Net Theory and the Modelling of Systems*, Prentice-Hall.

Post, A.J. (1986), Application of structured methodology to real-time industrial software development, *Software Engineering Journal*, November.

Rothon, N.M. (1979), Design Structure Diagrams: a new standard in flow diagrams, *Computer Bulletin Series 2*, **No.19**, pp4–6, March.

Ward, P.T. and Mellor, S.J. (1985), *Structured Development for Real-time Systems*, Vols.1, 2 and 3, Yourdon Press.

Warnier, J. (1981), *Logical Construction of Systems*, Van Nostrand Reinhold Co., New York.

Yourdon, E. and Constantine, L. (1978), *Structured Design*, Yourdon Press, New York.

FURTHER READING

British Standard Guide to Design Structure Diagrams for use in program design and other logic applications, BS 6224:1987, BSI, 2 Park St., London W1A 2BS.

IEEE Transactions on Software Engineering (1989), *Special Section on Petri Net Performance Models*, **Vol.15**, No.4, April.

Chapter Seven

Formal specification methods

From the early 1970s conventional digital and analogue electronic systems have gradually been superseded by microprocessor-based designs. Subsequent experience shows that their reliability rarely exceeded that of earlier designs, due mainly to software errors. The root cause was the lack of design formality and rigour in producing software. Yet in spite of this the micro has been tremendously successful in real-time systems. Clearly, the effects of software problems have been overstated. However, the one area which couldn't tolerate such error rates is that of safety-critical software. Consequently work was put in hand to investigate this, especially in the aerospace field. One early study was that started in 1976 by Elliott Brothers, London, 'the study of the design, development, analysis and testing of high integrity software for digital flight control systems'. This concluded that the most promising way forward was based on the semi-formal methods described in chapter 4. These proved to be very effective; yet error rates can still be unacceptably high. Better techniques are needed.

Formal methods are a relatively new discipline, their purpose being to eliminate software errors by using rigorous engineering practices. Very generally, they call for program specifications to be expressed in mathematical form, these being verifiable using mathematical methods. The purpose of this chapter is to:

- Show that formal specification methods **are** useful in software design.
- Justify the use of mathematically-based specification techniques.
- Describe their general concepts.
- Introduce two important specification languages, VDM and Z.
- Show how they are used in assessing program correctness.

7.1   FORMAL METHODS — ARE THEY USEFUL?

As new ideas and techniques emerge they sometimes suffer from a particularly unwelcome virus, the hype factor (look, for instance, at what has happened in the field of Artificial Intelligence). Unfortunately, overselling a product is not something found only in the commercial world; academics can be just as guilty as their industrial counterparts. At the moment formal methods are being promoted as the way to produce high quality, error-free software. But are they useful or are they merely 'buzz words' used to attract research grants?

The only real way to assess new methods is to see how well they work in practice; formal techniques are no different in this respect. However, because it is a fairly new topic, practical experience is limited. Even so, the results obtained so far are very encouraging, as illustrated in the following examples (Ince, 1987).

(a) IBM
A software team in the IBM Federal Systems Division, Bethesda, USA, implemented formal, mathematically-based, techniques in a project which (ultimately) consisted of 30,000 lines of code. The results were impressive. The software was delivered early, under budget, and the error rate was reduced enormously (compared with earlier, similar, projects). Further, the team was able to predict the future reliability of the software, i.e. the likely occurrence of software errors stated in terms of 'mean time between failures'.

(b) Merlin Geophysical
This is a company which gathers raw geological data during field exploration work and, using computer-based techniques, processes this into a useful and meaningful form. To support its operations it needs to maintain something like 400,000 lines of Fortran code. Previously it expected to allocate 60–70% of its resources to such maintenance activities. However, by using formal methods, it has reduced this figure to 10%.

These, I hope, answer the question set out as the section header: yes, formal methods appear to be useful. Moreover, they are practical. But don't be misled into thinking that there is only one right method, because, as defined by Alvey (1984),

'A formal method is a set of rigorous engineering practices which are generally based on formal systems and are applied to the development of engineering products such as software or hardware – a formal system is a well-defined system of notation together with well-defined rules for manipulating that notation which are based on sound mathematical theory.'

Thus formal methods are development tools. And, like all tools, they have be used in the right place, at the right time and in the right way. Here we are specifically concerned with their use for two purposes: specifying system requirements and proving the correctness of the resulting solutions.

7.2   THE SPECIFICATION PROBLEM — AGAIN

The problems encountered in defining system requirements (specification) have already been well and truly covered. But let us assume that we have managed to produce a complete statement of requirements for the system (or so we think). Now, at this point, some very important questions should be asked:

- Is the statement of requirements clear, understandable and unambiguous?
- Can we be absolutely sure that it is consistent and complete?
- Can we, as the specifiers, be completely sure that the software designer correctly and fully understands these requirements?
- Can we review the proposed design to check its correctness (i.e. does it meet its specification)?

Note well this last point, the check for correctness. To do this we compare text (the program) whose syntax is defined formally and precisely with text (the specification) whose syntax is defined – how? The inherent problems of natural language (e.g. ambiguity, redundancy, verbosity) cause difficulties in defining clearly the SOR. Using diagramming methods in the specification document can help considerably. But even then, users of the SOR can still end up with different views of the system requirements. Quite often users can agree collectively on the meaning of specifications; yet individuals may interpret them quite differently. This comes about usually because:

- The specification document is not sufficiently precise.
- The specification technique may be inherently ambiguous or ambivalent.

Therefore, if we wish to prove the correctness of a solution, we **must** define system specifications in a formal manner using a formally-and precisely-defined language. In practice this means that we need to augment the natural language specification with a formal specification.

7.3   WHY MATHEMATICS?

Suppose that we are given a specification for a liquid level controller which reads (in part), 'During the first phase of operation, liquid is to be pumped in to raise the level from its initial value to within 100 mm of the required set level at a flow rate Q_1. Now the second phase of operation is invoked. The flow rate is to be gradually reduced until it reaches zero at the set level point. At this stage, phase 3, the heater is . . .'. The control system designer, on reading this, will very soon realize that the specification is incomplete and ambiguous. Questions to be answered include:

- What is the initial level, and is it always the same?
- What is the value of the flow rate Q_1?
- What is the set level?
- During the final phase, is the flow rate reduced in a linear manner?
- When, precisely, is the flow rate to be reduced? That is, at 100 mm below the set level, is pumping done at the original rate or the new reduced rate?

In such a small section of text, omissions and errors are almost always picked up. But where specifications are large and complex, mistakes frequently go unnoticed right up to system test time.

Let's now add to this specification a mathematical description of the process, as follows:

(a) Phase 1
The level equation is

$$h = Q_1 t + h_0$$

This is valid in the range

$$h_0 \leqslant h < (H - 100)$$

where h   = actual level
 h_0 = initial level
 Q_1 = initial flow rate
 t   = time in seconds
 H = Set level

(b) Phase 2
This is valid in the range

$$[(H - 100) \leqslant h < H]$$

giving a level equation of

$$h = Q_2 t + (H - 100)$$

where Q_2 is the instantaneous flow rate, calculated as follows:

$$Q_2 = [(H - h)/100]Q_1$$

(c) Phase 3
This occurs when $(h \geqslant H)$

$$Q_3 = 0$$

Observe that the system behaviour has now been specified using a precise language (mathematics), which is rigorous, and is built on provable rules. So far, so good. But what have we gained by using a mathematical specification? Five factors, to be precise:

- Unambiguous communication.
- Consistency of specification.
- Correct specifications.
- Complete specifications.
- Specification clarity.

(a) Unambiguous communication
Mathematics are precise and unambiguous. The statement

$$h = Q_2 t + (H - 100)$$

has only one meaning. Consequently, when using this in a reference document, communication between designers, users, etc., is also unambiguous.

(b) Consistency of specification
All operating conditions must be consistent, as in

Phase 1: This is valid in the range $h_0 \leqslant h < (H - 100)$.
Phase 2: This is valid in the range $(H - 100) \leqslant h < H$.
Phase 3: This is valid for $h \geqslant H$.

Here the specified conditions cover the total operating range, with sub-ranges being explicit, non-overlapping and consistent.

(c) Correct specifications
The behaviour of the system can be evaluated in all its operating modes using mathematical analysis. Any mistakes made in the specification produce inconsistent results in this evaluation; hence they can be discovered fairly quickly. For instance, the specification above could include the statement '. . . tank filling is to be achieved in X seconds'. An analysis of the system equations will soon show whether this can be achieved given the known performance factors. In the example here the filling rate drops rapidly in the final stages, and might be unacceptably low. Consequently the specification could be altered to avoid this by putting a lower limit on the rate, as in:

$$Q_2 = [(H - h)/100]Q_1, \text{ subject to } Q_2(min) = Q_1/10$$

(d) Complete specifications
All system parameters **must** be included in order to form the defining equations correctly. Further, **all** values have to be given to make the equations soluble.

(e) Specification clarity
A mathematical specification can be written fully and correctly only when the specifier:

- Understands the problem properly.
- Can express it properly and clearly.
- Removes all ambiguous and ambivalent conditions.
- Has full system data, operating condition, etc., at hand.

Consequently, when formal specification documents are produced they are much more likely to be well thought out, balanced, objective, clear and concise.

Availability of data is a crucial factor in the design of real-time systems. Many projects begin by assuming a great deal about the system to be designed, i.e. uncertainties abound in multitude. So in such situations it is impossible to satisfy the final requirement listed above. After all, if you don't have the data how can you solve the equations? This factor seems to negate the use of mathematically-based specification methods. Surprisingly enough this isn't the case. True, the equations can't be solved until the data is available. But what it does is highlight **precisely** any missing information from the specification. And this is one of the most valuable items that the developer can have. As system design proceeds the missing bits can be filled in until finally the specification is complete. Some aspects may not even be obtained until system trials are carried out; this doesn't diminish its usefulness.

The example given here uses conventional mathematics to bridge the gap between concept and practice. In reality, formal specification methods are based on discrete mathematics.

7.4   FORMAL METHODS — GENERAL CONCEPTS

7.4.1   Introduction

As stated earlier, formal methods result in verified program code derived from mathematically-based system specifications. However, in all systems, statements of requirements are **always** produced using a natural language. Hence the first step along the formal route is to convert these into a formal specification (Fig.7.1). The next step is to validate the correctness of the specification and, once this is done, generate program code from the formal document. The resulting code is then verified, i.e. proved to be correct with respect to its mathematical specification. Often the formal document goes through a number of refinement stages. The purpose is to get a good match between the specification and the structure of the implementation language.

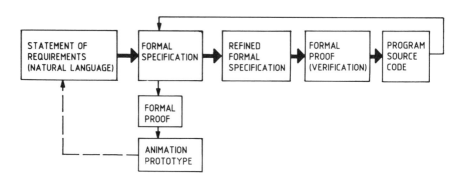

Fig.7.1 Formal specifications within the software design cycle

This, in essence, is how formal software methods work. Underlying it is the dependence of each step on the previous step. Now, we can loop around the 'formal specification-verification-code generation' stages until these are proved to be correct. Unfortunately this doesn't include the SOR. After all, it can't be proved that the system designer has specified what he wants. Mathematics unfortunately don't help us very much; other methods are needed.

One promising solution is that of animation prototyping, using the formal specification as the input to the animation. This sets up an 'SOR-FormalSpec-Animation' loop which is iteratively refined until the specification is agreed to be correct.

7.4.2   Formal specification languages

The basic requirements of a formal specification language are that it:

- Allows the functions and states of a program to be specified.
- Can be used to prove that the specification statements are **logically** correct.

The underlying structure is based on discrete mathematics. This is a fairly extensive subject, certainly beyond the bounds of this book. However, for those readers who wish to use formal methods, it is essential to become proficient in the topic. Suitable material can be found in the texts by Denvir (1986) and Woodcock and Loomes (1988).

A number of formal specification languages have been developed, Table 7.1 giving a list of those which are currently available (the more exotic ones being omitted). There are two basic categories, model-based and axiom-based. In many respects they are quite similar, using concepts and notation based on set theory. Typically, data items from the real world are modelled mathematically in terms of abstract data types (Fig.7.2).

Table 7.1 Some formal specification languages

Model based languages	Axion-based languages
Vienna Development Method (VDM)	LARCH
Z	ACT-ONE
INA-JO	OBJ
me too	CLEAR

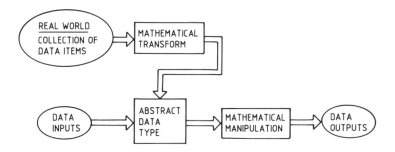

Fig.7.2 Formal specification – basic concept

Mathematical manipulation of the abstract data type is carried out using discrete mathematics so that, for any set of data inputs, the outputs are correct. In terms of the real-world situation, this describes **what** the outputs should be for particular input configurations, not **how** the results are calculated.

Model-based systems are well suited for the specification of sequential operations. Here we build a mathematical model of the state of the system and the operations which are to be carried out on this. This is then refined to give more detail and to move from an abstract mathematical description to the structures of the programming language. The operations themselves are likely to be broken down into sequences of simpler operations, the so-called decomposition process. When we can describe the system states and operations completely in terms of the programming language the specification process is complete.

The alternative method, the 'axiomatic' technique, specifies software by first developing system models and then defining the axioms which these must satisfy ('axiom – established principle, self-evident truth' – *OED*). Here there are no states as such, nor any idea of updating the values of the abstract data types. Instead, the properties of the specification are expressed as a series of algebraic equations relating the data types involved.

The two approaches are complementary in that they best specify different aspects of a problem. In some situations it is easier to produce a specification using model-based techniques, in others the algebraic approach is best. Experience of these in real-time systems is quite limited but, so far, model-based methods have given good results. Two particular languages stand out, VDM and Z.

7.5   VDM

7.5.1   Introduction

VDM stands for Vienna Development Method. It was first developed at IBM's Vienna Laboratories, but has since undergone substantial evolution, to improve and extend it. It is now sufficiently well established that attempts are being made to define a standard notation which it is hoped will become a British standard, and perhaps an international standard. This is important to ensure that the notation for all VDM specifications is consistent, thereby reducing the chance of misunderstandings. It will also facilitate the development of automatic computer support tools for the production and checking of VDM specifications. Until the BSI standard is published, Jones (1986) provides an accepted notation.

VDM is primarily a notation for a specification language, but, because of the underlying mathematics, it is possible to use it also for the design and development of programs, and to use the mathematics to help prove that the resulting program is correct. This is important for programs which must be particularly safe, reliable or secure.

The mathematics behind VDM comprise the theory of sets and the theory of logic, and a basic knowledge of these is required by anyone who is to write or implement VDM specifications. At first sight this might seem daunting, but most of the ideas will already be known by someone with experience of programming using a high-level language such as Pascal, or who has some experience of digital electronic design. A discussion of the mathematics is not possible here due to the available space, but good sources of information are Gries (1981) and Jones (1986).

7.5.2   Some simple principles

There are two fundamental requirements of a specification language:

- It should allow specifications to be written which say **what** is to be done without saying **how** it is achieved.
- It should permit the information content of data items to be defined without saying how the data is to be represented.

How can this be done? The first objective, the **what** is achieved by making the main part of the specification a statement (using the VDM notation) of what the conditions shall be after the piece of program has been executed. In ordinary English we frequently do this. For instance there is the simple description of a type which can often be found in a prospectus for a course:

'At the end of the course the student will have a knowledge of VDM sufficient for him to be able to write small specifications, and will have an elementary knowledge of set theory and predicate calculus.'

Note that this does not give any indication of **how** this desirable state of affairs is to be achieved!

In many cases such a prospectus will suggest who the course is suitable for, or will give some academic qualifications which are required, for instance:

'Students should have a degree in a numerate discipline, or five years' experience in software engineering.'

These two statements together provide a good specification for the course. Obviously it is a bit vague in places (how big is a small specification?), but together they provide a format similar to that of a VDM specification. The initial requirement is called the precondition – that is the condition which must be met if the course is to be successful. The statement of what is achieved is called the postcondition – that is the condition which will hold true after the course has run, assuming the precondition is true. Note that this says nothing about what would happen if the precondition were not true. For instance a student with a degree in an Arts subject may or may not complete the course successfully.

Obviously such a specification is in English and therefore subject to all the problems of ambiguity mentioned before. VDM specifications employ a similar format, the precondition and postcondition being written in a mathematical notation.

7.5.3   A simple example

Consider the example given in section 7.3.

'During the first phase of operation, liquid is to be pumped in to raise the level from its initial value to within 100 mm of the required set level at a flow Q_1. The rate is then to be gradually reduced until it reaches zero at the set level point.'

We will assume that we are going to specify the process in VDM for a piece of software running repeatedly to control the level. We can assume the program executes much faster than the vessel fills up. We will also assume that there is a way of altering the flow and measuring the level. Given that, we want to specify software which will control the process without imposing implementation details on the software designer.

There is an obvious condition which must prevail after each execution of the program. Written in English this is:

either
> the level is less than (H − 100) and the flow equals Q1

or
> the level is between (H − 100) and H and the flow is gradually reducing

or
> the level is equal to H and the flow is zero.

The second part '. . . and the flow is gradually reducing' is a little difficult; the way it is reducing is not really defined. However we do know that at that stage the flow will in some way be related to the level − in mathematical terms flow will be a function of the level, or

$$flow = f(level).$$

We can now write the English postcondition in mathematical notation:

$$level < (H - 100) \wedge flow = Q_1$$
$$\wedge$$
$$(H - 100) < level \wedge (level < H) \wedge flow = f(level)$$
$$\wedge$$
$$level = H \wedge flow = 0$$

[NOTE: '$\wedge$' means 'and' , and '$\vee$' means 'or'.]

This could almost be a VDM postcondition. However, we need to make it more precise by defining, if we can, what f(level) means. VDM allows us to define how f(level) works and to give it a name, in a similar manner to the way functions are defined in a high-level programming language. For the time being it can be defined as

CALC_REDUCING_FLOW (L: Real, Q: Real, H: Real) f: Real

What this means is that this piece of specification is a function called CALC_REDUCING_FLOW. It requires three inputs. All are Real numbers, one is called L (the level), one is called Q (the flow) and the other H (the set level). When it has executed it returns a value f (flow) which is another Real number.

What do we know about this function? Firstly it is only used, and is only required to work, when the level is within 100 mm of H. Therefore we can write a precondition thus:

$$\text{pre } L > (H - 100) \wedge L < H$$

We can also write down the postcondition. All that the English specification says is that the flow is gradually reducing. Hence we can write a postcondition thus:

$$\text{post } f < Q$$

Thus the whole specification of CALC_REDUCING_FLOW is:

CALC_REDUCING_FLOW (L:Real, Q:Real, H:Real) f:Real
pre $L > (H - 100) \wedge L < H$
post $< f < Q \wedge f > 0$

Note that an extra part has been added to the postcondition, to require that the flow must be greater than zero.

This is now a precise definition of how the flow is to be reduced, in accordance with the English specification, though because it does not say by how much the flow is to be reduced each time, it may give too much freedom to the implementor of the specification to be really useful. One strong indication of this is that although we specified that CALC_REDUCING_FLOW requires the value of the level, L, it is not used in the precondition or the postcondition. If there were time we should go back to the writer of the English specification and ask for a more precise statement of what is required.

We can now return to the overall specification for determining the flow. We will call this part of the specification FLOW.

We are already able to define the postcondition, but what about the precondition? The English specification does not give a precondition, but commonsense requires that there be one, namely that the initial value of the level is defined. We don't know what it could be so we must ask the writer of the English specification for more information:

'It could be anything from empty to H.'

At least now we know what we have to cope with, and can now write the specification for FLOW:

OPERATION FLOW

ext	rd level: R
	rd H : R
	rd Q_1 : R
	wr Q : R
pre	level $>= 0 \land$ level $<= H$
post	level $< (H - 100) \land$ flow = Q1
	$\lor$
	level $> (H - 100)$
	$\land$ (level $< H$)
	$\land$ flow = CALC_REDUCING_FLOW
	$\land$
	level = H $\land$ flow = 0

It is necessary to define the variables used in the specification, and some information about them. 'ext' means 'external' and indicates that the variables exist outside FLOW. 'rd' means 'read-only' and indicates that the value of the variable may not be altered. 'wr' means 'write', that is the value of this external variable can be altered as well as being read.

The above example shows us many of the main facets of a VDM specification, and demonstrates how a specification may be split into manageable parts, and how it is possible to specify what a piece of software is to achieve, without specifying how it is to be achieved. This latter process is known as implicit specification.

7.5.4   Another example

The above example concentrated on the WHAT part of the problem. This next example looks at some of the other areas important to creating accurate formal specifications.

Imagine we are trying to specify the control system for a simple conveyor belt. The conveyor can move in two directions, up or down. There is a button which can be pressed to start the conveyor, and another to stop it. In addition there are two buttons to define the direction, one for up, and the other for down. There are some rules for the control system:

- When the start button is released the conveyor is started.
- When the stop button is pressed the conveyor is stationary.
- When the up button is released the direction is set to up, and when the down button is released the direction is set to down.
- Direction buttons are ignored if the conveyor is moving.
- If more than one button is pressed ignore all buttons except the stop button (safety first!).

What are the important things about this system? There are only a very few:

- Whether it is stationary or moving.

- Which direction the conveyor is set to move in.
- What is happening to the buttons.

The system could be implemented in a number of ways:

- The control system looks at the buttons on a regular basis and decides what to do.
- The control system is activated every time a button is pressed or released.

Ideally the specification at its highest level will not require decisions to be made about these. Note that it is a change in the state of the buttons which is the important thing.

We also do not want at this stage to have to decide or worry about the nature of the signals coming from the buttons or the nature of the control signals being sent to the conveyor. It should not at this stage concern us what voltages the signals are or how they might be coded when received by the control system.

We can do this by using abstract types for these signals. Consider the direction of the conveyor. We can specify a data type 'dir' for the direction signal. This can have only the values 'up' or 'down'. We need to include this definition in the specification somehow, in an implicit form. We can write the following:

$$\text{TYPES}$$
$$\text{dir} == \{\text{up, down}\}$$

This defines a type dir; variables of type dir can have only the value up or down.

One problem we have not addressed so far is how to deal with inputs and outputs to and from the control system. One obvious way is to regard the reading of the buttons as the execution of some sort of function:

$$\text{buttons} = \text{read\_buttons}$$

or something similar. This is not good enough, however, because there is no input parameter to read_buttons, and in that case the mathematics will regard every call of read_buttons as returning the identical value, whereas we need a model which can give us different values on successive calls. We could model input in a way which overcomes this:

$$\text{input} = \text{read\_keyboard (input no)}$$
$$\Lambda$$
$$\text{input\_no} = \text{input\_no}^{\sim} + 1$$

This approach requires the introduction of a new variable 'input_no' which is an artificial addition, and does nothing to improve clarity.

[The '$\sim$' indicates that this is the original value of input_no.]

There is a way which requires no such additional variables, and can be easily written in VDM. That is to regard the inputs as a sequence of values waiting to be read. There are rules in VDM for dealing with sequences. Thus we can write:

inputs   : sequence of something (inputs is a list of something)
invalue : something   (invalue is a variable of type something)

Then to perform an input it is only necessary to specify

$$invalue = hd (inputs) \wedge inputs = tail (inputs \tilde{}).$$

That is take the head (hd) of the sequence as the value for invalue, and update the sequence of inputs by removing the head. This is shown diagrammatically in Fig 7.3.

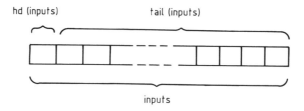

hd (inputs)   tail (inputs)

inputs

Fig.7.3

We can deal with outputs in a similar manner. For instance we could model the output of characters to a VDU as follows:

char   : character   (char is a variable of type character)
VDU_screen : sequence of character

Then to model an output we would specify

$$VDU\_screen = cons (char, VDU\_screen \tilde{})$$

['cons' is a function for making sequences. In this case it says update the value of VDU_screen by adding char to it.]

We can now return to the conveyor belt example. There are a number of important things about this system, which we shall call CONTROL_BOX, namely the button inputs, the control signal outputs and whether it is moving or not. We can start to write the specification:

CONTROL BOX :: button_inputs   : sequence of set of buttons
              control_signals : sequence of signals
              buttons_now   : set of buttons
              buttons_last   : set of buttons
              change   : indicator
              moving   : motion
              direction   : dirn

We have now given the specification a name, and have listed the main variables it will be concerned with. This collection of variables is often called the State.

We need to define the types used in the above part of the specification:

$$buttons == \{stopb, startb, upb, downb\}$$

That is, a variable of type buttons can only have the value stop, start, up, or down. Similarly:

signals	$== \{gos, ups,\} \{gos, downs\}, \{stops, ups\}, \{stops, downs\}$
indicator	$== \{same, different\}$
motion	$== \{stopped, move\}$
dirn	$== \{up, down\}$

The definition of type signals is a little more complicated than the others. There are only four values possible for a variable of type signals – all combinations of either up or down with either stopped or move.

We will now specify the operation which inputs the state of the buttons and checks to see if they have changed.

CHECK BUTTONS

ext	wr buttons_now	: set of buttons
	wr buttons_last	: set of buttons
	wr change	: indicator
	wr button_inputs	: list of buttons
pre	len (button_inputs) > 1	(there must be some inputs available)

post (buttons_now = buttons_last $\quad \Lambda \quad$ change = same
$\quad$ V
$\quad$ buttons_now /= buttons_last $\quad \Lambda \quad$ change = different)
Λ button_inputs = tail (button_inputs $^\sim$)
Λ buttons_now = hd (button_inputs $^\sim$)

What CHECK_BUTTONS does is to input a new value for the state of the buttons, and compares it with the old state of the buttons setting the indicator 'change' as appropriate, and updating the input stream.

We now need to decide if there is anything to do. We will have an operation called DECIDE for this.

DECIDE

ext	rd buttons_now	: set of buttons
	rd buttons_last	: set of buttons
	wr moving	: motion
	rd change	: indicator
	wr direction	: dirn

pre $\quad$ change = different Λ buttons_now $\neq$ buttons_last
post $\quad$ stopb $\notin$ buttons_last $\qquad\qquad$ (the stop button has just
$\quad\quad \Lambda$ stopb ϵ buttons_now $\qquad\qquad\qquad$ been pressed, so stop)

Λ moving = stopped
V
  buttons_now = { }   (the last button has been released)
  Λ (buttons_last = {startb}   (the start button released)
  Λ moving =   move   (so we can start to move)
V
  moving~ = stopped   (so we can change direction)
  Λ (buttons_last = {upb}
  Λ direction = up
V
  buttons_last = {downb} Λ direction = down))

ϵ means 'is contained in', $\notin$ means 'is not contained in'; $\neq$ means 'not equals'

This last postcondition looks a little complicated; what it says is:

       'If the stop button has just been pressed_stop'.

The only other time we take any action is when there is only one button pressed and it is then released. That means that this time there are no buttons pressed and last time there was only one. If that is the case, decide what to do. If the last time the start button was pressed then start the conveyor. If either of the direction buttons is the one just released then we must check to see if the conveyor is moving. Only if it is stopped can we set the direction.

Having made the appropriate decisions we can now send the output signals:

CONTROL

```
ext   wr control_signals : sequence of signals
      rd moving           : motion
      rd direction        : dirn
pre   true
post  control_signals =
          cons (TRANSFORM (moving, direction), control_signals~)
```

TRANSFORM is a function which works out which values to give to the output signals. It takes a pair of variables of abstract types 'motion' and 'dirn' and returns a set of signals of the appropriate value.

TRANSFORM (m : motion, d : dirn) ss : signals

```
pre   true
post  (m = stopped $\Lambda$ stops $\varepsilon$ ss
      V
      m = move $\Lambda$ gos $\epsilon$ ss)
      V
      (d = down $\Lambda$ downs $\epsilon$ ss
      d = up $\Lambda$ ups $\varepsilon$ ss)
```

We have now an almost complete VDM specification for the conveyor belt control system, the only piece missing being an operation to initialize the system if necessary. Although the original English specification was small and simple it was not very clear. Certainly some parts of it had implications which were not apparent. Writing a formal specification like the one above enables one to concentrate upon the important issues. It is not necessary to know what form the control signals take, or whether a button press is indicated by a high or a low voltage.

7.5.5   Summary

The above examples show the main features of the VDM notation, and give a simple but almost complete specification. It is not possible to describe all of the facilities VDM has to offer in the space available, but it is hoped that enough information is included to demonstrate how a VDM specification differs from conventional specifications, and to give some indication of the thought processes which lead to such a specification. The way in which formal specification languages allow one to concentrate on the WHAT, not the HOW is important, but this is difficult to convey to the reader. Practice is the best way to really get the feel of a formal specification language, and you are therefore recommended to try to write a VDM specification for a simple example such as those above.

7.6   Z

The Z specification method has been under development, mostly at the Programming Research Group of Oxford University, since the late 1970s. It is now reaching some level of maturity, and is indeed, to a very limited extent, being used in industry. However, most of the available material on Z is very academic in nature, which makes it very difficult for the non-academic to gain an understanding of the subject. This academic bias, and the perceived difficulty of the subject, are the most important factors in the slow uptake of the method by industry.

Some of the most useful published information about Z comes from Hayes (1987) which provides some useful case studies, Spivey (1989) which attempts to define the syntax, Spivey (1988) which gives the mathematical background and Woodcock (1988) which gives details of discrete mathematics but explained using Z. In addition, information is available in monograph and note form from the Programming Research Group of Oxford University. Care must be taken when reading Z documents because of the general inconsistency in detailed notation – Spivey (1989) is an attempt to improve this situation; however, some people believe that it is better to allow *ad hoc* extensions to be applied as required by individual practitioners!

The terms 'method', 'language' and 'notation' are often used freely when discussing what is usually called 'formal methods'. The use of these terms can be confusing as the distinction between the terms is blurred. The terms 'language' and 'notation' can, for our purposes, be used interchangeably, but the term 'method' is normally used as a shorthand for 'a way of doing things'. For our purposes we shall use the term 'method' to encompass the total idea – that is, the 'way of doing' together with 'notation' or 'language'.

There are in reality two parts to the Z 'method' – its notation, and a number of heuristics about how the notation can be applied.

7.6.1   The Z notation

It is not intended to give an exhaustive description of Z notation; however, enough information is presented to give a flavour of the language.

Z notation is based upon Set Theory and Predicate Calculus – well-known parts of discrete mathematics, together with a structuring known as Schema Calculus that is peculiar to Z.

Z is often illustrated by the definition of a simple data base. This type of example is convenient because it can be shown as a state system, which Z is very good at representing. However, data bases are fairly unusual in real-time embedded systems, so we shall attempt to model the fluid flow system described earlier in this chapter.

It is often convenient to assume the existence of some structures whose internal detail is of little interest at the time of specification. For our example we require types of VOLUME, TIME and FLOW-RATE. In Z these can be expressed as basic types as shown opposite.

This structure is known as a Schema. The Schema has two parts – a declaration part above the centre line, and a part giving the relationships of the declarations (known as predicates) below the centre line.

This first Schema defines the Basic Static State of the System, therefore the Schema must be included (how is explained later) when defining the system further. The predicates are therefore system invariants – they must be true for the system to be defined. The system is undefined if any of the predicates are violated.

Here we have decided to model the system by defining the interesting properties of the system as the sequences *Timein*, *Volout* and *Rateout*. The definition *Timein*: Seq TIME says that *Timein* is a variable of Type (Seq TIME) where Seq TIME is a sequence of TIME elements (sequences are described below). The italicizing has no particular significance except to highlight the variables and thus make them stand out.

It is necessary here to define what we mean in Z by a Sequence. A Sequence can be described in a number of ways. A simple definition says that a sequence is an ordered set of pairs such that the first element in each pair is an index, starting at 1 and incrementing by 1 for successive elements; and the second element is a variable of the object type being sequenced. This can be illustrated

[VOLUME, TIME, FLOW-RATE]

It is then usual to define the basic Static state of the System:

```
┌─SYSTEM──────────────────────────────────────┐
│                                             │
│     Timein      : Seq TIME                  │
│     Volout      : Seq VOLUME                 │
│     Rateout     : Seq FLOW-RATE             │
│     Setlevel    : VOLUME                     │
│ ─────────────────────────────────────────── │
│     # Timein = # Volout                      │
│     # Timein = # Rateout                     │
│                                             │
│     Timein(1) = 0                            │
│                                             │
│     ∀ n: dom Timein ● n > 1 ⟹               │
│                Timein (n) = Timein (n−1) + 1 │
│     ∀ n: dom Volout ● n > 1 ⟹               │
│                Volout (n) > = Volout (n−1)   │
│     ∀ n: dom Rateout ● n > 1 ⟹              │
│                Rateout (n) < = Rateout (n−1) │
│     ∃ n: dom Volout ● (n) = Setlevel ⟹      │
│                # Volout = n                  │
└─────────────────────────────────────────────┘
```

∀ means 'for all'; dom means 'domain'; ∃ means 'there exists'; ⟹ means 'imply'; ● means 'where' by an example. For instance, the days of the week can be modelled as follows:

DAYS == {'MON', 'TUE', 'WED', 'THU', 'FRI', 'SAT', 'SUN'}   ..1
Dayorder = Seq DAYS   ..2
Dayorder = {1 → 'MON'}   ..3
Dayorder (2) = 'TUE'   ..4
Dayorder = *Dayorder* U {3, 'WED'}   ..5
Dayorder = {1 → 'MON', 2 → 'TUE', 3 → 'WED'}   ..6
Dayorder = {(1, 'MON'), (2, 'TUE'), (3, 'WED')}   ..7

Statement 1 defines the Set DAYS as having members 'MON', 'TUE' etc.
Statement 2 defines the Sequence *Dayorder* as being a Sequence of DAYS.
Statement 3 defines *Dayorder* to be the Set with one element pair (1, 'MON').
The arrow → means maps to, i.e 1 maps to 'MON'.
Statement 4 shows how *Dayorder* can be considered as a function, it defines
that if the value 2 is applied to the function then 'TUE' will result.
Statement 5 defines *Dayorder* to be *Dayorder* Union the pair (3, 'WED').
All of the above may be slightly confusing but is in reality quite simple. It is
intended to show how, in Z, a sequence can be considered as:

       (a) A set of Pairs   (Statements 5 and 7)
       (b) A set of Mappings   (Statements 3 and 6)
       (c) A Function   (Statement 4)

Being able to consider a sequence in these different ways is very useful because
it allows the specifier to choose the most convenient mode for his purpose.

    Continuing with our original example, the use of sequences to define the
system allows a very elegant specification. This is because the use of sequences
transforms the problem from one of specifying a sequential system into one of
specifying a state system – input state *Timein* and output state *Volout* together
with *Rateout*.

    Below the line the first two predicates define the cardinality (#), or length, of
each sequence as being equal to the cardinality of each other sequence – note
that the length itself is not defined.

    The next predicate sets the first element of the sequence *Timein* to 0, and the
following predicate sets all of the remaining elements of *Timein* to 1 plus the
previous element value. The predicate can be read as:

    For all ($\forall$) n in the domain (dom) of *Timein* where ($\bullet$) n is greater than 1 we
can imply ($\Rightarrow$) that the n'th item in *Timein* (*Timein*(n)) is equal to the value
of the previous item in *Timein* plus 1 (*Timein* (n-1) + 1).

    The word 'domain' might be confusing to some but is quite simple; it means
all values that can be applied to a particular function (in this case *Timein*)
that could produce a valid output from the function.

    It should be noted again that no restriction has yet been placed on the length
of *Timein*, so although the predicate looks somewhat like a programming loop

it would be impossible to execute, because you don't know when to stop!

The next two predicates say that the volume must always stay the same or increase, and the rate must always stay the same or decrease.

The final predicate says that there exists ($\exists$) a value n in the domain of *Volout* such that the volume is equal to the *Setlevel* which implies that n is the length of *Volout*. Here we finally define the length of the sequence, but it is self-referred and cannot be determined until the system is 'executed'! Before the system can operate, information is required about the actual values of the initial state. This can be shown as follows:

INITIALIZE

$\triangle$ SYSTEM

Setlev?	: VOLUME
Initiallev?	: VOLUME
Initialrate?	: FLOW-RATE

Setlev? > *Initiallev?*

Setlevel' = *Setlev?*

Volout'(1) = *Initiallev?*
Rateout'(1) = *Initialrate?*

Timein' = *Timein*

$\forall$ n : dom *Volout* $\bullet$ n > 1 $\implies$
    Volout' (n) = *Volout* (n)

$\forall$ n : dom *Rateout* $\bullet$ n > 1 $\implies$
    Rateout'' (n) = *Rateout* (n)

The first line in the Schema ($\triangle$SYSTEM) refers to a Schema like SYSTEM but for each undecorated variable (e.g. *Timein*) another variable annotated with a single quote (') is also declared (e.g. *Timein'*). The annotated variable is considered to be the final state of the un-annotated variable. The statement *Volout'*(1) = *Initiallev?* therefore says that the final state of *Volout* item 1 is equal to the variable *Initiallev?*.

Variables annotated with a question mark (?) (e.g. *Setlev?*) are deemed to be input variables whose value is supplied from outside the Schema when the Schema is 'used'.

The function of this Schema is to read-in the input variables and initialize the states as appropriate. It should be noted that all variables that are otherwise unchanged (such as *Timein*) have their final states set to their initial values. This gives completeness to the specification at this stage.

The Phases can now be defined:

```
┌─PHASE1&2────────────────────────────────────────┐
│                                                  │
│  △SYSTEM                                          │
│  ─────────────────────────────────               │
│    ∀ n : dom Volout • n > 1                       │
│                                                  │
│      Volout (n) < (Setlevel − 100) ⟹             │
│          Rateout' (n) = Rateout (1)               │
│                                                  │
│      Volout (n) > = (Setlevel − 100) ⟹           │
│          Rateout' (n) = ((Volout (1) −           │
│                      Volout (n−1)) / 100) * Rateout (1) │
│                                                  │
│      Volout' (n) > = Volout (n−1) + Rateout' (n−1) * 1 │
│                                                  │
│    Volout' (1) = Volout (1)                       │
│    Rateout' (1) = Rateout (1)                     │
│                                                  │
│    Setlevel' = Setlevel                           │
│    Timein' = Timein                               │
└──────────────────────────────────────────────────┘
```

With the explanation of Z given so far the Schema should be clear. Basically when *Volout* (n) < (*Setlevel* − 100) then the original flow rate is required to be maintained. Outside of this range the flow rate is adjusted according to the formula. The volume *Volout* at any particular time is the previous volume plus the rate during the previous interval (multiplied by one time unit).

7.6.2   Z Heuristics

Using the Z 'Method' means using the notation in an appropriate manner such that the work is complete, consistent and understandable. This means that a number of 'rules' need to be followed, but these 'rules' cannot be succinctly described. We therefore choose to call the 'rules' Heuristics. According to *Collins New English Dictionary*, Heuristic means:

> 'Learning by observation, investigation and experiment'.

Heuristics are best displayed by example as in Hayes (1987) and Spivey, (1989).

For instance the example of section 7.6.1 is incomplete in a number of ways. For example, if an error occurs in the input data to Schema INITIALIZE, then the predicate *Setlev?* > *Initiallev?* could be untrue and the system reaction would be undefined. It is obvious that for a critical system all possible conditions must be catered for and Heuristics could exist to help ensure and show how completeness in this sense can be proved.

In addition, Heuristics define how a Z document should be formatted. For instance, it is good practice to include explanatory text between Schemas to make the specification understandable by those not expert in the Z notation, and to say why particular modelling techniques have been chosen.

If the specified system were to be implemented, then it would be necessary to evolve the specification into the design and finally to the code, and then prove that the code meets the requirements of the specification. The evolutionary process is known as Refinement, and has Heuristics to show how it can be achieved (Spivey, 1989).

The problem of incompleteness in Schema INITIALIZE can be solved by assuming a given type:

[REPORT]

and forming the following Schema:

```
┌─INITERR ───────────────────────────────────────────┐
│     ⌐ SYSTEM                                         │
│                                                      │
│     Setlev?        : VOLUME                          │
│     Initiallev?    : VOLUME                          │
│     Error!         : REPORT                          │
│     ─────────────────────────────                   │
│     Setlev? <= Initiallev?⟹Error! = Bad_data        │
│     V                                                │
│     Setlev? > Initiallev?⟹Error! = OK               │
└──────────────────────────────────────────────────────┘
```

The Schema contains new notation; Ξ SYSTEM is like $\triangle$SYSTEM but with all final states set to the initial state. This is obviously used where operations change none of the variables in the parent Schema, as here. The variable annotated with a pling (*Error!*) is similar to those annotated with a ? but the ! indicates that the variable is for output.

Here we have put both the pass and fail conditions in the error Schema. In practice the pass report would be placed in the original INITIALIZE Schema.

It is now necessary to join the two schemas INITIALIZE and INITERR together. This can be done using the Schema Calculus:

E_INIT $\triangleq$ INITIALIZE V INITERR

This forms the new Schema E_INIT as INITIALIZE or'ed with INITERR. This means that the declarations are combined and the predicates are or'ed together.

The new Schema would not normally be written out in full but for illustration see below:

```
┌─E_INIT ──────────────────────────────────────────────┐
│        △SYSTEM                                         │
│                                                       │
│        Setlev?        : VOLUME                         │
│        Initiallev?    : VOLUME                         │
│        Initialrate?   : FLOW-RATE                      │
│        Error!         : REPORT                         │
├───────────────────────────────────────────────       │
│        Setlev? > Initiallev? ⟹                        │
│                                                       │
│            Error! = OK                                 │
│                                                       │
│            Setlevel' = Setlev?                         │
│                                                       │
│            Volout' (1) = Initiallev?                   │
│            Rateout' (1) = Initialrate?                 │
│                                                       │
│            Timein' = Timein                            │
│                                                       │
│            ∀ n : dom Volout • n > 1 ⟹                 │
│                          Volout' (n) = Volout (n)      │
│                                                       │
│            ∀ n : dom Rateout • n > 1 ⟹               │
│                          Rateout' (n) = Rateout (n)    │
│        ∨                                               │
│            Setlev? <= Initiallev? ⟹                   │
│                      Error! = Bad_data                 │
└───────────────────────────────────────────────────────┘
```

Note that the inequality $Setlev? > Initiallev?$ from INITIALIZE needed to become a condition when forming E_INIT from INITIALIZE and INITERR.

7.6.3   Summary

We hope that this section has enabled the reader to get a flavour of the Z Method. There is of course much more to Z than described here, and for more detail the reader is referred to Spivey (1989). It must be kept in mind that the Method is evolving, and while difficult to use manually, the increasing availability of Software Support Tools for Formal Methods will make using the Method (and particularly checking the Specifications for completeness) much simpler.

It should be noted that Z includes no facilities for modelling real-time aspects such as concurrency and interrupts. However, work is progressing (at Oxford University and elsewhere) to incorporate these aspects into Z using ideas from CSP (Communicating Sequential Processes) (Hoare, 1985).

7.7   FINAL COMMENTS

Formal methods can make a significant impact on software design and development. Note though that the operative word is 'can'. Much depends on management commitment, technical expertise of designers and the usability of specification toolsets. The effects produced show in three areas: safety, costs and contractual aspects.

Formal methods are the only way to prove that implementations are correct with respect to their specifications. Consequently, in safety critical systems, these techniques provide a high degree of confidence in the delivered software.

Costs are affected by a number of factors, including reducing the number of design errors, automating the design process, and simplifying software maintenance. First, consider how and why errors are eliminated. Specification documents have to be clear, correct and complete (or omissions clearly noted). And they have to be produced early on in the project. Therefore, during the design phase, fewer mistakes are likely to be made due to misunderstanding these. Moreover, such mistakes are likely to be found fairly quickly. Second, because formal specification methods are mathematically based, these can be automated. This should improve productivity, thus reducing costs. Finally, software maintenance, which usually suffers because of poor documentation, becomes a much easier task. Not only is the original design fully documented but all changes must also be fully and explicitly shown.

Contractual aspects are something which don't rate very highly in software texts. Yet, for a commercial company, they are extremely important. Particularly worrying are charges that the software fails to work as specified. When specifications are vague, open to differing interpretations and incomplete, handling this problem can be a nightmare. But if specifications are rigorous there is little to argue about.

These are the positive features of formal specification methods. Against these must be set concerns regarding the costs involved in using these and doubts about the likely productivity gains. A company which intends to use formal methods either has to train its staff or recruit experienced practitioners. Both are expensive options. Are the improvements in quality and productivity going to pay for this? In any case, these methods cannot prove the correctness of the informal specification, the starting point for the project.

Notwithstanding these drawbacks, formal methods have an important role to play in the software design process. At present it is a small role, being limited mainly to safety–critical software design. This is bound to expand as the techniques and its advantages become more widely known.

REFERENCES

Alvey (1984), Software engineering – Programme for formal methods in system development, Alvey Programme Document, April, DTI, Millbank, London SW1P 4QU.

Collins New English Dictionary.

Denvir, T. (1986), *Introduction to Discrete Mathematics for Software Engineering*, Macmillan Education Ltd., Basingstoke, Hants, UK, ISBN 0–333–40737–7.

Gries, D. (1981), *The Science of Programming*, Springer-Verlag, New York, ISBN 0–387–90641–X.

Hayes, I.J. (1987), *Specification Case Studies*, Prentice-Hall.

Hoare, C.A.R. (1985), *Communicating Sequential Processes*, Prentice-Hall.

Ince, D.C. (1987), Next to Godliness, Datalink, February, pp18.

Jones, C.B. (1986), *Systematic Software Development Using VDM*, Prentice-Hall International (UK), ISBN 0–13–880717–5.

Spivey, J.M. (1988), *The Z Notation – a Reference Manual*, Cambridge University Press.

Spivey, J.M. (1989), *Understanding Z – a Specification Language and its Formal Semantics*, Cambridge University Press.

Woodcock, J.C.P. and Loomes, M. (1988), *Software Engineering Mathematics – Formal Methods Demystified*, Pitman Publishing, London, ISBN 0–273– 02673–9.

FURTHER READING

Backhouse, R.C. (1986), *Program Construction and Verification*, Prentice-Hall.

Burstall, R.M. and Goguen, J.A. (1981), An informal introduction to specifications using Clear, in *The Correctness Problem in Computer Science*, (ed. R.S. Boyer and J.S. Stothers-Moore) Academic Press.

Ehrig, H. *et al.* (1983), *ACT ONE – an Algebraic Specification Language with Two Levels of Semantics*, Berich-NV, Technical University of Berlin.

Ehrig, H. and Mahr, B. (1985), *Fundamentals of Algebraic Specification 1*, Springer-Verlag.

Goguen, J.A. and Tardo, J. (1979), An introduction to OBJ: a language for writing and testing formal algebraic software specifications, Conference proceedings on *Specifications of Reliable Software*, pp170–189, IEEE.

Guttag, J.V. *et al.* (1985), Larch in five easy pieces, Digital Systems Research Center Report, July.

Meilliar-Smith, P.M. and Schwartz, R.L. (1982), SIFT: a fault tolerant flight control system, *IEEE Transactions on Computers*, Vol.C-31, No.7, pp616–630, July.

Milner, R. (1980), A calculus of communicating systems, Lecture notes in computing science, **vol.92**, Springer-Verlag.

Rowles, J. (1988), Formal specification and execution viewed as complementary aspects of software design – a case study, *Technical Report SETC/IN/230*, STC Technology, Newcastle-under-Lyme, Staffs, ST5 1EZ, UK.

Stone, R.G. and Cooke, D.G. (1987), *Program Construction*, Cambridge University Press.

Zave, P. (1982), An operational approach to requirements specification for embedded systems, *IEEE Transactions on Software Engineering*, Vol.SE-8, pp250–269, May.

Chapter Eight

Languages for real-time systems

There are two quite different views on how to choose a programming language. The first is held (usually) by academics, compiler writers and standards committees. Here, language features are carefully listed, defined and assessed; then languages are compared on a point-by-point basis using an unbiased, objective approach. The second method, used by most practising software designers, assesses languages within the context of their own work. Evaluation is supposedly objective. In fact it tends to be highly subjective, prejudiced and emotional, opinions being held with a form of religious fervour. Rational arguments rarely change religious beliefs.

Even accepting that exponents of new languages might be given a fair hearing, there are other, significant, factors to be considered. Many have nothing to do with languages; instead they are tied up with commercial pressures of cost, manpower availability and customer preference. Without a doubt, these are major concerns for any company; their influence on engineering decisions should never be underestimated. Technically brilliant languages can fail purely on commercial grounds.

This chapter aims to show:

- The requirements of languages for use in real-time systems.
- The importance of design, compilation and readability factors.
- Modern high-level language constructs involving variables, data typing, program flow control, exception handling and low-level features.
- Interfacing to and use of 'foreign' high-level languages and assembler coding.
- The current language situation, together with a comparison of Ada, C, Pascal and Modula-2.

The approach used is to discuss language features which are considered to be 'good'. These features are then used as a template against which modern languages are assessed. Although this is reasonably straightforward, the problem comes in defining their **relative** importance. This is left to the reader although guidance is given (based on a set of personal prejudiced views). Readers unfamiliar with compilation and assembly operations are recommended to consult chapter 11, *Development tools*.

8.1   CHOOSING A PROGRAMMING LANGUAGE —
THE REAL QUESTIONS

In choosing a programming language, the starting point is to show **what** is important in embedded software code writing. Consider the following scenario. A highly enthusiastic academic is trying to persuade an overworked, slightly cynical and less-than-enthusiastic software engineer to adopt a new programming language. The questions posed by the engineer highlight what, to him, are important.

Let's start with costs and effort, Fig.8.1.

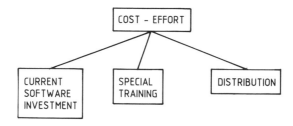

Fig.8.1 Resource implications

Q. We've got a major investment in our current software. Do we have to throw it all away and start afresh? Or can we include source files already written in other languages with this particular language?

Q. If we use this language, will our staff need special training (or can they easily build on their current knowledge)?

Q. How much time and effort is it going to take to distribute this information through the company and to set up the new development environments?

Moving onto design aspects, Fig.8.2.

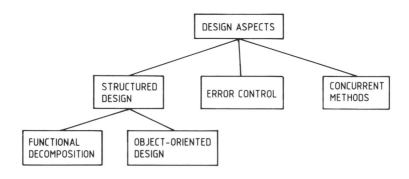

Fig.8.2 Design implications

Q. We seem to design software systems by bending reality to suit our languages and design methods. How well do **these** language constructs mirror the real world?

Q. How well does the language let me, as a designer, express my ideas?

Q. Does the language help us avoid making mistakes when writing programs in the first place?

Q. Our designs use diagramming methods. Do the language constructs provide support for such techniques?

Q. How easy is it to write multitasking software using this language?

Now what about the higher-level aspects of software development, Fig.8.3.

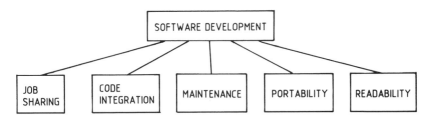

Fig.8.3 High-level software development aspects

Q. Quite often our design timescales are short, so we have to split the work between a number of programmers. How easily can this be done using the proposed language? Is integration of code difficult?

Q. One difficulty we constantly face is updating software without introducing new (and usually unforeseen) mistakes into it. How will this language help us here?

Q. How portable are programs produced using this language?

Q. Is the language sufficiently flexible to let us devise text layout styles so that it's easier to use, read, change, test?

Q. As a project leader I'm often called on when problems come up. Inevitably this means checking out source code. Will the document be easy to read? Does it take up many pages? Will it be easy to grasp the meaning of the program? How easy will it be for me to **misunderstand** it?

And at a more detailed level, Fig.8.4.

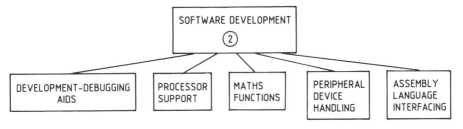

Fig.8.4 Detailed software development features

Q. We use a number of different processors in our hardware. How extensive is the current range of compilers which produce ROMable code? How portable is the code between compilers? Is there support for in-target debugging? How good is this?

Q. What about mathematical operations? What features are available as standard? What number types and sizes are included? Are there inbuilt safety factors concerning maths working?

Q. In our embedded designs we have a large and diverse range of peripheral devices. Can I access this hardware – easily?

Finally, in the target system, Fig.8.5.

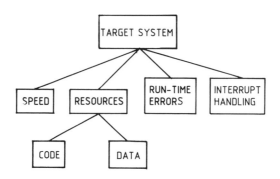

Fig.8.5 Target system/considerations

Q. How fast is the object code produced by this language?

Q. If we find it's too slow can we write time-critical sections in assembly language and then integrate this with the high-level code?

Q. We often have to work with a limited amount of memory. Will the object code produced from this source language fit into my available space?

Q. Are there features in the language for handling run-time errors?

Q. How easy is it to handle interrupts?

From these it is clear that a language can't be assessed in isolation from its development environment. Software engineers frequently produce very good designs even when using a poor language – given the support of a comprehensive software toolset. Conversely, some rubbish has been produced using the best of programming languages. But this is beyond the control of the language designer.

8.2   HIGH-LEVEL LANGUAGES — REQUIREMENTS

The questions above state basically what the user wants. More formally these requirements can be grouped as:

• Acceptable initial cost, effort and disruption.

- Easy integration within current design practices.
- Language flexibility.
- Portability.
- Program readability.
- Execution speed and memory requirements (efficiency).
- Security at compile time.
- Security at run time.

The first two items listed vary considerably from company to company. Thus they can't easily be tackled by the language designer; therefore emphasis is placed on the other objectives. Language features which help to meet these include:

- Program syntax and layout rules.
- Modular design and compilation methods.
- Variable usage – scope, visibility, lifetime and declaration.
- Abstract data typing.
- Program flow control structures.
- Low-level facilities.
- Exception handling.
- Interfaces to assembly language routines.
- Interfaces to other high-level languages.
- Multitasking constructs.

Note that there isn't a one-to-one relationship between the questions raised earlier and the items of the requirements list. Similarly there isn't a one-to-one correspondence between the requirements and language features lists. In general, individual program constructs usually provide solutions to a number of requirements.

8.3 PROGRAM SYNTAX AND LAYOUT RULES — THE READABILITY FACTOR

We can write readable programs only if the language syntax and layout rules allow us to. A number of factors affect this, including:

- Case sensitivity and mixing.
- Identification of words reserved for specific program usage.
- Constraints on naming identifiers.
- Clarity of program maths symbols.
- Format rules.

(a) Case sensitivity and mixing
Examine the following small section of a program:

```
IF OILTYPE = 'A' THEN WRITESTRING ('OIL IS SAE 20'); WRITELN;
ELSE WRITESTRING ('BAD ENTRY'); WRITELN;
```

Now consider a rewritten form:

```
IF Oiltype = 'A' THEN Writestring ('Oil is SAE 20'); Writeln;
ELSE Writestring ('Bad Entry'); Writeln;
```

An important point, not obvious in a small example, is that lower-case text is generally easier to read than upper case. Why this should be so is a question of psychology – but the effect is well known in the printing industry. Second, case mixing within a word makes for readability. It also allows the use of alternatives in writing identifier names, as in

```
HIGHTEMPALARM – > HIGH_TEMP_ALARM – > High_Temp_Alarm
– > HighTempAlarm
```

(b) Identifying reserved words

All languages use defined constructs as part of their structure, e.g. repetition, selection, logical operations, etc. Specific words are reserved to implement such features and may not be used for any other purpose. These reserved words act like signposts, guiding the reader through the program, indicating what it does and how it does it. Therefore it is important to be able to find these easily within the program text. Three general approaches are used, shown here for the word 'procedure'.

(i)   Case not considered: PROCEDURE or **procedure**. Here the reserved word is written in the same case as the rest of the text.
(ii) Case ignored, but special identifying marks used: 'PROCEDURE' or 'procedure'.
(iii) Case defined and the language is case sensitive: PROCEDURE or procedure, but only one of these is correct.

The first method is poor because the program writer has to find some way of making reserved words stand out. In the second, reserved words are more easily found, especially if lower case is used elsewhere in the text. The third method works well **provided** the rest of the program is written predominantly in a different form.

Some languages allow only one case to be used. Others don't worry whether text is written in upper or lower case (as long as reserved words are done correctly). That is, they are case insensitive. Others, though, **are** case sensitive. Consequently, in such a language,

HIGHTEMPALARM – – – HighTempAlarm – – – Hightempalarm

are regarded as three different words.

(c) Naming identifiers

Identifiers are symbolic names used to represent items within a program. If a programmer uses meaningful names, programs instantly become readable. Compare for instance the following as alternatives in naming a program variable:

x – – – –> HITEMP – – –> High_Gearbox_Temp – – – –> HighGearboxTemp

Names become more meaningful, recognizable (hence readable) as they look more like the real-world values they represent. Therefore the greater the number of letters and digits that can be used in any one identifier, the better. Some older languages aren't very flexible, six characters being a typical maximum. In some instances the number is unlimited but only the first few are analysed by the compiler. In such cases, for instance, HITEMP and HITEMPALARM are the same variable as far as the compiler is concerned.

Clear, meaningful and simple names make a program easy to read and understand. Even so, it's easy to go to extremes when there's no restraint on the number of characters used.

(d) Clarity of program maths symbols

For maths working in particular, it is essential to understand two factors: the meaning of program symbols and their precedence. This applies to both conventional arithmetic and logic functions. Software engineers should have a good basic grounding in maths; therefore program rules and notation which mirror coventional mathematics work best. For instance, compare an algebraic expression with its program counterpart:

$$Y = 2C + BD + 5 \text{ – – – – – – – – –>} \quad Y := 2 * C + B * D + 5;$$

This is easy to follow because the symbols are similar to conventional ones. And, provided operator precedence follows familiar rules, the equation form can be quickly checked for correctness.

Therefore a good language will support all basic arithmetic functions, using rules closely related to conventional maths. It is extremely useful if a maths library package comes as part of the language, again using recognizable symbols, e.g. 'sin' for sine, etc.

(e) Format rules

Most languages give the programmer a good deal of flexibility in laying out text. Some, the 'free format' ones, impose hardly any restrictions. This, unfortunately, is a two-edged sword. When used sensibly, text layout can be standardized in a highly readable form. When used without thought, programs can become quite difficult to follow, as in:

REPEAT WriteString('input data');ReadReal(x1);WriteLn;x2:=x2+x1;
WriteString('the value of x2 is');WriteReal(x2,15);WriteLn;UNTILx1>100.0;

Not too difficult over two lines, but difficult when dealing with page upon page of code.

8.4 PROGRAM DESIGN AND COMPILATION METHODS

8.4.1 Overview

It was shown in chapter 4 that software can be constructed using three basic methods: monolithic, modular and independent techniques. Now consider these in the context of software design and compilation (Fig.8.6).

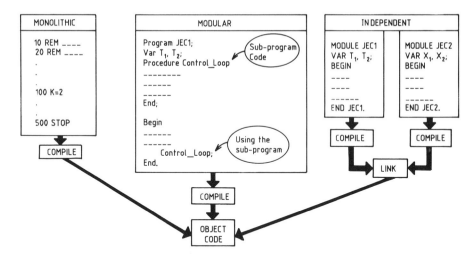

Fig.8.6 Alternative compilation methods

Monolithic program development is simple and straightforward. Here the source program is written out in its entirety as a series of successive statements, i.e. one large block. Compilation to object code may then be carried out.

Modular methods allow us to use a 'building-block' approach in the design of the software. The blocks are realized as a series of subtasks (or subprograms) based on the use of procedures and functions. But compilation of the source code is, as in monolithic designs, still carried out on the complete program.

With independent techniques the fundamental program building block is the module, individual modules being written and compiled as complete items. These come together only at the final stage of 'linkage'. Bennett (1988) defines two compilation methods which support this approach, 'independent' and 'separate'. These differ in their compilation and linkage operations. For instance, suppose that code in module 1 references a procedure held in module 2. When 'independent' compilation is used, no cross-checks are made between the procedure call and the procedure format. Thus it would be possible to use an incorrect format – wrong number of parameters, for instance – and still compile correctly. We rely on the linker to find such mistakes. On the other hand, 'separate' compilation methods do not allow this problem to arise in the first place. They demand that the compiler be given specific information concerning external code at compile time.

8.4.2 Monolithic, modular and independent operations — an evaluation

(a) Monolithic operation
The monolithic method works best where one person only is concerned with the design-and-build programme. Consequently it is most suitable for small, simple tasks. But, as a project becomes more complex, the program becomes equally complex. In the end only one person may understand it, the original designer. Further, the technique inherently makes it very difficult to split the job among a number of designers (Fig.8.7).

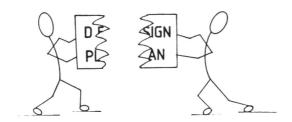

Fig.8.7 Work sharing in a monolithic design

Now consider what happens when a program revision is requested. First, the complete document has to be assessed, a time-consuming and costly effort. Second, any change – no matter how small – results in a full program recompilation. Then, and only then, can change effects be evaluated. In complex systems even a single revision may produce 'knock-on' reactions, leading to undesirable (and unpredicted) side effects. Ergo, monolithic designs are difficult to maintain once they're in service.

(b)   Modular operation

By breaking a single large program into a series of smaller ones even quite complex designs can be managed comfortably. And individual subtasks may be handled simultaneously by different designers. Consequently, designs become more understandable and can be completed more quickly. This requires, however, that the job be properly co-ordinated.

When an existing program has to be modified, the modular method is decisively better than the monolithic approach. Individual changes are likely to be localized, possibly affecting only one sub-task. Hence their consequences can be quickly evaluated. Further, they are less likely to produce unwanted side effects. But, when any change is made, full recompilation must be carried out.

Apart from this last point, does the modular approach have any other major drawback? Unfortunately, yes – but at least it occurs only when the design is split amongst a group. In any design some information must be made generally available, the so-called global data. Thus, it may also be modified by any individual programmer. Unless stringent project control procedures are implemented, changes to global values (especially undocumented ones) can produce design chaos.

(c)   Independent operation

This has all the design features of the modular method, with two further advantages. First, the number of global data items is considerably reduced. Second, should a program change be needed, only the module affected by this needs to be recompiled (Fig.8.8). This minimizes the time taken to implement and test changes; it also reduces the likelihood of side effects.

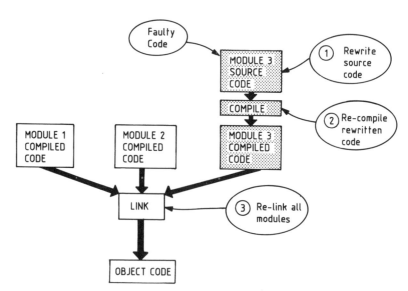

Fig.8.8 Design modification procedure – independent operation

Table 8.1 compares the advantages and weaknesses of the three methods discussed above. Here both 'independent' and 'separate' methods are grouped together as they both require similar control mechanisms. For error-free code production tight cross-checking must always be done, either at compilation or linkage time (note – even more confusingly – some authors use 'independent' to mean the same as 'modular').

Independent (separate) compilation is recommended for high quality work.

Table 8.1 Comparison of compilation methods

Compilation method	For	Against
Monolithic	Simple to use. Suitable for small programs.	Large programs are difficult to handle. Program document soon becomes complex. Difficult for more than one designer to work on the job. Revisions can be costly and time consuming. Unwanted effects may easily be inserted when doing changes.
Modular	Overall structure can be made highly 'visible' using modularity of design. Design can be split among a number of programmers, giving faster program development. Changes are easier to implement. Side effects are reduced. Standard program building blocks can be developed (e.g. I/O to console).	Any change means a complete program recompilation. Global variables are a source of potential danger.
Independent	As for the modular compilation method. Global data items minimized.	More complex cross-referencing needed.

8.5   VARIABLE USAGE — SCOPE, VISIBILITY, LIFETIME AND DECLARATION

8.5.1   Visibility and scope

Modern software engineering methods demand the use of techniques which:

- Develop programs from sets of building blocks.
- Allow a number of programmers to work simultaneously on a project.
- Hide information.
- Provide program stability.

The first two items have little to do with the use of program variables (well, not directly). But, once we decide on a building-block approach, the way variables are used **does** become important. Information hiding and program stability are profoundly affected by this factor. Further, when program development is split between designers, variable usage must be carefully controlled.

The area of a program in which an identifier is visible is called its 'scope'. Within these areas it can be accessed and, if required, changed. If it is visible in all areas of a program it is said to be 'global'. Conversely, if it can be seen in only part of the program, it is 'local' to that section. Two methods are used to enforce locality: the module and the procedure.

What are the advantages of using local variables? The major one is that it helps us to produce reliable, maintainable programs. An identifier is bound to its procedure or module; therefore it cannot be accessed from other parts of the program. By limiting scope, identifiers become easily visible and hence controllable. Accidental access to, and modification of, such items is eliminated. Moreover, the same names can be used for different variables provided their scopes don't overlap. In large projects this minimizes the number of global names, making it easier for programmers to spot name clashes.

8.5.2   Mixing global and local variables

Given the right language then, in theory, global variables don't need to be used (for variables, also read constants in this context). In practice this tends to become clumsy; hence global variables are always used. The question is, how do we decide whether items should be global or local? One proven method is to declare as global objects which reside at defined locations in the processor system (either memory or I/O). All other items become local. But this rule can't be applied in a simple go/no-go manner; much depends on the language being used.

So what are the rules for handling the combination of local **and** global items? There are minor variations between languages, but most follow the general concepts of Fig.8.9.

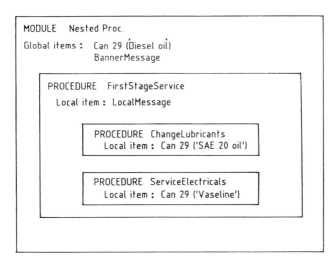

Item	Scope	Where Visible
Can 29 ('Diesel oil')	Module 'Nested Proc'	Everywhere except the two innermost procedures
Banner Message	Module 'Nested Proc'	Everywhere
Local Message	Within all three procedures	Within all three procedures
Can 29 ('SAE 20 oil')	Procedure 'ChangeLubricants'	Procedure 'ChargeLubricants'
Can 29 ('Vaseline')	Procedure 'ServiceElectricals'	Procedure 'ServiceElectricals'

Fig.8.9 Scope and visibility within modules and procedures

8.5.3   The lifetime of variables

Assume our program has 100 variables. Does that mean that 100 RAM store locations have to be permanently allocated for these? Well, it depends. Certain variables exist (are 'alive') for as long as a program runs. These are defined to be 'static'. Others are activated and then disposed of as determined by the program, the 'dynamic' ones. All programs **need** static variables; this isn't so for dynamic ones. In fact, the idea of dynamic variables is generally unknown in assembly language programming. So why use them? The answer is, they save on RAM space. As far as variables are concerned, storage is needed only for the maximum number active at any one time: not the total number used in the program.

   Normally program or global variables are static, procedure variables being dynamic. But, if procedure variables **are** static, the demands on RAM store may limit the use of procedurization as a design technique.

8.5.4   Declarations

Any object (constants and variables) used in a program must be 'declared' to the compiler. The primary reasons are twofold. It allows the compiler to build up a list of all program symbols (a symbol table), required by the compilation process. Further, it provides information regarding the storage space needed for these objects.

Two different declaration techniques are used. In one, declaration is an implicit process. Here the programmer chooses a name for an object and uses it as required in the program. When the program is compiled the first use of the name acts as its declaration. In the other case declarations are explicit; that is, the programmer must list the objects outside the executable part of the program.

Explicit declarations are the preferred method. Using information from the symbol table the compiler can check that such items are used correctly in the program. In contrast, implicit declarations are extremely unsafe, for two reasons. First, any single, simple spelling mistake creates a new object which will be accepted as valid by the compiler. The mistake shows only at run time, the most difficult point to track down errors. Second, object types (e.g. integer, real, etc.) have to be extracted automatically by the compiler. One well-known method used for this relates object type to the first letter of its name. For example, if the first letters are I to N then it's an integer. The opportunities for making mistakes in this situation are immense.

8.6   DATA TYPES —CONCEPTS AND USES

8.6.1   Background

The use of data types is an abstraction process, being a fundamental instrument of high-level language working. Before looking into this in detail it is worth considering the problems that typing can eliminate. These are most troublesome in assembly language work, where typing is pretty primitive. Let's assume that the only types available to us are defined to be bytes, words (16 bits) and double words (32 bits). Now:

Q. Is it possible to examine the contents of a data store and define its meaning? Well, only as a binary number.
Q. What happens if you try to store a data word in the wrong location? The system will do exactly what you tell it to do, within type constraints (and sometimes not even then).
Q. If you mistakenly add two different quantities together, what happens? They usually get added together.
Q. By examining detailed operations carried out on the data can you deduce the

program function? Only if the text is littered with comments and you have a good understanding of the processor instruction set.

It isn't surprising that mistakes are made at this level, the most serious ones being algorithmic and logical. This situation arises because we concentrate mainly on machine details and data-handling features, not on the problem itself. Data typing, however, helps us to focus on what we're trying to do (that is, to solve a particular problem) instead of getting trapped in the finer points of machine detail.

8.6.2   Abstraction and data types

Show Fig.8.10 to an electronic engineer and ask him what it is. The answer is likely to be 'a capacitor', although in reality it's nothing more than marks on a piece of paper. What he means is that it 'represents' a capacitor in his mind. Not that it has a particular shape and size, etc., but that it has the electrical circuit properties defined as capacitance. Now this is an important point; it demonstrates our ability to separate concepts from implementations. Moreover, once we work in abstract terms, the same physical item can be viewed in quite different ways, Fig.8.11.

Fig.8.10 The basic idea of abstraction

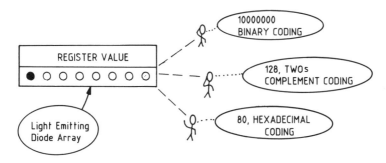

Fig.8.11 Reality and concepts

In terms of languages a data type is also a conceptual idea. Each type defined within a programming language has two attributes:

(a)   A set of values.
(b)   A set of operations which can be carried out on these values.

Consider, for instance, type integer. This has a set of values consisting of whole numbers usually lying in the range $-32,768$ to $+32,767$, the step size being 1 (one). Some of the operations which may be carried out on these values include addition, subtraction, multiplication, etc. Note that we haven't said anything about how integer values are held within the machine itself. Thus at the programming level we work with an abstract concept; particular implementations only become important when used in target machines.

Most modern languages are designed to be 'strongly typed', that is, subject to the following rules:

- Every data object must belong to one (unique) type.
- Associated with each type is a set of values and operations.
- Every operator used with a data type must belong to the set defined for that type.
- Where assignments are carried out, data objects must be of the same type (unless actively overridden).

It is fundamental to high-level language design that data objects should be named and not accessed using memory addresses. This can't hold in all situations though, a point covered in low-level programming.

Typing has a strong bearing on program design and maintenance, its objective being to enhance program reliability. By using type information the compiler can pick up many errors which otherwise would go through to the run-time code. Weakly-typed languages do little to enforce type rules. Therefore it is recommended that strongly-typed languages should be used for real-time systems programming.

8.6.3   Inventing your own data types

All languages have a predefined set of data types, such as integer, real, character, etc. In some cases user-defined types may be added to this set. Now, why should we want to devise new data types in the first place? This feature isn't available on older languages, including many used in real-time systems.

The reason stems from the fact that the number of predefined types is relatively small. As a result any individual type (e.g. integer) may represent a wide range of variables which, logically, are incompatible (from the programmer's point of view). Now, the compiler can look for type incompatibility; logical compatibility checking is beyond its powers. Consider the following simple example (Listing 8.1) for computing the average of four analogue measurements.

```
VAR
    NewValue,TotalValue,AverageValue,Num:INTEGER;

    ............................................
    TotalValue:=0;
    FOR Num:= 1 TO 4 DO
        ReadInt(NewValue); WriteLn;
        TotalValue:=TotalValue + NewValue;
    END; (*end of for*)

    AverageValue:=TotalValue DIV 4;
    WriteString('The average value is');
    WriteInt(AverageValue,5); WriteLn;
```

Listing 8.1

If for any reason the programmer had written

TotalValue:=TotalValue + Num;

the compiler would accept it as a perfectly valid statement; yet logically it is completely wrong. What can be done to help the compiler stop us implementing such code? It can't possibly spot flaws in program logic; after all each program is unique. The answer is, first invent new data types, then use these to distinguish between logically different items. In effect, force the compiler to check for name equivalence instead of structural compatibility. This isn't foolproof – but it does significantly improve the situation.

8.6.4   Defining new types — enumerated types

Types which can be defined by the programmer are usually enumerated ones. That is, we have to list the values of the type, the ordinality of the values being given by the listing order. For example, we could invent a type, 'Digital1Status', to represent the possible states of a motor controller (Fig.8.12). How do we benefit from using programmer-defined types? Look at the program abstract of Listing 8.2.

First, for the two user-defined types (Digital1Status, Digital2Status) we've clearly and unambiguously spelt out all possible conditions. The reader doesn't have to interpret the meaning of the source code. Second, the names used are logically associated with the type attributes. This makes the program easier to read, understand and maintain. Third, we've built in extra safety factors. Consider that, by accident, we write

BearingTemp:=off;

When the program is compiled a 'type incompatibility' error message will be flagged up.

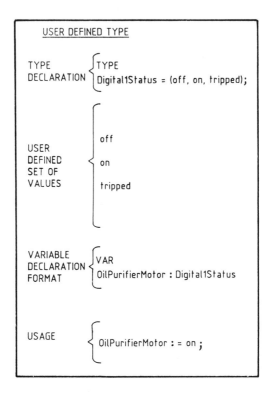

Fig.8.12 User-defined enumerated type

```
TYPE Digital1Status = (off, on, tripped);
     Digital2Status = (low, high);

VAR
   OilPurifierMotor, CPPpumpmotor:Digital1Status;
   BearingTemp, SealTemp:Digital2Status;

BEGIN
   CPPpumpmotor:=on;
   OilPurifierMotor:=tripped;
   BearingTemp:=high;
END.
```

Listing 8.2

For the small number of variables shown here such a mistake is unlikely. In large systems, where the number of program objects runs into thousands, this is a definite hazard.

8.6.5   Subrange types

There are situations where the range of a variable needs to be limited ('constrained'), often for reasons of safety. Let's look at a specific example (Fig.8.13). Assume a number is represented in a processor using 16 bits, counting in straight binary. The program uses this number to set the output of a 12-bit Digital-to-Analogue (DAC) converter.

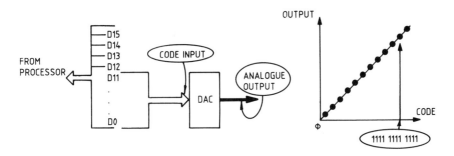

Fig.8.13 Working with a subrange value

Because the DAC is a 12-bit type, the four most significant bits are irrelevant; that is, it uses only a subrange of the total number range. When decimal 4095 (binary 0000_111111111111) is fed to the DAC it produces full range output; for zero (0000_000000000000) it produces its minimum value. Unfortunately it does the same for 4096 (0001_000000000000). Visualize this device being used to set the blade pitch of a ship's propeller. For a 4095 output maximum ahead pitch is set, giving full power ahead. If the output is incremented just by 1 (giving 4096) the DAC signal will go from full ahead to full astern pitch. At the very best this would result in an embarrassing situation.

In many languages the only way to avert this is to positively check for out-of-range conditions. That puts the responsibility entirely onto the programmer; no support is given by the language. As a result, one single 'mistake' in a syntactically correct program could produce catastrophe. But if the language includes subrange constructs, such mistakes can be minimized.

A subrange is defined as a contiguous subset of a given data type (Fig.8.14). For the DAC example the declaration section defines the subrange, as follows:

```
TYPE
    DacRange = [0..4095];
VAR
    DAC1:DacRange;
```

Consequently, should mistakes such as

```
DAC1:=4096;
```

be made in the source code, the compiler would flag up an error.

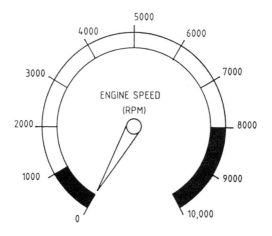

FULL RANGE .... 0–10,000 RPM
NORMAL SPEED RANGE .... 1000–7,000 RPM
OVERSPEED RANGE.......................... 7,000–9,000
DESTRUCTION RANGE .... 9,000+

SUBRANGES OF THE
TOTAL SPEED RANGE

Fig.8.14 Subrange concept

Subranges may also be used with enumerated types (Fig.8.15). This could be used, for example, in the part program shown below (Listing 8.3). Here an enumerated type 'Digital1Status' is first defined. Following this is the declaration of a subrange of it, 'PartDigital1Status', its lower bound being 'off', the upper one, 'standby'. As a result the oil purifier motor can be defined to be in one of five conditions, but the CPP pump motor in only three.

```
TYPE
        Digital 1 Status = ( primed, off, on , standby, tripped);
TYPE
        Part Digital 1 Status = (off ..... Stanby);
```

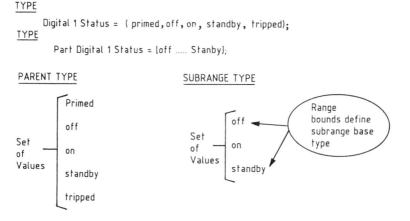

Fig.8.15

```
      TYPE Digital1Status = (primed, off, on, standby, tripped);
           PartDigital1Status = [off..standby];
      VAR
         OilPurifierMotor:Digital1Status;
         CPPpumpmotor:PartDigital1Status;

      BEGIN
         CPPpumpmotor:=on;
         OilPurifierMotor:=standby;
      END.
```

Listing 8.3

Sub-ranges may not give protection against out-of-range values at run time. It is possible that values lying outside the defined subrange **could** be computed. If run-time checks aren't performed on numerical values these will be accepted as valid, with the attendant consequences. Even when such checks **are** done, serious thought must be given to the resultant responses (see section 8.9, *Exception handling*).

Subranges are most useful when developing programs, mainly to identify mistakes of logic. They also make it easier to read and understand programs.

8.6.6   Derived types

Derived types are those invented by the programmer, usually being based on standard language ones. The reasons for their use are to minimize errors and to make the program more readable – not necessarily at the same time. For example, the declaration

```
            TYPE
            NavWeaponsSystem:REAL;
            EngineDataSystem:REAL;
            VAR
            Groundspeed, Altitude: NavWeaponsSystem;
            Airspeed, JetPipeTemp: EngineDataSystem;
```

creates derived types 'NavWeaponsSystem' and 'EngineDataSystem', both having a parent type 'REAL'. In a strongly–typed language it isn't possible to mix variables of different types (without explicit type overriding). Thus the statement

Groundspeed:=Airspeed;

would be flagged up as an error by the compiler.

In a weakly–typed language this would be taken as valid, because the parent types are the same. But, even here, derived types can be used for reasons of program readability, as in Listing 8.4.

```
TYPE
    Distance:REAL;
    Velocity:REAL;
    Time:REAL;
VAR
    Waypoint0, Waypoint1, Waypoint2: Distance;
    Time0, Time1,Time2: Time;
    Velocity0to1, Velocity1to2: Velocity;

BEGIN
    Velocity0to1:=(Waypoint1 - Waypoint0)/(Time1 - Time0);
END.
```

Listing 8.4

We rely on the programmer to pick up logical errors such as

$$Velocity1to2:=(Waypoint1 - Waypoint0)/(Time1 - Time0);$$

With weak typing, to spot illogical and incorrect operations, it is important to use types correctly and consistently.

8.6.7   Procedure types

If a language lets us treat procedures as variables then it is possible to perform operations on them as an entity. One particular feature, the assignment operation, is important, as it allows us to:

- Change the function of a procedure without changing its name.
- Use a named procedure in place of a standard one.

We can make a program much more readable and understandable using this approach (after all, that's why we use names for identifiers).

As an example, suppose that we have to take in a complex number in polar form (i.e. $R \angle \theta$) and calculate its cartesian values $A + jB$. The basic mathematical relationships are:

$$A = R(\cos \theta) \ldots \text{the Real part}$$
$$B = R(\sin \theta) \ldots \text{the Imaginary part}$$

Frequently these operations are mistakenly interchanged (i.e. $A=R(\sin \theta)$). Such mistakes can be eliminated by replacing the standard sine and cosine calculation procedures with well-named user-defined procedures. First, the procedure type must be established, Listing 8.5. Then procedure variable names are declared. Finally, assignment of procedures to these variables is done in the body of the program. Note that these new procedures do exactly the same job as the ones they replace; therefore they must have exactly the same structure.

```
TYPE
    CartesianCalculation = PROCEDURE(REAL): REAL;

VAR
    Radius, Theta, A, jB :REAL;
    RealPart, ImaginaryPart :CartesianCalculation;

BEGIN
    RealPart:=sin;
    ImaginaryPart:=cos;
    A:=Radius * RealPart(Theta);
    jB:=Radius * ImaginaryPart(Theta);
END.
```

Listing 8.5

8.6.8   Structured types

Structured types allow the programmer to work collectively with groupings of data items (which generally relate to each other). The basic requirements of such a data structure are that:

● It must allow data objects to be grouped together. This includes objects of the same type ('homogeneous') and those of different types ('heterogeneous').
● It must let us handle individual objects within the group as well as manipulating the group (or parts of the group) as a single entity.
● Where appropriate it must enable single items to be accessed at random. In other situations it should allow us to work with large quantities of data using sequential accessing methods.
● Accessing information should be both simple and efficient.

To meet these requirements a number of different data structures have been produced:

● Arrays.
● Sets.
● Records.
● Dynamic structures.

Each has particular features and uses.

(a)   Arrays
The array structure is provided in virtually all high-level languages, being used with homogeneous data objects. Only its main features need be noted as it should be a familiar construct to all software engineers. It is a data type which:

● Holds a related set of individual items ('elements').
● Is uniquely identified by a single name.

- Allows the whole set of elements to be handled as a single variable.
- Enables each element to be manipulated separately.
- Is easy to manage.

Modern languages offer features for:

- Multidimensional array structures.
- Forming new types from array structures.
- Using user-defined enumerated types as array bounds.
- Using undefined array sizes as formal parameters of procedures ('open arrays').

The array is extremely powerful in supporting complex or large mathematical operations such as matrix manipulation. Its disadvantage is that it is relatively inflexible for general purpose work, as all elements must be the same type.

(b) Sets

Sets are similar to arrays in many ways. First, individual elements of a set belong to some base type. Second, all elements are of the same base type ('homogeneous'). Third, elements can be accessed directly, i.e. it is a direct access method. Now for the differences. The maximum number of elements contained within a set is defined at declaration time; however, the actual number present at any time can be changed by the program. As such the contents can range from an empty set (null set) through to a full one (all components present). Further, set elements are constants. Thus it is impossible to alter their values. All that can be done is to check whether a set element is present, add elements to the set, or delete elements as required.

Various operators can be used on set variables, those in Table 8.2 being representative. The results of such operations are evaluated using relational operators such as those of Table 8.3. Sets are used mainly for:

- Mathematical operations.
- Validity testing.
- Control of individual bits within computer words.

Bit management is probably the most important application for the embedded systems programmer. Using this construct single bits of a processor word can be handled quickly and easily. Yet this can be written at a high level, providing visibility, clarity and security.

One last point concerning sets is their size, that is, the number of elements within the set. Practical systems considerably limit set sizes (16 elements is not unusual). Further, sizes vary between different computers or compilers. Therefore set operations tend to be highly unportable features of programs.

(c) Records

As shown previously, all data elements within array and set structures are the same type. This is sufficient to satisfy most engineering and scientific needs. Unfortunately these constructs are unsuited for handling large amounts of

Table 8.2 Operators used with set variables

Operator	Name	Logical	Example	Result
+	Union	OR	X + Y	The resulting set has elements which occur in X or Y or both.
*	Intersection	AND	X * Y	The resulting set elements belong to both X and Y.
~	Difference	DIFF	X~Y	The resulting set has elements which occur in X and are not in Y.
/	Symmetric difference	EX-OR	X/Y	The resulting set has elements which occur in either X or Y, but not in both.

Table 8.3 Set relational operators

=	Equality		X = Y	Boolean result, true if X = Y.
<>	Inequality		X<>Y	Boolean, true if X and Y are not equal
<=	Inclusion (set is contained in)		X<=Y	Boolean, true if set X is contained in set Y.
>=	Inclusion (set contains)		X>=Y	Boolean, true if set X contains set Y.
IN	Membership		x IN Y	Boolean, true if ELEMENT x is contained in SET Y.

data, especially data involving different types. Data structures are needed which allow different types to be mixed together. Further, it is desirable to manipulate the contents of these structures both collectively and individually. And it must be possible to work with large quantities of data.

The type which meets these requirements is the record, this being defined as a direct access, heterogeneous, fixed-size data structure. It has the following features:

- It allows a mix of data types.
- The complete data structure can be handled as if it is a single object.
- Each component (element) within the structure can be accessed and manipulated individually.
- Names are used to identify the complete structure and its elements.

When building a record, four items have to be declared to the compiler:

- The name of the record structure.
- The fact that it is a record.
- The individual components of the record.
- The type of each component.

Consider the requirements to form a record for a control loop (Fig.8.16). The declaration format is typically:

```
TYPE
   ControlLoop = RECORD
                  Alarm :BOOLEAN;
                  InputSignal :REAL;
                  OutputCommand :INTEGER;
                END;
```

Variables belonging to this record type are declared in the usual way:

```
VAR
   PortEngineController, StbdEngineController :ControlLoop;
```

Thus each variable has a set of individual components, these being Alarm, InputSignal and OutputCommand. When used in a program they are accessed by name, as in:

```
PortEngineController.InputSignal
StbdEngineController.InputSignal
PortEngineController.Alarm
```

The record structure simplifies many data-handling tasks, even in small programs. No modern language should be without it.

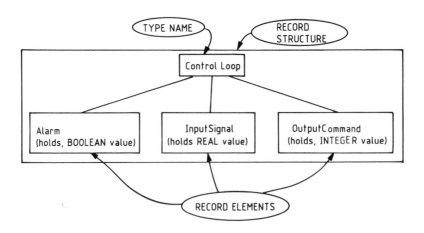

Fig.8.16 Structure of record type 'ControlLoop'

(d)   Dynamic data structures and pointers

There are occasions when systems must handle large amounts of data, placing considerable demands on computer storage space. Data like this is usually dynamic, i.e. in a constant state of change. Consequently, during a program run, the amount of storage space needed at any particular time can vary considerably.

All structures discussed so far have one common feature; their sizes are fixed by program constructs. When sizing them, a worst-case approach must be used; i.e. cater for the maximum needed. But where data is dynamic this clearly is inefficient. In fact small systems may not have enough RAM space to cope with such demands. What's the best way to deal with this?

To meet such needs Dynamic Data Structures have been devised. These structures are created and then disposed of as required; during use they expand and contract as store requirements change. In practice this has led to the use of sequential data storage techniques for dealing with dynamic variables. Variables stored within a dynamic structure do not have individual names, only data values and locations. Consequently, access to such variables is done using address (pointer) information, not names.

Dynamic data types are usually organized as lists or trees, but unlike arrays, etc., are not explicitly defined as such. Instead they are built up using the pointer type, one declaration format being;

```
TYPE
    LogPointer = POINTER TO RunningHours;
    RunningHours = [0..9000];
VAR
    Log :LogPointer;
```

Thus, 'LogPointer' is a pointer type, by type definition. It points to another type, in this case 'RunningHours'. The variable 'Log' is of type 'LogPointer'.

One important use of pointers in embedded systems is for building up operating system constructs. Without this, code would have to be written in assembly language. So even though pointer operations are inherently insecure, they should be provided as part of a modern language.

8.7   PROGRAM FLOW CONTROL

8.7.1   General

It may seem simplistic to say that all programs can be written using only the three structures outlined in chapter 4. Yet, with one exception, this really is the case with well-designed software. The exception occurs only when special steps need to be taken to get out of extreme difficulties – which should be a rare event in embedded systems. Even here recovery techniques should be precisely formed and controlled.

The three structures of sequence, selection and iteration form the basic syntax for Structured Programming techniques; all programs can be constructed using just these. Most languages allow the programmer to transfer program control unconditionally, usually by using the GOTO function. Modern software design practice avoids GOTO constructs as their use can result in badly-structured programs. However, for embedded applications, the GOTO or its equivalent is essential for handling dangerous exception conditions.

8.7.2   Simple selection

There are a number of variations on the simple selection construct, these being:

- The IF-THEN statement.
- The IF-THEN-ELSE statement.
- NESTED-IF statements.

IF-THEN is the simplest version of the selection statement, having the structure of Fig.8.17a. More generally though, we want to carry out alternative actions as a result of the evaluation, one set for true, the other for false. The IF-THEN-ELSE control structure is designed for this, Fig.8.17b.

In some situations, to arrive at an answer, a series of decisions have to be made. Using the IF statement this can be done, as follows:

```
IF <condition A> THEN
    If <condition X> THEN <action 1> ELSE <action 2>
ELSE
    IF <condition Y> THEN <action 3> ELSE <action 4>
END
```

This is described as the NESTED-IF operation (Fig.8.17c).

8.7.3   Multiple selections —ELSE-IF and CASE statements

Often we are faced with having to select one path only from many options. This requirement **could** be handled by using either a sequence of IF-THEN statements, as in

```
IF <X> THEN <action 1>;
IF <Y> THEN <action 2>;
etc.
```

or by a series of IF-THEN-ELSE actions. The first case, although it will work, does not by itself ensure that the operations are mutually exclusive. A little bit of creative programming will soon put an end to such good intentions. The second, using multiple IF-THEN-ELSE's, results in a complicated program structure which is difficult to read and understand. Two methods of dealing with situations such as these are provided in some modern languages, the ELSE-IF and CASE functions.

(a) ELSE-IF

This selection operation allows a single choice to be made in a straightforward manner, as in:

```
IF        <X> THEN <action 1>
ELSE-IF <Y> THEN <action 2>
ELSE-IF <Z> THEN <action 3>
END
```

The flow of operations is shown in Fig.8.17d.

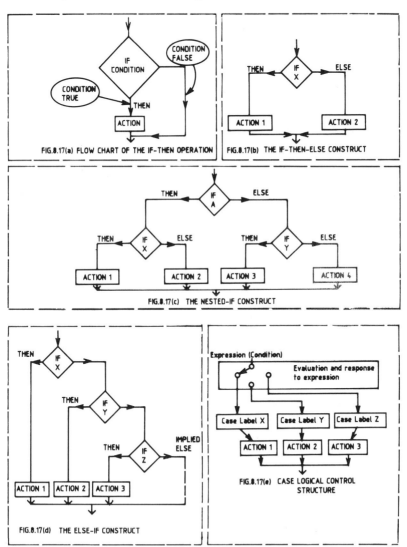

FIG.8.17(a) FLOW CHART OF THE IF-THEN OPERATION

FIG.8.17(b) THE IF-THEN-ELSE CONSTRUCT

FIG.8.17(c) THE NESTED-IF CONSTRUCT

FIG.8.17(d) THE ELSE-IF CONSTRUCT

FIG.8.17(e) CASE LOGICAL CONTROL STRUCTURE

Fig.8.17 Selection constructs

(b)   Case

An easier way of handling multiple-choice problems is the selector switch construct, usually called the CASE statement. Here the switch (Fig.8.17e) selects one course of action from a number of choices.

The CASE syntax usually has the form:

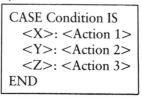

```
CASE Condition IS
   <X>: <Action 1>
   <Y>: <Action 2>
   <Z>: <Action 3>
END
```

The route selected for use is determined by the value of 'Condition'.

8.7.4   Repetition or 'Loop Control'

Very broadly, repetitive constructs can be split into two groups (Fig.8.18). Within the first set, repetition depends upon program conditions, the number of loops set by the state of some control variable. This also includes the case where the program never loops. In contrast, repetitive actions may be defined quite precisely by the program code itself; termination takes place only after the correct number of iterations have been carried out.

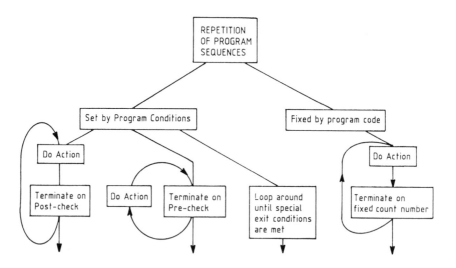

Fig.8.18 Repetition constructs

Thus the four basic iterative control structures are (Fig.8.19):

- Post-check loop (the REPEAT-UNTIL construct).
- Pre-check loop (WHILE-DO construct).

- Check within loop (the LOOP construct).
- Fixed looping conditions (the FOR-TO construct).

With REPEAT-UNTIL operation we first do the required action and then check the test condition (Fig.8.19a). If this condition isn't satisfied then the action is repeated and a further test carried out. Finally when the test conditions are fulfilled control passes to the next sequential statement in the program.

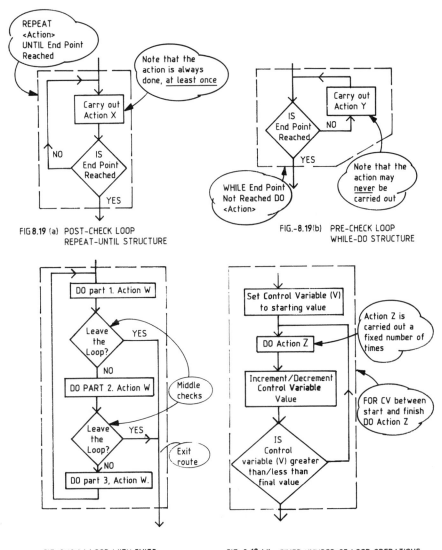

FIG 8.19 (a) POST-CHECK LOOP
REPEAT-UNTIL STRUCTURE

FIG.-8.19(b) PRE-CHECK LOOP
WHILE-DO STRUCTURE

FIG. 8.19 (c) LOOP WITH EXITS

FIG. 8.19 (d) FIXED NUMBER OF LOOP OPERATIONS
FOR-TO STRUCTURE

Fig.8.19 Repetition control structures

When using the WHILE-DO statement the test condition is evaluated before the action is carried out (Fig.8.19b). Depending on the result, two outcomes are possible. One is that no action is performed and control passes on to the next program statement. Otherwise the defined action is implemented and the test condition is once more evaluated.

The LOOP-EXIT construct (Fig.8.19c) is extremely useful because it:

- Can result in more readable code.
- Minimizes the need for GOTO operations.
- Enables the programmer to implement multiple terminating conditions in a simple fashion.

This is not a universally held view (Sale, 1988).

When the number of iterations can be defined in the program code, the FOR-TO construct is usually used (Fig.8.19d).

8.7.5   The importance of flow control constructs

It isn't often realized that **all** flow control constructs can be devised using just two operations: the combination of IF-THEN-ELSE and GOTO (this, though, requires that the language uses either line numbering or labels). Unfortunately, with such an approach, it becomes difficult to see exactly which operation is being carried out. In contrast, highly readable code results by using program statements which relate directly to specific control structures. Therefore, a good modern programming language should provide a full range of control structures.

8.8   INTERFACING TO OTHER LANGUAGES

8.8.1   Assembly language interfacing

For professional work it is a primary requirement to work whenever possible with high-level languages. These are easy to understand, straightforward to maintain, and much less likely to hold unwitting mistakes. Nevertheless, there will be occasions when the high-level approach fails. Therefore we must be able to integrate assembly language into the high-level code.

This is a fundamental requirement for all high-level languages. Two methods are commonplace, using either code inserts or linked assembly routines (Fig.8.20). Code inserts ('inline code') are program statements which are placed directly in the high-level source code. Either assembler mnemonics or machine instruction hexadecimal values can be used. To use assembly statements the compiler first generates intermediate code; it then submits this to an assembler process. This is a highly flexible programming method; unluckily, few compilers offer this feature. The second method doesn't involve an assembler and has the advantage of producing fast and small code. It also allows the programmer to manipulate processor registers, etc., knowing that unforeseen effects won't be generated by the compiler. This method, when combined with a good high-level language, eliminates the need for separate assembly language routines. But, to use it, the programmer must have an expert knowledge of microprocessor machine language.

The most common method of assembly language interfacing is to first write assembler operations as separate routines: then link these in with the compiled code of the high-level language. One highly desirable feature is the ability to reference high-level designators (e.g. variables) from assembly code (and vice versa). For professional work this should be mandatory. The degree of cross-checking performed by the linker on the high-level and assembler routines (e.g. version numbers) is important.

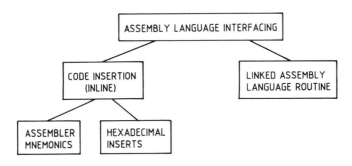

Fig.8.20 Linking assembly language operations

8.8.2 High-level language interfacing

From a technical point of view there isn't a need to interface to other high-level languages. However, should a company decide to use a new language it can't afford to throw away its existing software investment. It must be possible to integrate existing work with new developments. Unless a language provides this facility it may well be rejected on commercial grounds. The important factors here are the:

- Range of language interfaces available.
- Ease of interfacing.
- Degree of cross-checking of 'foreign' language routines.

Note that these features are frequently compiler, not language, dependent.

8.9   EXCEPTION HANDLING

Exceptions are 'errors or fault conditions which make further execution of a program meaningless' (*Dictionary of Computing*). For embedded systems this definition should have the words 'and/or dangerous' added. When errors do occur, the usual response is to invoke an exception handler routine; this decides what action should be carried out. It can be seen that there are three distinct issues here:

- What errors should be detected?
- Who provides the error detection mechanism?
- What should be done once the exception is identified?

The final item is application-dependent; thus it is beyond the scope of the language (although it's probably the most difficult question to answer). In a data processing environment it may be sufficient to halt the program; for embedded working this may be even more dangerous than the original error condition.

The first two items **are** language related, these being another contentious issue. The questions are, how much should be built into the language itself, and how much should the programmer handle explicitly? Now, certain errors may occur on any processor system. Others, though, are specific to system and hardware design. It is recommended that:

- Languages should provide certain basic automatic error detection facilities at run time, especially for maths handling. These include number overflow, divide by zero, array bound violations, etc.
- The programmer should be able to switch off these checks if required to speed up execution times.
- The language should provide a set of procedures by which the programmer can check for error conditions and invoke appropriate responses.

Doing it this way removes a significant burden from the programmer; he doesn't have to include code to check for all possible error conditions. It also keeps the source text clear; automatic checks require no program code. It highlights those error checks which the programmer **does** insert. And finally, by grouping error handling routines together, it is easier to assess system safety.

8.10 ACCESSING PROCESSOR HARDWARE — LOW-LEVEL FACILITIES

8.10.1 Introduction — the need for device access

Do we need to manipulate hardware at the chip level? Well, if the computer system comes equipped with its own operating system, then we don't. In such cases direct control of the hardware is done by systems software, our own programs being defined as applications software (Fig.8.21). However, many computer-based real-time engineering functions don't use standard operating systems. Software tends to be tailor-made for the task in hand, with little or no distinction between systems and applications software. In fact, software in smaller embedded systems is considered to be 'applications' only, interacting directly with the computer hardware (Fig.8.22). Adapting hardware behaviour to meet varying requirements is not restricted to just embedded designs. The systems programmer, for instance, faces similar problems when installing operating systems on new or modified hardware.

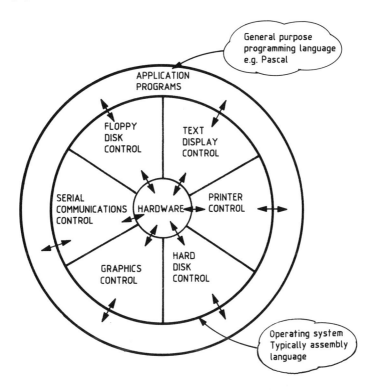

Fig.8.21 General purpose machine – hardware/software structure

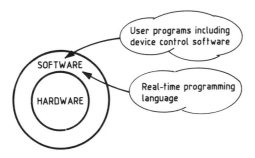

Fig.8.22 Embedded real-time compute – hardware/software structure

A second set of problems arises when dealing with designs which use different processors. A brief comparison is given in Table 8.4 of the Intel 8085 and 8086 microprocessors; this shows how much variation can be found even in devices from the same manufacturer. Even when the processor is fixed, designs still differ concerning:

- Use of memory space for code, data, heap and stack.
- Amount of code in read-only store.
- Amount of read/write store.
- Special store provisions, such as non-volatile devices.
- Address locations of these devices.
- Location, size and activating methods for interrupt-driven programs.

Table 8.4 Outline comparison – Intel 8085 vs 8086

	8085	*8086*
Address range	64 kByte	1 MByte
Data word size	8 bits	16 bits
Serial I/O	Yes	No
Vectored hardware interrupts	4	1
Software interrupts	No	Yes

8.10.2 Facilities needed to access devices

Access facilities can be grouped roughly into four areas:

- Memory accesses, for the control of code, data, heap and stack operations.
- Peripheral device interfacing and control.
- Interrupt handling.
- Support of special machine operations.

(a) Memory operations
Memory chips are mapped into the processor address space, their locations being determined mainly by processor characteristics. For instance, EPROM must be mapped at the bottom of memory in the Z80 (Fig.8.23). This comes about because, on power-up, program execution begins at location 0000H. The 8086, however, restarts with its instruction pointer pointing to location FFFF0H. For this processor EPROM must be located at the top of memory.

Thus the software engineer must take into account the mapping scheme in use when compiling the program (as it's rather difficult to write information into EPROM).

In some situations we have to access information residing at specific memory locations (absolute addresses). Here the need is to specify precisely the addresses of these memory locations. Such features should be standard within the language.

(b) Management of peripheral devices
Virtually everything except processor and memory devices come into this

category. Included are items such as programmable timers, interrupt controllers, serial I/O controllers, maths chips, analogue-to-digital converters, etc.; the list is immense. Generally, though, they have three factors in common:

- They are mapped at specific absolute addresses.
- Both read and write operations are performed on them.
- Individual bits within a data word have specific meanings.

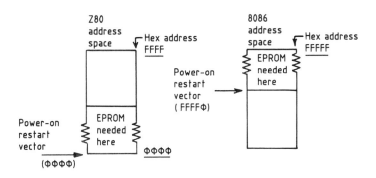

Fig.8.23 Mapping of memory devices

Where peripherals are mapped into memory then, to the processor, they look like RAM. Thus addressing and read/write operations need no further discussion. However, bit management is a different matter. This facility is required for two main reasons. We may, in the first instance, want to establish the status of the device being accessed. In the second we may wish to change its operational mode. Both status and control information is handled using word (in smaller systems, byte) data transfers. For such applications the information carried by the word is set by individual bits within the word. Therefore, when interacting with peripherals, we must be able to examine and modify data words bit by bit. And for the sake of clarity and reliability, bit-handling should be supported within the high-level language itself.

(c) Interrupt handling
The role of interrupts has been discussed elsewhere. But no matter how these are implemented, we always end up using absolute addressing methods. Two alternative techniques are shown here. In the first one the interrupt program is located at a defined absolute address in memory; the processor is then 'vectored' to this when the interrupt is activated (Fig.8.24).

Alternatively, the compiler fixes the program location; we then 'plant' the necessary reference to this at an absolutely defined address in the interrupt vector area. When an interrupt occurs, program control is initially transferred to the appropriate location in the vector area. The program residing here is usually quite short. Normally it performs limited housekeeping functions and then transfers program execution to its interrupt program.

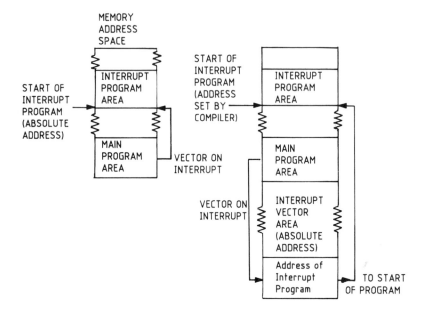

Fig.8.24 Interrupt operations

Interrupt handling obviously is machine specific. This causes great difficulty in trying to standardize such operations in any general purpose high-level language. To avoid using assembly language, two features should be provided. The language should provide constructs which allow the programmer to implement interrupts in his own fashion. It should also provide an interrupt-handling mechanism which is non-standard but supplied as part of the compiler.

(d)   Special machine instructions
Occasionally processors provide facilities which are unique to their design. For instance, on Intel processors, data can be transferred quickly and efficiently using IN and OUT instructions. Peripheral devices which respond to these are mapped into the so-called I/O space. Clearly such instructions cannot be included as standard within the language; yet we should still be able to invoke all facilities provided by the processor. It is desirable that such features are included within the language package, as a non-standard extension.

8.11 MISCELLANEOUS ITEMS

8.11.1 Macros and macro-processors

A *macro-instruction* ('macro' for short) is an instruction inserted in the source code, representing a sequence of program statements. When the source file is compiled the macro is replaced prior to compilation by the statement set. This is done by a *macro-processor* program. Macros perform much the same task as procedures except that:

- Executable (object) code is generated for each insertion of the macro; in the case of a procedure, code is generated once only.
- Execution times are faster as there isn't any saving or restoring of processor information.

These are powerful mechanisms, particularly when parameters can be used with the macro call (as with procedures). They are especially useful when structured design methods are used. Most implementations of top-down modular structures use procedures as building blocks. But this has one (not so obvious) drawback. That is, as the levels in the structure increase so do the number of nested procedure calls. The save/restore overhead can be substantial in such cases. Expansion factors of two to three are commonplace (compared with straight code). In contrast, the macro allows the designer to implement top-down designs with minimal effect on run time. The trade-off for this is code size, faster run times requiring more object code. Unfortunately there aren't simple rules for calculating the code ratio between macro and procedure implementations. A further complication is that small procedures may have as much code for save/restore instructions as that in the procedure body itself.

A second factor, particularly important for small embedded systems, is the demand placed by nested procedures on RAM space. Each time a procedure is called, processor status must be preserved. Further, variables local to the procedure also need RAM space. Add to this the need to store parameters, especially those copied into the procedure ('value' parameters). With nesting these can mount up dramatically, resulting in the processor running out of RAM space and consequent failure of the program:

Few languages provide the macro facility as standard. Where it isn't available it is recommended that a language-independent pre-processor be used.

8.11.2 Variable initialization

Some languages enable a value to be assigned to a variable at the time of its declaration – 'variable initialization'. The compiler itself generates object code to set the variable to this value; no statements need be made in the program. Opinions differ concerning the usefulness of this feature. What **is** useful is a compiler check to ensure that variables have values assigned to them before they are used. In many cases it doesn't matter that variables aren't initialized; in others it may be crucial. Without automatic initialization checks, responsibility lies entirely with the programmer.

8.11.3 Constant expressions

In high-level language working all program items should be given names. This includes constant values as well as variable ones. A fairly standard declaration form is:

```
CONST
  pi = 3.14159;
```

where the right-hand side of the equation is defined to be a constant expression. If the language allows this to be treated in the same way as normal expressions then it's possible to build up constructs as:

```
CONST
  pi = 3.14159;
  f = 50;
  omega = 2*pi*f;
```

The readability of the source code can be greatly improved using such methods.

8.11.4 Concurrent constructs

It is important that a general purpose programming language contains constructs for building concurrent programs (chapter 9). This allows the programmer to implement the high-level features – scheduling, mutual exclusion and task communication – of operating systems. These can be applied both to single and multiprocessor systems, being tailored to suit the application.

8.12 LANGUAGES FOR REAL-TIME SYSTEMS —SURVEY

8.12.1 General

Over the last three decades many programming languages have been developed; few have achieved widespread use. Those discussed here have been selected using the criteria of suitability, availability, and current and future interest (Fig.8.25). For a wider view of the subject the texts by Taylor and Morgan (1980) and Foulger (1982) should be consulted.

Of these, the ones which are likely to be significant during the next decade are compared in some detail (mind you, there's an element of crystal-ball gazing here). This doesn't extend to a point-by-point description of the languages. There seems little value in doing this; details can be found in the language texts. Further, there isn't much reason for discussing in depth the older languages, no matter how successful they've been. These will gradually be replaced by newer ones.

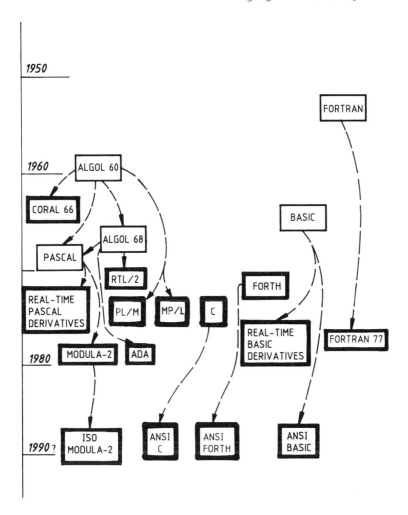

Fig.8.25 Languages for real-time embedded systems

8.12.2 FORTRAN

FORTRAN (FORmula TRANslation Language) is really the forerunner of modern high-level languages, although most real-time languages derive (somehow) from Algol. It was developed by IBM in the late 1950s as their standard scientific programming language. However, its structure (or rather, lack of it), global scoping and weak typing made it an unlikely candidate for real-time applications. Significant improvements were made with the introduction of FORTRAN 77, with versions for ROM being available. Even so, it has generally been ignored for embedded work and isn't a serious contender for future use in this area.

8.12.3 BASIC

BASIC (Beginners All-purpose Symbolic Instruction Code) was designed in 1965 at Dartmouth College, USA, by Kemeny and Kertz. It was intended to be a simple, easy-to-learn language, geared mainly to input and output via keyboard and screen. Certainly it was never intended for real-time systems use. However it rapidly became very popular and, consequently, widely used. Its features have been extended until now we have compilable, structured versions incorporating low-level and multitasking facilities. It is highly popular with engineers who have had little education in structured and/or assembly languages. This is especially true in the mechanical, civil and chemical industries. Purists tend to sneer at BASIC. But its very simplicity allows less experienced programmers to produce better software than they would using Pascal, say. It is likely to be given a further boost with the introduction of an American National Standards Institute (ANSI) standard.

BASIC is not compared further because, fundamentally, there isn't a basis for comparison. With so many variations about, it would have to be done taking specific implementations into account.

8.12.4 CORAL66

CORAL66 (Computer On-line Real-time Application Language) was produced in 1966 by what is now the Royal Signals and Radar Establishment. This became the standard defence language in the UK, microprocessor compilers being available as early as the late 1970s. It was designed specifically for real-time use, its features making low-level programming simple and straightforward. It also includes assembly language insertion facilities, macros and floating-point arithmetic. Multitasking is not supported within the language; instead this is usually done in conjunction with the MASCOT system (chapter 10). It has been standardized by the British Standards Institute, specification BS 5905:1980.

The real-time features of CORAL are those against which all other languages should be measured. However, the language has been replaced to a certain extent by versions of real-time Pascal; in the future its role will be taken over by Ada. There is little point in discussing it any further.

8.12.5 Pascal

Pascal was designed by Professor Nicklaus Wirth, Institute for Technology, ETH, Zurich, circa 1970, primarily as a teaching tool. It rapidly became popular in universities, polytechnics and the like, becoming a standard teaching language. As a result, by the end of the 1970s, it was being used in professional computing circles. The original defining document is *Pascal – User Manual and Report*, by K. Jensen and N. Wirth. Subsequently it has been standardized as

BS 6192:1982 and ISO 7185:1982 (identical).

In its original form it didn't accommodate embedded system features. But, because of its popularity, many extensions have been made and it is now a highly popular language in the real-time world. Like BASIC, these variations make it difficult to evaluate it as a single unified language. However, general comments are made later in conjunction with its successor, Modula-2.

8.12.6 RTL/2

RTL/2 (Real Time Language Two) was developed in ICI about 1971 by J. Barnes for company use in real-time process control applications. Later it was released commercially through Systems Designers Ltd. (SDL), being widely used within the chemical industry. It is considered by many to be a major improvement on CORAL66. Unfortunately it hasn't made a significant impact in real-time systems applications, and is unlikely to do so in the future. It is standardized by BSI as BS 5904:1980, fuller details given in the text by Barnes (1976).

8.12.7 C

C was designed by Dennis Ritchie at Bell labs in 1972. At that time most systems implementation languages were written in assembler, with their attendant drawbacks. C's purpose was to give the programmer almost as much flexibility as assembler but using high-level language constructs. It was also aimed to be as efficient as assembler. Initially it was used to write the UNIX operating system, only appearing in the embedded world (to any great extent) in the 1980s. Since then its use has blossomed tremendously; in fact it is probably the single most important real-time language. The reasons for this are that:

- The number and variety of support tools are immense.
- The development environments are sophisticated and advanced.
- C compilers are available for almost all major microprocessors.

The language is still evolving, with standards being prepared by ANSI (document X3.159). Further developments have been made concerning concurrency (concurrent C) and object-oriented programming (C++, Stroustrup, 1987). More is said on C later.

8.12.8 Forth

Forth is unlike all other languages considered here. It has been described as '. . . a bit like Lisp, a bit like assembler, but in the last analysis, Forth is a language apart' (Dettmer, 1988). It was designed by Charles Moore in the late 1960s, and was made available by Forth Inc. in the early 1970s. Its main advantages for real-time work are that it generates efficient code, executes quickly, allows easy control of hardware devices and can be developed relatively quickly. Users of Forth tend to have a messianic belief in its capabilities; yet it still remains a minority language. There's no doubt that it will be around for a long time, although C will probably diminish its use. For an introduction to Forth see the article by Dettmer (1988).

8.12.9 PL/M and MPL

PL/M (Programming Language/Microcomputers) was developed by Intel, starting with PL/M-80 in 1976 for the 8080 microprocessor. This is a block-structured language, derived from PL/1 from the Algol stable. Versions have been produced for other Intel processors: PL/M-51, PL/M-86 and PL/M-96. MPL is the Motorola equivalent, designed for the 6800 and 68000 range of processors. These languages are generally less powerful than, say, RTL/2 and extended Pascals, but have significant strengths:

- They are specifically designed for ROMable microprocessor systems.
- They work within the integrated Microcomputer Development System environment provided by the processor manufacturers.
- Interfacing to assembly language is simple and straightforward.
- Integrated debugging tools are provided for these.

The drawback is that they can be used only on specific micros. It is likely that their use will reduce somewhat, mostly due to the greater availability of C compilers.

8.12.10   Ada

Any real-time systems software engineer who hasn't heard of Ada must have spent the last few years in a monastery. This language project began in the mid-1970s (the High Order Language Working Group, HOLWG) when the US Department of Defense decided to rationalize language working. A survey had shown that not only were many different languages being used (according to Bennett (1988), over 300), but many were highly specialized. Language requirements were set out in a number of documents, starting with Strawman in 1975 (Fig.8.26). Four separate design studies were undertaken, defined as Blue, Yellow, Red and Green.

The goals set for these by the HOLWG were (listed in order of importance):

- Cost.
- Responsiveness.
- Timeliness.
- Flexibility.
- Reliability.
- Maintainability.
- Training.
- Transportability.

- Readability.
- Writeability.
- Efficiency.
- Acceptability.

Eventually, in 1979, Green was selected as the winner, the language being named Ada in honour of Countess Augusta Ada Lovelace (Charles Babbage's assistant and daughter of Byron).

		LANGUAGE	LANGUAGE SUPPORT ENVIRONMENT
1975	April	STRAWMAN	
	August	WOODENMAN	
1976	June	TINMAN	
1977	January	IRONMAN	
1978	June	STEELMAN	
	July		SANDMAN
	December		PEBBLEMAN
1979	May	Honeywell Bull design selected	
1980	February		STONEMAN
	December	APPROVAL AS MIL-STD-1815	
1983	February	APPROVAL AS ANSI/MIL-STD-1815	

Fig.8.26 Ada language development

The final language requirements document, Steelman, was produced in 1978. This was followed in 1980 by Stoneman, the final Ada programming support environment requirements document. It was also decreed that no sub-sets or super-sets of the language would be permitted (Ada was trademarked). Only one document forms the definitive statement of the language, the ANSI Ada standard language reference manual. For further details see Elbert (1986).

Ada has a number of features which can have a major impact on program design, development and maintenance. The most important ones are packages, tasks, exceptions and generics. Packages are fundamental high-level software units used for the construction of modular programs. Tasks are the basic building blocks of concurrent programs. Exception handling – a critical activity for real-time systems – is an integral part of the language. Finally, generics enable the designer to produce general purpose software 'templates', and then tailor ('instantiate') them for specific uses. Thus the language inherently supports modularization, separate compilation, concurrency, exception handling, reliability and modifiability. It also promotes good readability, high programmer productivity and genuine program portability.

Little experience has yet been obtained in embedded applications. Also, many significant problems have been encountered along the way, due mainly to its attempt to be a 'do-all' language. This makes compiler writing a nightmare job. Much is made of the validation suite. Yet many aspects important to the embedded systems designer are not (yet) covered by this. Substantial defects have been found in fully validated compilers (personal research). Much has been made of the fact that the language was designed for real-time applications. In reality it was designed with extremely large systems in mind, mainly by computer scientists, with little input from the embedded systems community.

Ada also has its critics, including a foremost UK computer scientist, Professor C.A.R. Hoare. He expressed great concern for and considerable criticism of the language in his 1980 Turing Award lecture (Hoare, 1980). But Ada **will** succeed, given the driving forces behind it and the vested interests involved. Therefore it will have to be assimilated by those working in defence applications. For these reasons its features will be looked at in more detail.

8.12.11   Modula-2

Modula-2 was developed by Nicklaus Wirth between 1977 and 1980, being derived from Pascal and Modula. It was designed to improve on Pascal, particularly with regard to systems programming and concurrency. One of its aims is to allow programs to be written entirely in Modula, without resorting to assembler. To do this it incorporates many low-level facilities including device and interrupt handling. Its other major feature is its modular approach to software construction, using a combination of program, local and library modules. This is a major step forward over Pascal, similar constructs being available in Ada. In fact, it has often been said that Modula-2 forms an easy stepping-stone from conventional block-structured languages to Ada.

Modula-2 is rapidly replacing Pascal as a teaching language; hence it is also expected to replace it in general use within the next few years. At the moment the defining document is Wirth's book (1988), but a BSI/ISO standard is in its final approval stages.

8.13   A COMPARISON OF ADA, C AND MODULA-2/PASCAL

8.13.1   Introductory remarks

Various methods have been proposed for comparing languages. Wirth (1980), for instance, advocates that they should be evaluated solely by their definitions, without reference to compilers or implementations. Experience, though, has shown that such separations are hard to achieve. It is impossible in a text like this to take implementations into account sensibly; they change so quickly. It is therefore strongly recommended that, before plunging into a new language, the available support tools are carefully evaluated.

The approach adopted here is to compare the languages on a series of very specific features, as follows:

- Syntax
- Operators, assignments and expressions.
- Type philosophy and data types.
- Control flow constructs.
- Routine and scope.
- Separate compilation and enforcement of type consistency.
- Exception handling.
- High-level access to absolute addresses.
- Assembly language interfacing.
- Bit manipulation.
- Concurrency.
- Efficiency and code size.

This is based on work carried out by M. Bowring (1985).

8.13.2 Syntax

(a) Ada

Readability was a basic consideration in the Ada design. Hence it avoids cryptic encoded symbols, generally using English-like constructs. The syntax is well defined using a simple variant of the Backus–Naur notation. Its character set is that of the American Standard Code for Information Interchange (ASCII). The language is case insensitive although a convention has grown up concerning reserved words; frequently these are written in lower-case text. An example program fragment is:

```
if HYDRAULIC_PUMP_SPEED > 2000 then
      SHUTDOWN (HYDRAULIC_PUMP);
   end if;
```

It is considered by some Ada programmers that the use of lower-case for reserved words is a fundamental mistake. This can, in their opinion, make the source code quite difficult to read.

(b) C

Until the ANSI standard is finalized it is difficult to define precisely the syntax of C. What – at this time – is considered to be the reference manual (Kernighan and Ritchie, 1988) only contains a syntax summary which 'is intended more for aiding comprehension than as an exact statement of the language'. The style is terse, uses unconventional operator symbols and has complex precedence rules. As a result C programs can be extremely difficult to read. For instance, one line from the reference manual reads:

for (i=0; i<lim−1 && (c=getchar()) EOF && c' '; ++i)

Because of the operator complex precedence levels, C programs tend to be overparenthesized. When combined with mixing of types in expressions, this can be very dangerous; missing or extra parentheses result in valid but unintentional results. There is no convention for identifying reserved words. For critical applications these are serious issues.

It is known that because of these problems, one defence contractor allows programming staff to use only a limited, controlled subset of the language.

(c) Modula-2/Pascal

Both Modula-2 and Pascal are designed to be highly readable. Modula-2 is case sensitive, Pascal isn't. Case mixing can be used in Modula-2, though reserved words must be written in upper case. A specimen example is:

IF HydraulicPumpSpeed > 2000 THEN
    Shutdown (HydraulicPump);
END;

Case sensitivity only appears to be an irritating point to those who haven't used the language. Declaration rules are simpler than Pascal, leading to more readable text. The languages are defined using Extended Backus–Naur Form notation.

8.13.3 Operators, assignments and expressions

(a) Ada

Ada has six classes of operator, having the precedence levels set out below:

- Level 1: Abs, not, ** (i.e. absolute, logical negation, exponentiation).
- Level 2: Multiplying: *, /, mod, rem.
- Level 3: Unary adding: +, −.
- Level 4: Binary adding: +, −, & (& is concatenation).
- Level 5: Relational: =, /=, <, <=, >, >=.
- Level 6: Logical: and, and then, or, or else, xor.

For each operator the types with which it can be used, and the result types, are defined. However, operators can be overloaded (see 'types').

(b) C

C has a large number of operators, with 15 levels of precedence. In some cases the notation is extremely cryptic. For instance,

'&&' is 'AND', '||' is OR,

X=10;   is an assignment statement, whereas   X==10;   is equality.

```
X=10;
Y=++X;
```
means
```
X=10;
X=X+1;
Y=X;
```

i.e. Y has the value 11.

But
```
X=10;
Y=X++;
```
means
```
X=10;
Y=X;
X=X+1;
```

i.e. Y has the value 10.

Bit manipulation is standard within the language, including bitwise logical operations. Assignments may be made in expressions. This can easily lead to side effects, resulting in unreliable programs. Arithmetic can be used with pointer types, which gives extremely efficient memory management. It is also highly prone to error.

(c) Modula-2/Pascal
Modula-2 has four classes of operator, the precedence being:

- Level 1: NOT, ~.
- Level 2: *, /, DIV, MOD, AND. (* also has the meaning 'set intersection', / also being used for symmetric set difference).
- Level 3: +, −, OR. (+ also means set union; −, set difference).
- Level 4: =, <>, <, <=, >, >=, IN (IN, <= and >= being used with sets).

The / symbol is not applicable to Pascal sets.

8.13.4 Type philosophy and data types

(a) Ada
Ada is probably the most strongly-typed language currently available. Basic types include Boolean, Integer, Real, Character, Array, Record, Enumeration and Access (pointer). Integers are implementation defined as type INTEGER (LONG_INTEGER and SHORT_INTEGER are optional extensions). A useful construct of Ada allows the programmer to specify a variable range of an integer – without having to define its type. The compiler then maps it onto the integer type most appropriate for that specific implementation. This is significant in terms of program portability.

Real types fall into two categories, floating point and fixed point. They differ in the specification of their error bounds, that is the accuracy constraint.

Type mixing is forbidden. Type conversions are allowed, but these are all fully defined to provide complete compiler checking. Unchecked type conversions are also permitted, using a predefined subprogram UNCHECKED_CONVER-

SION. Derived types can be obtained from a 'parent', but these are treated as logically distinct entities. The same identifier can be used to represent more than one subprogram, i.e. there may be more than one possible meaning for an identifier in the text. This is called overloading. In such cases the compiler resolves the apparent ambiguity from the context of the identifier.

Arrays of variable length can be declared.

(b)   C

C is weakly typed, the predefined ones being CHAR, INT, LONG, FLOAT (single precision 32 bit) and DOUBLE (64 bit). The qualifiers SHORT, LONG and UNSIGNED can be applied to INTs. Arrays can be built, including multidimensional ones; records may also be constructed. There aren't Boolean, enumerated or subrange types. Typing can be broken in many ways. Implicit conversions occur; further, compilers may allow unexpected type conversions to take place. Pointers can point to static variables outside the normal scope of their routine, and address arithmetic can be performed. Explicit type conversions can be done using the CAST mechanism.

(c)   Modula-2/Pascal

Modula-2 and Pascal are both strongly typed, Modula more so. Standard types in both are CHAR, INT, REAL, ARRAY, RECORD, BOOLEAN, POINTER and SET. Pascal has type STRING. Modula has types CARDINAL, LONGINT, LONGREAL, BITSET, WORD, ADDRESS and PROC. Enumerated and subrange types can be formed. Some implicit type-changing takes place in Pascal; none is allowed in Modula. Modula provides for explicit type conversion and also type transfer operations. This latter action doesn't change the data format into that of a new type; it merely interprets the existing data as if it belongs to the new type.

There are two ways to overcome the strong typing rules when using records. One concerns the use of the WITH-DO construct, the other involves variant records.

8.13.5   Control flow constructs

(a)   Ada

Ada supports the following control flow constructs:

(i)   Selection

                    if . . . then . . . end if;
                    if . . . then . . . else . . . end if;
                    if . . . then . . . elsif . . . elsif . . . end if;
                    case <expression> is . . . end case;

With CASE, the final choice must be made using the 'others' construct. This enables the programmer to cover all incoming values to the case construct which are not among those explicitly defined.

(ii)   Repetition

>   loop . . . end loop;
>   while <condition> loop . . . end loop;
>   for <identifier in range> loop . . . end loop;

Any loop can contain an exit statement. The for-loop does not have a 'step-by' construct.

(iii)   Unconditional transfer of control: GOTO.

The label to which control is transferred must be in scope.

(b)   C

(i)   Selection

>   IF . . . ELSE . . .;
>   IF . . . ELSE IF . . . ELSE . . .;
>   SWITCH <expression> LABEL_CASE0 . . . LABEL_CASE1 . . .;

The logic for IF-THENs is similar to that of Ada, except that THEN is considered to be superfluous. SWITCH provides a structure similar to CASE but with one major difference. When statements corresponding to a particular switch label are executed, control doesn't pass from the switch construct (as would be expected). Instead it drops through to the next case condition. This is much less secure than the conventional CASE structure. An optional DEFAULT clause can be included to allow for no matching of the case labels.

(ii)   Repetition

>   WHILE <expression> . . .;
>   DO . . . WHILE <expression>;
>   FOR <expr1, expr2, expr3> . . .;

'Expression' is usually a logical relationship, but in fact can be any expression which has an integer value. The FOR loop allows the programmer to set various loop conditions, involving initial conditions, to specify loop continuation decisions ('CONTINUE') and to perform different actions at the end of the loop. Immediate loop exiting is done using BREAK. These constructs are highly flexible, highly abusable and therefore inherently insecure. Consider the obscurity and complexity of the following:

>   for (X=10, Y=A+20; X<Y; X++, Y--) {. . . . . .}

(iii)   Unconditional transfer of control: GOTO, but only to a label within the same function.

Braces are used to set the boundaries of the statement blocks. These tend to be less readable than more conventional methods.

(c)   Modula-2/Pascal

(i)   Selection

    IF . . . THEN . . . END;
    IF . . . THEN . . . ELSE . . . END;
    IF . . . THEN . . . ELSIF . . . ELSIF . . . ELSE . . . END; (not Pascal).
    CASE . . . OF . . . Label1 . . . Label2 . . . ELSE . . . END;

The ELSE is optional in CASE, a potential weakness.

(ii)   Repetition

        FOR . . . DO . . . END;
        FOR . . . BY . . . DO . . . END; (not Pascal).
        REPEAT . . . UNTIL . . .;
        WHILE . . . DO . . . END;
        LOOP . . . END; (not Pascal).

(iii)   Unconditional transfer of control
The GOTO is available only in Pascal. The label to which control is transferred must have been declared and be in scope. In Modula-2, the only operations giving unconditional transfers are EXIT (from a loop) and RETURN (from a procedure).

Both Modula-2 and Ada are significantly superior to C in terms of readability and security, but less flexible.

8.13.6   Structure and scope

(a)   Ada
The basic program building blocks of Ada programs are subprograms (procedures and functions), packages and tasks. Procedures and functions are similar to those found in other high-level languages. Packages are used to group logically-related subprograms and data together, confining their scope to the individual package. Tasks are program units designed to support the implementation of concurrency of operation.

A package normally consists of two parts, the specification and the body. The body contains the implementation details, i.e. the program source code itself. The specification lists the items of the package which are made visible to other program units. Tasks, like packages, also consist of a specification and body. The specification part defines the interface of the task with other program units; the body contains task implementation details. Task synchronization and communication are provided by the rendezvous.

There are no global data areas, all communication between packages being explicitly controlled. Scoping rules for subprograms are similar to those given in section 8.5. Subprogram headings specify the mode of the formal parameters, these being input, output and input/output types. Functions are restricted to 'in' parameters only.

(b)   C

A C program may be formed using a collection of subunits called Functions. Whether this has the structure of a conventional function or a procedure can only be distinguished by its syntax. There is no reserved word 'procedure'. The function 'main' consists of a program block which may contain calls to any externally defined functions.

The scope of an identifier depends on how its storage class has been declared. External variables, declared at the top of the MAIN source file, are global. Variables declared within a function have local scope and may not be accessed by any other function. These, defined to be of class AUTO, are dynamic. That is, their values are not kept between function calls. If values **are** required to be maintained then such variables may be declared as STATIC. But, in all this, scoping rules may be easily overcome through misuse of pointers.

Program blocks (i.e. compound statements) may be nested in a conventional block-structured manner.

(c)   Modula-2/Pascal

Standard Pascal is structured as a single compilation unit whereas most embedded implementations allow for separate compilation. Thus there isn't a simple base for comparison; each implementation must be assessed on its own merits.

The major building blocks of Modula-2 are modules, these being Program, Library and Local types. Each program consists of one program module, a number of library modules and usually a few local modules. Each library module consists of two separate parts, a DEFINITION and an IMPLEMENTATION section. The implementation part consists of the source code, the definition part acting as the interface between this and other modules. It lists program items within the implementation module which may be accessed by these modules.

This modular structure separates **what** a program does from **how** it does it. The interfaces are highly secure in that explicit actions must be made to breach them, so avoiding accidental side effects.

Within modules, the standard building blocks are procedures and functions. Variables declared within these have local scope and are dynamic. Static variables are those declared at the top of the module, their scope being that of the module itself. Global variables do not exist; all access must be explicitly made via a defined access mechanism (the IMPORT–EXPORT constructs).

8.13.7 Separate compilation and enforcement of type consistency

(a)   Ada

The compilation units of Ada are:

- Subprograms – specification.
- Subprograms – body.
- Package – specification.
- Package – body.

It is the function of the compiler to resolve names and check for type correctness and compatibility between separately compiled units.

(b) C

A single C program may consist of a number of source files, these being separately compilable. Also, precompiled routines may be loaded from libraries. Name resolution is done by the linker but type checking is omitted unless the LINT program (or a variant) is used.

(c) Modula-2/Pascal

For the reasons given earlier Pascal implementations should be assessed individually.

In Modula-2 the compilation units are:

- Program modules.
- Definition modules.
- Implementation modules.

Local modules are used within program and implementation modules but they are not compilation units in their own right.

It is the function of the compiler to resolve names and check for type correctness and compatibility between separately compiled units.

8.13.8 Exception handling

(a) Ada

Ada is extremely powerful because it specifically provides a mechanism to respond to exceptions. This 'exception handler' operates in conjunction with both standard and user-defined error conditions. When exceptions are user-defined, an explicit statement ('raise') is required to invoke the exception handler. This mechanism can be augmented by the use of 'GOTO', 'RETURN' and 'EXIT' statements. Return is used to force a premature return from a function or procedure: exit to get out of a loop.

(b) C

Exception handling in C must be implemented by the programmer using one or more of the following constructs:

- GOTO.
- RETURN (from a Function).
- BREAK (from a loop).

- CONTINUE (skip rest of loop, do next iteration).

No run-time checks have to be built into the compiler.

(c) Modula-2/Pascal
In Pascal the GOTO statement can be used. There is no GOTO in Modula-2, although EXIT (from a loop) and RETURN (from a procedure) can be used. Run-time checks are usually performed on specific error conditions such as stack overflow, array bound violations, etc. These tend to be implementation-dependent; exception handling features are, as yet, unresolved within the standard language definition. In practice, though, implementing user-defined exceptions is straightforward. It is done by writing the exception handler as an unparameterized procedure (type PROC), and invoking it when required.

8.13.9 High-level access to absolute addresses

(a) Ada
Ada contains an implementation-dependent package, SYSTEM. This contains a type ADDRESS which may be used to specify the absolute addresses of:

- The location of a program variable.
- The start point of a subprogram, package or task body.
- A hardware interrupt vector.

Although the details of SYSTEM are implementation-dependent, its structure and content are defined by the language reference manual.

(b) C
All such features are totally implementation-dependent.

(c) Modula-2/Pascal
There aren't facilities in standard Pascal to access absolute addresses. Modula-2, like Ada, uses an implementation SYSTEM module to handle absolute addressing. Interrupt operations can be written entirely by the programmer or implemented using the standard procedure IOTRANSFER. This is located within the SYSTEM module.

8.13.10 Assembly language and machine code interfacing

(a) Ada
Assembly language and machine code interfacing may be done in Ada only by using a subprogram. Such subprograms must contain only low-level statements; no Ada language statements are allowed. Each instruction is structured as a record type, located in the predefined package MACHINE_CODE. It is not a language requirement that implementations have to provide this package.

(b) C

Assembler routines may be written in separate external routines, communicating with the C program via function entry and return parameters. Macros may be written in assembler but care must be taken to avoid overwriting problems when using this feature.

(c) Modula-2/Pascal

Neither language contains features for handling assembly language or machine code inserts. This, in reality, isn't a major drawback as all implementations which generate ROMable code provide it as an extension. But until such facilities are defined within the language, they remain a serious omission.

8.13.11   Bit manipulation

(a) Ada

By using an enumerated type it is possible to represent the bit pattern of individual words. Also, arrays of Boolean elements can be formed, each element corresponding to a bit within a word. The standard logical operators can be applied to such constructs.

(b) C

C has a useful variety of bitwise functions, allowing AND, OR, XOR, NOT and SHIFT operations to be performed on variables. Both left and right shift can be carried out.

(c) Modula-2/Pascal

The set structure of Pascal and Modula-2 can be used for bit-handling operations. From this, different set sizes can be made to hold byte (8 bit), word (16 bit) and double-word (32 bit) values. Note that set size may be implementation-dependent.

Modula-2 contains the construct BITSET, this being defined as a set of enumerated cardinal values. The standard set operators can be applied, making bit handling a fairly straightforward task except for bit shifting.

8.13.12   Concurrency

(a) Ada

Support for concurrent processing in Ada is provided by the TASK structure. Each task consists of declarations and a set of instructions; it is executed concurrently with all other program tasks. Task synchronization and communication is effected by the RENDEZVOUS mechanism. Experience in embedded systems indicates that the rendezvous is less powerful and flexible than its proponents claim it to be. Note it supports synchronized communication only.

(b) C

C itself doesn't contain explicit concurrent constructs but should present no problems for such designs. After all, it was used in the first place to write the UNIX operating system.

A variant, Concurrent C, is now available.

(c) Modula-2/Pascal

Standard Pascal doesn't support concurrency, although an extended implementation, Concurrent Pascal, has been produced.

Modula-2 was designed to support the writing of concurrent programs, essentially on uniprocessor systems. The basic building block is the co-routine, this being implemented as a process (or task). Each concurrent task is written as a process – a parameterless procedure – having its own code and data area. Simple concurrency can be attained using the TRANSFER mechanism; for more sophisticated systems the programmer needs to devise synchronization, communication and mutual exclusion features. These can be readily achieved using standard program constructs.

8.13.13   Efficiency and code size

This is so compiler-dependent that generalizations can't easily be made. Given in Table 8.5 are the results of a number of evaluations carried out; readers may draw their own conclusions.

Table 8.5 Performance of high-level languages

Compiler	Sieve program – link/execution on an IBM PC-AT, MS-DOS 3.3	
Stoney Brook Modula 2 .... 4.0 seconds	(V1.06)
Logitech Modula 2 .... 12.5	(V3.03
Turbo C 4.1	(V1.0)
Microsoft Fortran77 .... 9.8	(V3.4)
Turbo Pascal 3.4	(V4.0)
Alsys Ada 46.1	

Source: IEEE, *Software*, November 1988

8.14 ASSEMBLY LANGUAGE PROGRAMMING

For professional programming, assembly language working should be avoided wherever possible. Justification for this is given both explicitly and implicitly in many parts of this book, embracing topics such as:

- Inherent insecurity of the basic coding method.
- Lack of scoping control.
- Extremely weak data typing.

- Limited (or non-existent) flow control mechanisms.
- Difficulty in understanding program intent (readability factor).
- Non-portability of source code to other processors.
- Difficulty in maintaining the software.

But, having said that, there are still occasions when it must or should be used. The reasons include:

- Lack of a high-level language.
- Hardware testing.
- Interrupt handling.
- Peripheral and subsystem interfacing.
- Speed of program execution.
- Program (code) and data size.

(a)   HLL availability

When manufacturers release new processors they're always accompanied by an assembler package. Sometimes the manufacturer's own HLL version for the processor (e.g. PL/M) is made available at the same time. It is rare for the release to include a high-level language, although C compilers usually follow on fairly quickly (in some ways C may be regarded as a very high-level general purpose assembly language). Therefore the software writer has little choice in the matter. Clearly this is significant in the Ada and Modula-2 worlds.

(b)   Hardware testing

Hardware testing, especially when faults are present, must be very precisely controlled. This can be done most easily, clearly and with confidence by using assembly language instructions. HLLs are totally inappropriate – the tester must have full control of the object test code (compiled code is a problem here).

(c)   Interrupt handling

Many HLLs don't give the programmer any means of interacting with interrupts. Yet interrupts are an integral part of most embedded designs (note that, where possible, interrupts are avoided in safety critical software). Therefore, in such cases, the programmer has little option but to resort to assembly language routines.

(d)   Peripheral and subsystem interfacing

There are occasions when interfacing to peripherals and subsystems can be difficult (or even impossible) from an HLL. For instance, it isn't unusual for 8-bit peripherals to be used in a 16-bit system. Here the HLL may not even recognize the existence of data objects smaller than 16 bits; device control has to be done using assembly language. In other cases devices are mapped in the input/output address space of the processor; yet the HLL may not support such operations.

(e) Program performance aspects

Execution times and program store requirements are parameters frequently mentioned in the context of embedded systems programming. Two particular areas deserve special attention: high technology (especially defence) and the mass consumer market.

In high-tech areas such as avionics, fighting vehicles and the like, speed and space have always been important. But now, with major improvements in EPROM and RAM packing densities, storage is rarely a problem. Speed of response, though, remains just as important as ever. In the consumer area low cost is a fundamental goal. This means that processor designs use minimum silicon, which means minimal storage. Speed of response isn't usually a major difficulty.

Maximum computer throughput combined with minimum store (both ROM and RAM) **can** be attained using assembly language programming. The operative word is 'can', as many factors affect the outcome. Three points need special note: programmer competence, design methods and compiler performance.

Programmer competence has a profound impact on the performance of the target system. There is a marked difference (in terms of speed and store) between programs produced by good designers and those developed by mediocrities. So, for fast and tight programs it isn't just enough to program in assembler; the right man must be used for the job. In contrast, when HLLs are used, programmer variability is small.

In many applications the space constraint comes about because only a small amount of RAM is available (ROM packing densities and costs are significantly better). And HLL programs usually use much more RAM space than their assembler counterparts.

It should be pointed out that space and speed penalties are not necessarily inherent in HLL working. Often these are caused by the program design methods, not the language itself. Where procedures are used extensively as program building blocks, heavy demands are placed on temporary data storage. The same is true when designs are implemented using tasking (concurrent) structures. Both methods also impose time constraints. Experience has shown that by minimizing procedure nesting, a speed improvement of between 2–3 can be attained (this is highly dependent on individual programs). The solutions to these problems lie in the hands of the programmer.

Probably the most important factor affecting target system performance – in terms of code size and execution speed – is the compiler. Different compilers, designed for the same HLL and target processor, produce quite different results; variations of 4:1 have been experienced. A good compiler, when used with a good optimizing suite, will come close to equalling the performance of the best assembly language programmers. Certainly the results will be better than those produced on average from assembler writing.

8.15   A CLOSING COMMENT

Since this chapter was first written one particular language – C ++ – has very rapidly become a 'hot' issue. Its increasing popularity is tied up with the equally rapid increase in the use of object-oriented design techniques. Another reason for its acceptance is its close relationship to C.

C++ originated in Bell labs, deigned by Bjarne Stroustrup. It first appeared as 'C with clauses' in 1980, followed by release E in 1984, with the first proper release (version V1.0) in 1985. The latest version, V2.0, was released in June 1989. This is now taken to be the language defining document for all new C++ compilers and development tools.

What induced Stroustrup to develop a new language? Mainly it was due to – in his opinion – deficiencies in C itself. It did not provide good support for modern design and programming methods, and some program organizational features were poor. But the decision to base C++ on C (and to make it compatible with the C language) was made for very practical reasons, as follows:

- C was already well established as a systems programming language;
- it was mature, with a large number of proven compilers available;
- many software development tools (e.g., editors, debuggers, etc.) had been developed for C;
- a large set of C libraries had been produced;
- within Bell Laboratories and AT&T (its parent company), C was widely used. Thus training staff to use the new language was not going to be a major problem.

Therefore the starting point for stroustrup was the existing C language. However his objectives were to make major improvements to it, in particular to provide:

- support for modern design and programming practices;
- well structured program organization;
- high portability;
- efficiency;
- strong type checking;
- simple interfacing to 'foreign' languages;
- support for object oriented programming features (e.g., classes, inheritance, constructors, etc.).

At the moment the language does not include exception handling methods nor support for concurrent programming.

The first implementations used a two-stage compilation process. First the C++ code was submitted to the 'Cfront compiler which generated C code. This output was then compiled using a standard C compiler. The new generation of C++ compilers are 'native', that is, there is no intermediate C code stage (even so, C can be regarded as a subset of C++).

There is no doubt that C++ will become a major force in certain programming areas. Already implementations are available which run on VAX minicomputers. Sun workstations and personal computers, under UNIX and DOS operating systems. What will enhance the acceptance of C++ is that standardisation work is already under way under the auspices of ANSI.

How relevant and effective is C++ in the programming of real-time systems? This is a difficult question to answer; what we have at the moment is a 'bandwagon' effect. This is not meant to detract from the language: far from it. But it is clear that many users are asking for C++ without really understanding why they actually want it. However, given the success of C, it seems highly likely that C++ will follow in its footsteps.

What is the future on the programming language scene? The most likely outcomes are that, outside the professional software engineering world, Basic and Fortran will thrive. C will dominate the microprocessor world. Modula-2 will replace Pascal. And Ada will eventually become the standard defence language. It is less clear what will happen to languages specifically aimed at distributed systems. The reasons are twofold. First, at the present time, these aren't in widespread use. Second, many consider it better to develop distributed language features from standard programming language constructs. For those who wish to follow this topic up see Bennett (1988).

It was pointed out at the start of this chapter that languages are an emotive issue. It would be naïve to believe that experienced users are likely to change their (probably prejudiced) views after reading this (almost certainly prejudiced) text. But let's hope that it has brought new light to the subject. And for those contemplating using a HLL for the first time, it may provide reasonable guidance.

REFERENCES

Barnes, J.G.P. (1976), *RTL/2: Design and Philosophy*, Heyden, London.

Bennett, S. (1988), *Real-time Computer Control*, Prentice-Hall, London, ISBN 0–13–762485–9.

Bowring, M.F.B. (1985), High-level languages for safety critical microprocessor systems, M.Sc. thesis, Loughborough University.

Dettmer, R. (1988), Go fast, go forth, *IEE Review*, **Vol.34**, No.11, December 1988, pp423–426.

Elbert, T.F. (1986), *Embedded Programming in ADA*, Van Nostrand Reinhold Company, New York, ISBN 0–422–22350–1.

Foulger, R.J. (1982), Programming embedded microprocessors, NCC Publications, Manchester, UK, ISBN 0–85012–336–4.

Hoare, C.A.R. (1980), The Emperor's old clothes, 1980 Turing Award lecture, *Communications of the ACM*, **24(2)**, pp75–83, February.

Kernighan, B.W. and Ritchie, D.M. (1988), *The C programming language*, second edition, Prentice-Hall.

Sale, A. (1987), *Modula-2, Discipline and Design*, Addison Wesley, New York, ISBN 0–201–12921–3.

Stroustrup, B. (1987), *The C++ Programming Language*, Addison-Wesley.

Taylor, D. and Morgan, L. (1980), *High-Level Languages for Microprocessor Projects*, NCC Publications, Manchester, ISBN 0–85012–233–3.

Wirth, N. (1980), Programming languages: what to demand and how to assess them, in *Software Engineering* (ed R.H. Perrot), Academic Press, New York.

Wirth, N. (1988), *Programming in Modula-2*, fourth corrected edition, Springer-Verlag, Berlin, ISBN 3–540–15078–1.

FURTHER READING

Attikiouzel, J. (1984), *Pascal for Electronic Engineers*, Van Nostrand Reinhold (UK), Wokingham, Berks, UK, ISBN 0–442–30597–4.

Baron, N.S. (1986), *Computer Languages*, Penguin Books, ISBN 0–14–022807–1.

Brodie, L. (1986), *Starting Forth*, 2nd edn, Prentice-Hall.

Buhr, R.J.A. (1984), *System Design With Ada*, Prentice-Hall, Inc, New Jersey, ISBN 0–13–881623–9.

Cooling, J.E. (1988), *Modula-2 for Microcomputer Systems*, Van Nostrand Reinhold (International), ISBN 0–278–00046–0.

Feuer, A.R. and Gehani, N.H. (eds. 1984), *Comparing and Assessing Programming Languages: Ada C Pascal*, Prentice-Hall.

McCracken, D.D. (1978), *A Guide to PL/M Programming for Microcomputer Applications*, Addison-Wesley Publishing Co., ISBN 0–201–04575–3.

Motorola (1979), *M6800 Resident MPL Language Reference Manual*, Motorola Inc.

Sandmayr, H. (1981), A comparison of languages: Coral, Pascal, Pearl, Ada and ESL, *Computers in Industry*, **Vol.2**, No.2, June 1981.

Webb, J.T. (1978), *CORAL66 Programming*, NCC Publications, Manchester, UK, ISBN 0–85012–193–0.

Chapter Nine

Operating systems for real-time applications

In the world of large computers, operating systems (OSs) have been with us for quite some time. In fact the elementary ones go back to the 1950s. Major steps were made in the 1960s, and by the mid 1970s their concepts, structures, functions and interfaces were well established.

The micro arrived about 1970. It would seem logical that operating systems would find rapid application in microprocessor-based installations. Yet by the mid 1980s few such implementations used what could be described as formally-designed OSs. True, CP/M was released in 1975, and was later put into silicon by Intel. But it made little impact on the real-time system field. There were two factors working here, one relating to machine limits, the other to the design culture surrounding the micro.

The early micros were quite limited in their computing capabilities, speed of operation and memory capacity. Trying to impose an operating system structure on this base wouldn't work. Another (major) factor was that microprocessor programmers generally didn't have the background or knowledge to implement an OS. During the last few years, however, there've been major strides in both areas. As a result, operating systems have now become an important topic in real-time applications.

The purpose of this chapter is to describe the basics of real-time OSs (RTOSs), setting out to show:

- What, in general terms, an RTOS does.
- Why we use real-time operating systems.
- How they work, in detailed terms.
- What the benefits and drawbacks are.

9.1 WHY USE AN OPERATING SYSTEM?

Embedded microcomputer systems have now been around for many years. The majority don't use operating systems as understood by, say, mainframe designers. Therefore it seems reasonable to conclude that we don't need these in embedded applications. True. But what isn't apparent (at first sight) are the profound effects produced by using operating systems. Specifically, OS support has a major impact on software dependability, productivity and maintainability.

Consider the small, relatively simple, real-time system of Fig.9.1. Here the requirement is to measure temperature using a sensing probe, digitize the sensor output and display the results on a portable meter. This is a straightforward and well-defined task. In such a case how would the software be designed? Most likely we'd see a 'single thread' program, that is, a single contiguous set of instructions running as a continuous loop. This doesn't, of course, preclude the use of subroutines or procedures. It would include both general (high-level) program operations and machine/device specific ones (low-level programming). There aren't any real timing constraints (provided results are produced fairly quickly), thus simplifying the program design. After all, if the program cycle time varies from run to run (say due to the use of conditional constructs), who cares? Therefore, this is a perfectly reasonable way of designing programs for small applications. But can it be improved?

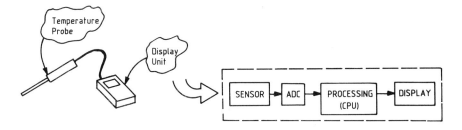

Fig.9.1 A simple processor-based real-time system

In the main, low-level operations are concerned with system hardware and related activities. Even if a high-level language is used, the programmer must have expert knowledge of the machine hardware and functioning. And that highlights one of the issues related to conventional programming of micros: the hardware/software expertise needed to achieve good designs. Even for this simple example the programmer needs a considerable degree of hardware **and** software skills.

Now examine a similar but more complex system, Fig.9.2, typical of many small-to-medium applications. Its primary function is to control the temperature in an engine jet pipe. This temperature is measured using the sensor, the resulting analogue signal is digitized, an error signal is calculated internally in the computer, and a correcting signal is output to the fuel valves via the DAC. The unit, however, is also required to perform several secondary tasks. First, the pilots need to have access to all system information via the keypad/display unit. Second, the flight recorder must be able to acquire the same information using a serial data link.

Given these requirements how do we go about writing the program? The simplest approach would be to use the single thread method. But, given the operational requirements above, such a solution is unlikely to be satisfactory. The problem stems from the inherent 'asynchronous parallelism' of the tasks. What this means is that we have a number of distinct tasks, which, in the real world:

- May have to be serviced at random (and not preset) times – the asynchronous aspect.
- May have to be processed simultaneously, i.e. in parallel.

These aspects are normally handled by using interrupt-driven programs. In such designs, each interrupt routine can be regarded as a separate task. All aspects of task handling (e.g. safety, security, timing, etc.) are thus the responsibility of the programmer.

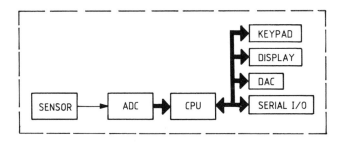

Fig.9.2 A more complex example

The central function of the operating system is to remove this burden from the code writer (all other OS features follow from this). It screens the complexities of the computer from the programmer, leaving him to concentrate on the job in hand. Detailed knowledge of interrupts, timers, analogue-to-digital converters, etc. are no longer needed. As a result, the computer can be treated as a 'virtual' machine, providing facilities for safe, correct, efficient and timely operation. In other words, it makes life easy (or, at least, easier).

9.2   BASIC FEATURES OF REAL-TIME OPERATING SYSTEMS

9.2.1   System requirements

Taking into account the factors discussed above, our hardware and operating system software must support:

- Task structuring of programs.
- Parallelism (concurrency) of operations.
- Use of system resources at predetermined times.
- Use of system resources at random times.
- Task implementation with minimal hardware knowledge.

- Task implementations as logically separate units (task abstraction).

These apply to all operating systems; but that doesn't mean that all OSs are designed in the same way or with the same objectives.

In all computer applications, two major benefits stem from using operating systems: reduced costs and increased reliability. Nevertheless, the way in which machines are used has a profound effect on the design philosophy of their OSs. For instance, a mainframe environment is quite volatile. The number, complexity and size of tasks handled at any one time are probably unknown (once it's been in service for a while, that is). In such cases a primary requirement is to increase throughput. On the other hand, in embedded applications, tasks are very clearly defined. The processor **must** be capable of handling the total computer loading within quite specific timescales (if it doesn't, the system is in real trouble). Therefore, although the OS must be efficient, we are more concerned with predictability of performance. Moreover, reliability of operation is paramount.

Now let's take a more detailed view of the problem. Consider Fig.9.3, which shows the processes to be executed by the jet pipe temperature (JPT) controller of Fig.9.2.

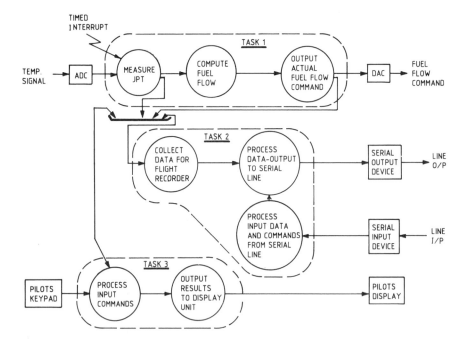

Fig.9.3 Simplified process structure diagram of Fig.9.2

There are three major tasks: JPT control, flight recorder interfacing and pilot interfacing. Each one **could** be run on a separate processor, i.e. multiprocessing.

In such a small system this would be extremely expensive, very complex and a massive technical overkill. Therefore one processor only is used. This, in fact, is the situation in most embedded systems.

It is impossible to have true concurrency in a single processor system; after all, only one task can run at any one time. Task executions are said to be 'quasi-concurrent'. In this text, single processor multitask designs are called 'multitasking' systems, to distinguish them from multiprocessing techniques (this definition isn't quite correct, but fits in with common use).

What we have then are three separate but interdependent tasks. This raises a number of interesting problems, the solutions being provided by the multitasking software of the operating system (Fig.9.4).

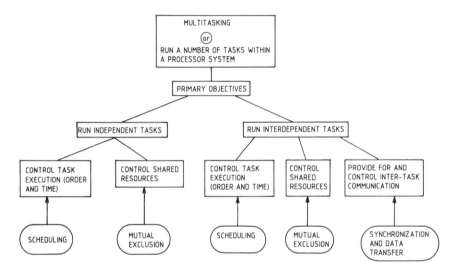

Fig.9.4 Objectives of multitasking software

First, we have to decide WHEN and WHY tasks should run – 'task scheduling'. Then we have to police the use of resources shared between tasks, to prevent damage or corruption to such resources – 'mutual exclusion'. Finally, as tasks (in this example) must be able to 'speak' to each other, communication facilities are needed – 'synchronization and data transfer'.

In a multitasking system it is possible to have tasks which are functionally independent. For instance, one can implement several separate control channels on a single board digital controller. These tasks proceed about their business without any need to communicate with each other. In fact, each task acts as if it has sole use of the computer. But that doesn't necessarily mean that each task has its own resources; there may still be a need to share system facilities. For instance, each control loop may have to report its status regularly to a remote computer over one common digital link. So we still have to include mutual exclusion features in such designs.

9.2.2   Executives, kernels and operating systems

We haven't yet said what an OS is. One starting point is the *Oxford Dictionary of Computing* definition as an OS being 'the set of software products that jointly controls the system resources and the processes using these resources on a computer'. Nevertheless, trying to define precisely what an OS is and how it is constructed is more difficult. Many have the same overall structure but differ, often considerably, in detail (Deitel, 1984). Embedded operating systems are smaller and simpler than mini/mainframe types. The structure shown in Fig.9.5 is typical of modern designs, formed from a relatively small software set. Note that it consists of a series of well-defined but distinct functions.

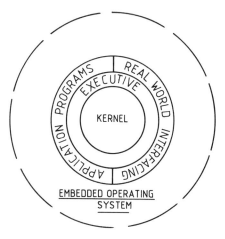

Fig.9.5 Overall operating system structure

First consider the middle ring, the 'executive'. This is where control functions are concentrated, the executive being the overall controller of all computer programs. User tasks (programs) interface with other system activities (including other tasks) via the executive. This is quite different from single thread designs where task actions are distributed throughout the program. Here each task is written separately, calling on system resources via the executive. The executive itself directly controls all scheduling, mutual exclusion, data transfer and synchronization activities. To do this it calls on detailed facilities provided by the inner ring, the kernel. In a sense, the executive behaves as the manager, the kernel as the executor. At this stage the detailed functions of the executive/kernel combination won't be spelt out; instead they'll be developed as we go along.

One part of the outer ring, labelled 'application programs', is self-explanatory. The other, 'real-world interfacing', consists of software which handles the hardware of the system. Such hardware, which varies from design to design, is driven by standard software routines. This typically includes programmable timers, configurable I/O ports, serial communication devices,

ADCs, DACs, keyboard controllers, and the like. Tasks do not directly access these; all operations are controlled by the executive.

In summary then, each task may be written as if **it** is the sole user of the system. The programmer appears to have complete access to, and control of, system resources. If communication with other tasks is required, this can be implemented using clear and simple methods. All system functions can be accessed using standard techniques (as developed for that system); no knowledge of hardware or low-level programming is needed. Finally, the programmer doesn't have to resort to defensive programming methods to ensure safe system operation.

How well we achieve these goals depends entirely on the design of the executive and kernel.

9.3 SCHEDULING — CONCEPTS

9.3.1 Introduction

This section deals with the underlying concepts of scheduling, using an analogy to a real-world non-computer task. Let's make one restriction; it applies to single CPU systems only.

The problem is a simple (perhaps unrealistic) one. Assume that a firm has only one truck (the CPU), but has a number of drivers (tasks or processes). Only one driver can use the truck at any one time. Further, each driver is specialized in one, and only one, task. In these circumstances, what is the 'best' way for the transport manager to organize his schedules (the 'scheduling' problem)?

9.3.2 Cyclic scheduling

One of the simplest solutions is that shown in Fig.9.6, the 'cyclic scheduler'. First, a queue of drivers is formed. The 'head of queue' is then given full use of the truck until he completes his job. It is then passed on to the next driver in the queue, who carries out his work, who then passes it on, and so on. All changeover activities are controlled by the scheduler/dispatcher (part of the executive); he does not, though, control task activities themselves. This method, described as first-in first-out (FIFO) scheduling, could be used to implement the measurement and display tasks of Fig.9.1. Certainly it would work where tasks are independent, as, for instance, running two control loops using a single control processor.

Notice that time plays no part in FIFO scheduling. Yet many tasks must be executed at predetermined and accurate time intervals. To achieve this we need to add a timing unit **and** another task: the 'idle' one (Fig.9.7). This acts as a buffer, absorbing any variations ('jitter') in task execution times.

If we use this simple scheduling scheme we're likely to meet some very real problems. First, consider what happens if a driver fails to return the truck (i.e.

a task gets stuck). In the basic cyclic scheduler the system instantly grinds to a halt. When timing control is used the situation is different, but just as serious. Here the dispatcher always retrieves the truck from a stuck task, thus restarting the cycle. Thus, each timed cycle begins correctly. But tasks only execute until the 'stuck' one is reached; following ones are never activated.

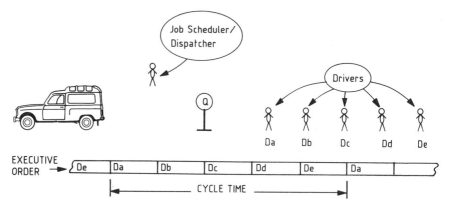

Fig.9.6 Cyclic scheduling

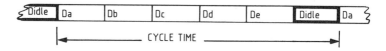

Fig.9.7 Timed cyclic scheduling

Second, system performance is affected mostly by long, not short, tasks. No matter how short tasks are, they still have to wait for their designated slot. Yet it might be that one short job could be done many times within the time slot of the long jobs. It might even be satisfactory to interleave the long job with multiple executions of the short one (Fig.9.8). This usually makes better use of system resources (i.e. the truck or CPU). Unfortunately, there isn't any way this can be done using FIFO scheduling.

| Da (Part 1) | Db | Da (Part 2) | Db | Da (Part 3) | Db |

Fig.9.8 Interleaving of jobs

Third, if a new driver (task) joins the system, he goes to the end of the queue. Accordingly, there could be a long delay before that job is carried out. In other words, the organization reacts slowly for requests to run new tasks.

These limitations are unacceptable for most systems, especially where fast responses are needed. One improvement is to set timing constraints on task execution, the 'time slicing' approach.

9.3.3   Time slicing

Here the scheduler/dispatcher is given a clock for the timing of jobs and the means to recall trucks (Fig.9.9). Tasks are still carried out on a first-in first-out basis. Now, though, each driver is allocated a fixed time for use of the truck, the 'time slice'. When time is up, the truck **must** be passed on to the next user (task), even if the current task hasn't finished. This task is resumed at its next allotted time slot, exactly from where it left off. It is then run for a preset period of time, put into suspension, and so on. Note: the basic unit of time is called the 'tick'.

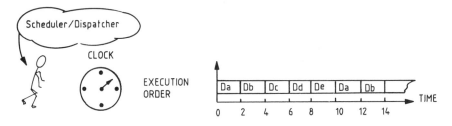

Fig.9.9 Time slicing of tasks

Such a process is called 'pre-emptive' scheduling. That is, the running task is replaced (pre-empted) by the next-to-run task. More generally, this applies whenever the resource (the CPU) can be taken away from the current user. Now this raises a problem not found in simple cyclic (non-pre-emptive) operations. With non-pre-emptive designs tasks run to completion. But in pre-emptive systems tasks don't necessarily finish in a single time slot; a number are needed. Stopping and restarting must be done without these being apparent to the user (i.e. 'transparent'). The only way to do this is to restart using precisely the conditions pertaining at shut-down. And, to achieve this, we must do two things. First, save all task information at the time of pre-emption. Second, restore this at the restart time.

So, whenever a task is pre-empted, two extra operations take place. Initially, current information is stored away for later retrieval, then information relating to the new task is retrieved from **its** store. This is called 'context switching', the related time being the 'context switch time'. Context switching is an important factor in real-time operations because it takes up processor time. Consequently it reduces the available computing time, becoming a system overhead.

This scheduling, where tasks are dispatched FIFO for preset time slots, is also called 'round-robin' scheduling. Its advantages are improved responsiveness and better use of shared resources. But in practice it needs to be modified because tasks:

- Vary in importance.
- Don't always run at regular intervals.
- May only run when specified conditions are met.

9.3.4   Task priorities

So far we have assumed that all tasks have equal status or priority. Hence the execution sequence is arbitrary, depending on how the system was set up in the first place. In reality a particular execution order may be required, and so tasks are allocated priorities (Fig.9.10). If this order remains fixed then we have a **static** priority scheme. If it can be changed during program execution then it is said to be **dynamic**. Priorities can be changed either by some external event or by a running task. Suppose, for instance, that during one run of task Db it changes the original priority order, setting De higher than Dd (Fig.9.11). This doesn't produce an immediate effect; its consequences can be seen later on in the execution time sequence. Such implementations are defined as 'pre-emptive round-robin scheduling algorithms'.

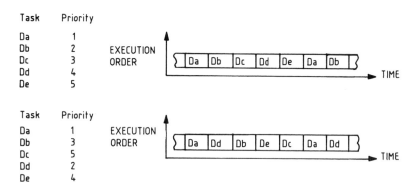

Fig.9.10 Setting task priorities

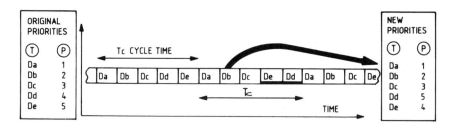

Fig.9.11 Dynamically changing priorities

The reason for using dynamic priority schemes is to improve flexibility and responsiveness. It is, however, more complex and also imposes a greater time overhead. Further, it has an inbuilt danger, that of blocking out tasks for long time periods. Observe that, when priorities are changed, the queue order is shuffled. And the task which next runs at the end of each time slice is that having the highest priority. Hence, if priorities continually change as programs run, low priority tasks **could** be blocked out. Not permanently, of course. They will eventually run at some time. But the responsiveness to such tasks may be pretty awful.

9.3.5   Using queues

So far only one queue has been used, consisting of all drivers, ready to perform their tasks when called upon. This we'll define to be the READY queue. In reality the situation is more complex because tasks aren't always ready to run. They may, for instance, have to wait until specific conditions are met **before** joining the ready queue. While 'not-ready' they are said to be in the BLOCKED or SUSPENDED state, and are held in the waiting queue (Fig.9.12). This is still a simplified situation because, in practice, it is necessary to use a number of suspended queues (Fig.9.13).

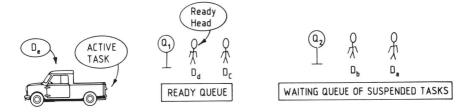

Fig.9.12 Ready and suspended task states

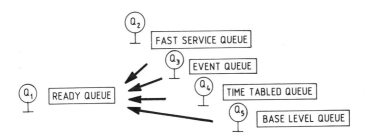

Fig.9.13 Types of queue

First there are task requests which must be serviced very quickly, a 'fast service' operation. An example of this in the JPT system (Fig.9.3) is the need to respond rapidly to incoming signals on the serial line.

Second, some tasks are suspended until specific events occur. Consider the keyboard handling task of the JPT system. This would normally be left blocked until a key is pressed (the 'event').

Next there are tasks which have to be run at regular, predetermined intervals, that is, timetabled jobs. Measuring the sensor input signal, for instance, is something which would be done in this way.

Finally, jobs which don't fall into any of these categories are done only when free time is available. These are defined to be 'base level' tasks. Updating the display could very well operate like this.

The state transitions which occur during task scheduling are given in Fig.9.14. This is self-explanatory. It can be seen that tasks are readied from the suspended state when particular conditions occur. These include the completion of some event, elapse of a specific time interval, or some combination of event and time.

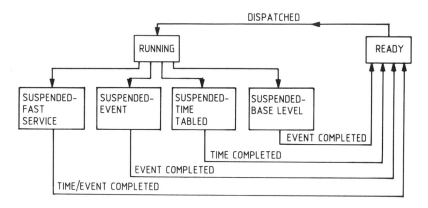

Fig.9.14 Task state transitions

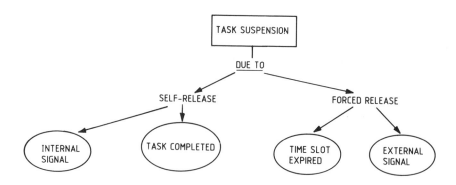

Fig.9.15 Reasons for task suspension

When a task goes into the suspended state it 'releases' the CPU for use by other tasks (Fig.9.15). Release is either self-induced or externally effected.

Self-release can be initiated by the running task itself, in two ways. First, it may have completed the required operation and so gives up the CPU. Second, it may relinquish control as a result of signals generated within its own program (internal events). Otherwise it must be forced to give up the resource (pre-empted).

When tasks are given priorities, operations become even more complex. A simple instance is given in Fig.9.16, showing how priorities determine task positions in both ready and suspended queues. It also shows how the ready queue changes as new tasks are readied.

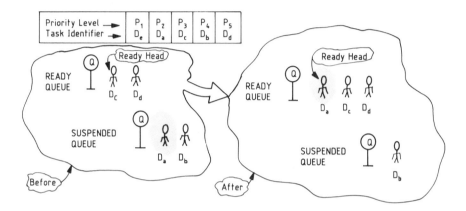

Fig.9.16 Effect of priorities on queue states

9.4   SCHEDULING — IMPLEMENTATION

9.4.1   Implementing queues — the task control block

The basic item used for constructing queues is a task description unit or 'task control block' (TCB). Information held in the TCB enables the executive to control all scheduling activities. Note, however, that TCBs carry task status and control information; they don't hold the program (task) code itself.

There isn't a unique design of TCB. Nevertheless, certain features have to be included, Fig.9.17. Within the TCB are a number of elements or 'fields'. These are used as follows:

- 1 – Identifies the task.
- 2 – Shows whether the task is ready to run or is suspended.
- 3 – Defines the priority of the task within the system.
- 4 – Gives the identifier of the task which follows (this applies to ready queues, suspended queues, and any other queues which may be implemented in the system).

1	Task Identifier
2	Status
3	Priority
4	NEXT TASK

Fig.9.17 Task control block structure

Queues ('lists') are formed by linking individual TCBs together using pointers. For instance, the ready list (Fig.9.18) consists of task X followed by Y, then A, finally terminating in the Idle task. The Idle task, usually needed in embedded work, shows that it is the end point by pointing to 'nil'.

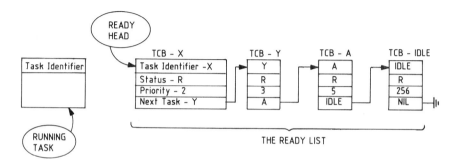

Fig.9.18 Ready list organization

Suspended lists can be formed in much the same way, Fig.9.19. The operating system may use one or more suspended list constructs; this depends entirely on individual designs. Task order within individual lists can be changed using one simple mechanism: the pointer construct. Reordering of tasks, moving tasks between lists, adding new tasks to the system – all can be achieved merely by altering pointer values.

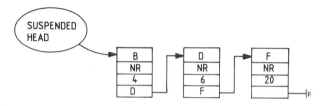

Fig.9.19 Suspended list organization

The task identifier field may be used to fulfil an extra role: a pointer to the so-called 'process descriptor' (PD). Dynamic information concerning the state of the process (task) is held in the PD, Fig.9.20. Each task has its own private PD and, in some designs, the descriptors may be located within the TCB itself.

One important point concerning the TCB and the PD is that both contain dynamic information. Thus they have to be located in RAM.

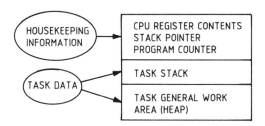

Fig.9.20 Process descriptor structure

9.4.2   The tick

The tick is an elapsed time counter, updated by interrupts from the system real-time clock (Fig.9.21). It is often implemented as a time-of-day (TOD) counter, supporting four major functions:

- Scheduling timing.
- Polling control (related to scheduling)
- Time delay generation (related to scheduling).
- Calendar time recording.

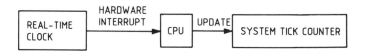

Fig.9.21 Updating the tick

(a)   Scheduling timing
Here the real-time clock sets the time slot for scheduling. It would normally be used to underpin a pre-emptive round-robin scheduling algorithm.

(b)   Polling control
Where tasks are event-driven, how is the processor made to respond to the event? One common solution, especially for time-critical events, is to use interrupts. But for many applications, interrupt-driven solutions aren't right; polling for status information is preferred. This solution could, for instance, be used with the keyboard handling task of the JPT system, Fig.9.2. Here the keyboard status is scanned ('polled') at regular intervals, set by the tick. If a

key is pressed the keyboard handler task is activated; otherwise it remains suspended. With this approach the executive never loses control of the system, which may happen when using interrupts.

(c)   Time delay generation
This feature is needed in most real-time systems, especially for process control work. Moreover, many applications use multiple time delays, with significant variations in the timing requirements. For instance, a combustion controller may wait for 250 milliseconds while checking flame conditions after generating an ignition command. On the other hand, a temperature controller may wait for one hour between turning a heater on and running the control loop. These diverse demands can be met, fairly painlessly, by using the tick.

(d)   Calendar time recording
In specific instances, system activation, control and status recording must be tied to the normal calendar clock. A count of hours, minutes and seconds – a 24-hour clock – can be implemented using the tick counter. The tick could also be used for months, days, etc. But remember, when processor power is switched off, everything stops (including the tick). Therefore, for embedded applications, it is better to use special battery-backed TOD clocks for long-term timing.

9.4.3   System responsiveness

How quickly does a task get service in a multitasking environment? Unfortunately there isn't a simple answer – it's interlinked with task priorities (Fig.9.22). High priority tasks of the 'fast service queue' type are only readied when service is required. But the reaction time ('interrupt latency') is small, typically in the range 25–100 microseconds. This assumes, though, that the task is allowed to run (a higher priority one may be executing at the time of interrupt).

When task execution is interlinked with the tick, some time variation or 'jitter' is experienced. This is small for the higher-priority jobs, getting larger as priorities reduce. Only tasks which can tolerate quite slow responses are implemented at the lowest (base) level. Further, the use of priorities may be abandoned down here. Instead, round-robin scheduling is likely to be used.

From what has been said, the tick period has a significant effect on system responsiveness. The issue isn't clear-cut, however, being interlinked with scheduling strategies. For real-time working it is a primary design requirement that **all** tasks be completed within an alloted time period. So CPU performance is the limiting factor here. In cases like this there seems little point in pre-empting important tasks, i.e. a task, once activated, should run to completion. This is a reasonable approach provided the current task has highest priority, any waiting (ready) tasks being of lower priority. But now suppose that a task is readied having a higher priority than the running one. In this instance a task swap takes place. The running task is returned to the head-of-queue position,

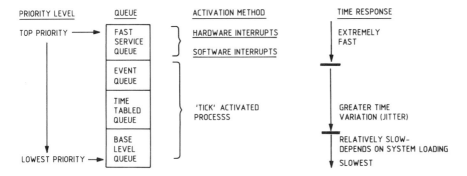

Fig.9.22 System responsiveness

its place being taken by the new task.

To support this strategy each task is given a specific priority; all tasks above the base level must have individual, different, priority settings. Base-level tasks may have the same priority level, being executed in round-robin fashion.

Assume that a currently executing task reaches completion. It then stops, indicating a 'not-ready' status; only at the next 'tick' does the executive regain control of the system. To minimize this 'wasted' time it makes sense to have a short tick period. Yet this may cause problems. The tick, remember, is updated on an interrupt from the real-time clock. This results in the current task being replaced by the tick handler (a 'context switch'). All current information must be saved before this handler is loaded up and set going. Which not only takes time, but contributes nothing to processing performance. So, as the tick period is reduced, the available task processing time also falls. Ultimately, for very high rates, tasks would never be executed; the processor would spend its time just servicing the tick (a ridiculous situation, of course).

Choosing the timing rate of the system isn't easy. It is determined both by response requirements **and** scheduling methods. For fast real-time applications it usually lies in the range 1–100 milliseconds.

9.4.4   By-passing the scheduler

Under most circumstances all tasking control is handled by the scheduler. For instance, when an interrupt occurs, the interrupt handler only readies the appropriate task; it doesn't activate it – that is the responsibility of the scheduler. So far, so good. But this could lead to an unacceptable delay between requesting service and getting it. And unfortunately there are situations where this cannot be tolerated, e.g. system exceptions. To cope with these we completely by-pass the operating system and go directly to a special interrupt handling routine. What this routine does depends on the system application, design and the exception condition which invoked it in the first place. But great care and thought needs to be put into its construction.

9.4.5   Code sharing and re-entrancy

The most widely-used building blocks of modern programs are the procedure (for high-level languages) and the subroutine (assembly language programming). These are invoked as and when required by running tasks. Now, in a multitasking system, each application process (task) is written separately and the object code loaded into separate sections of EPROM. As a result tasks may appear to be independent, but this isn't true. They are interlinked via their common program building blocks, the procedures or subroutines.

Consider the following scenario. A general procedure uses a specified set of RAM locations. It is invoked by task 1, which begins to manipulate data in the RAM locations. Task 1 is pre-empted by task 2, which then also calls the same procedure and operates on the same data locations. Some time later task 1 resumes, being totally unaware that the RAM data has been altered – and chaos ensues. To avoid this problem each task (process) is allocated its own private stack and workspace. All procedure parameters are normally kept on the stack, all local variables residing in the workspace. Now shared code can be used with safety because each task keeps its own data to itself. Such code is said to be 're-entrant'.

9.4.6   Scheduling strategy — a final comment

Many scheduling strategies have been devised and put into service (Deitel, 1984). But these have been designed mainly for commercial applications, being quite unsuited for real-time systems. The constraints and features of real-time applications are well covered by Allworth (1981) and Leigh (1988). Taking these into account, successful scheduling strategies follow a particular pattern (Fig.9.23). First, tasks above base level are set in priority order. Once such a task is set running it goes to completion unless pre-empted by a higher priority task. It is resumed at the first opportunity.

These tasks, when in possession of the CPU resource, can lose it to the executive in two ways. In the first case it voluntarily gives up the CPU because it no longer wants or needs it, 'self-release'. This arises, for instance, where a process cannot proceed any further until some event occurs. It also happens where the task is completed and the process has no further need for the CPU. The second reason for losing the CPU is a 'forced release' action. Usually this results from the readying of a higher priority task, forcing the current task to give up the processor on the next tick count.

Base-level tasks are normally run round-robin, at equal priority settings. Both self and forced release mechanisms are used as described above, together with a third forced release mode. Each task is forced to give up the CPU (even if it hasn't finished) when its allocated time slot expires.

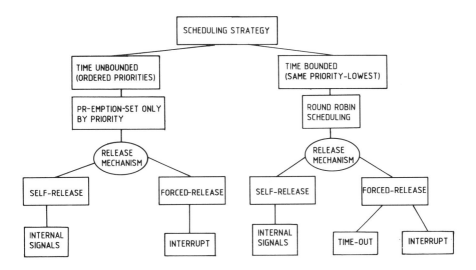

Fig.9.23 Embedded systems scheduling strategy

9.5   CONTROL OF SHARED RESOURCES —MUTUAL EXCLUSION

9.5.1   The problem of using shared resources

In a single CPU system the processor is a shared resource. Now there aren't contention problems when sharing it between the various processes; everything is controlled by the scheduler. But this isn't true for the rest of the system. Different tasks may well want to use the same hardware or store area – simultaneously. Without controlling access to these common resources, contention problems soon arise. Consider, for instance, what can happen in the following situation. Here a control algorithm is executed at regular intervals, interrupt-driven by a timer process (Fig.9.24). Part of the data used comes from the coefficient's data pool. The coefficient values are derived from engineering units input from a keyboard-display unit. Now, the problem here is a simple one. What would be the result if the control loop was activated while the coefficients were being updated? Up to eight bytes may be used for each coefficient; only one or two can be changed at a time. Therefore a value might only be part-updated when a task switch takes place. If this happened the results could well be disastrous.

How can we tackle this problem? In very general terms the solution is clear. Make sure that a shared resource can be accessed by one, and only one, process at any one time. That is, implement a 'mutual exclusion' strategy. The difficulties come, however, when we try to institute specific methods.

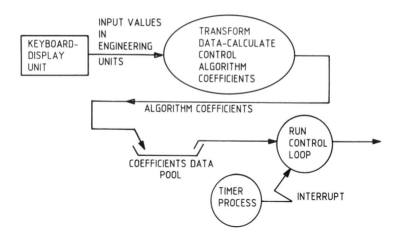

Fig.9.24 Shared data between processes

9.5.2   Flawed solutions to the mutual exclusion question

Flawed solutions are those which:

- Appear to work, but fail under certain circumstances.
- Are very restrictive in operation.
- Are highly inefficient or extremely difficult to implement.

Such offerings are not acceptable for real-time systems.

It may seem a negative (or even pointless) exercise to discuss techniques which aren't used. Not so. By understanding these methods and their drawbacks it is easier to appreciate what structures **do** work.

In the following sections the use of flags and control variables for mutual exclusion are covered. Concepts only are discussed; no programs are given. However, implementations in pseudo-code form can be seen in Deitel (1984) and Leigh (1988).

(a)   The single flag approach

Imagine that, to control access to a shared (or 'common') item, we put it in a special room (Fig.9.25). A gatehouse is provided for each task wishing to use the resource; this is its means of access. An indicator flag is used to show whether or not a task is in the room (in the 'critical area'). The flag can only be seen, raised or lowered from within a gatehouse (any gatehouse, in fact).

Assume initially that the critical area is empty, the flag being down. User 1, who wishes to use the resource, enters his gatehouse. He first checks the flag status. Finding it down, he knows that the resource is free for use. Now, as a separate, distinct, activity, he raises it, and then enters the critical area. At this point user 2 arrives on the scene, also wanting access to the shared item (Fig.9.26).

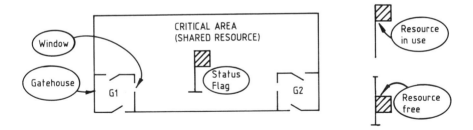

Fig.9.25 The single flag approach

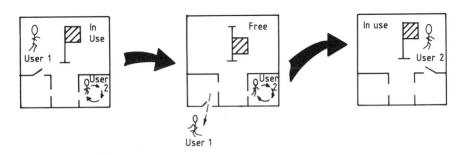

Fig.9.26 Mutual exclusion in action (single flag signal)

He enters his gatehouse and checks the flag. As it is up (resource in use), he waits here, constantly rechecking the flag status. Eventually user 1 leaves, his last job being to lower the flag, indicating 'resource available'. When user 2 next checks the resource status, he finds it free. Consequently he raises the flag and enters the critical area, now being its sole owner.

This all looks pretty good. Mutual exclusion has been successfully achieved using a fairly simple mechanism. Or has it? Consider the following scenario. The resource is free when user 1 enters gatehouse 1. He checks the flag. Finding it down, he turns to raise it. Just at this moment user 2 enters his gatehouse and checks the flag; he also finds it down. So, as far as he is concerned, his way is clear to enter the critical area. What he doesn't realize is that user 1 is also doing the same thing. Clash!

Here protection breaks down because there is a time lapse between user 1 checking the flag and then changing its status. In computing terms, for a single processor system, this is equivalent to:

(1)   Loading a variable into a processor register.
(2)   Checking its status.
(3)   If the variable says 'free' then change to 'not free' else, recheck.

During this sequence, user 1 (i.e task 1) could very well be pre-empted. If that happens **after** loading up the variable but **before** changing its status, then we may have problems (assuming the status is 'free'). Suppose that the pre-empting task is user 2. It checks the flag status, finds the resource free, and enters the critical area. When task 1 resumes, it also finds that the resource is free, enters the critical area – and so the mutual exclusion mechanism has failed. Failures are much more likely in multiprocessor systems as such designs have true task concurrency.

Note that gatehouses are analogous to the procedures of high-level languages. Critical areas represent the sections of code which provide access to the shared resource; these are contained within the procedures.

(b)   A safe, single flag mutual exclusion technique – the turn-flag

Let's see if a modified flag operation can achieve safe mutual exclusion. The flag, instead of showing resource free/in-use, now indicates which task can NEXT use the resource (Fig.9.27).

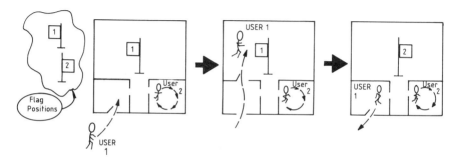

Fig.9.27 The turn-flag solution

It retains this number until the task designated by NEXT has finished with the resource. Only then is it changed. Consider the situation shown in Fig.9.27. Assume initially that the turn-flag shows '1', i.e. task 1 has been given the right to use the shared resource. Task 2 enters its gatehouse, finds the resource unavailable, and waits. Periodically it checks the turn-flag condition. At some later point, task 1, now wanting to use the resource, also enters its gatehouse. It sees the turn-flag set to '1', and therefore proceeds into the critical area. When it has finished it leaves this area, returning to the gatehouse. It then sets the turn-flag to '2', and leaves the area entirely. Task 2, on checking the flag status, finds that it is now authorized to use the shared resource. It therefore enters its critical area. If, by any chance, task 1 returns during this interval, it is blocked out as the turn-flag shows '2'. Ergo, mutual exclusion has been achieved.

Unfortunately there is a price to be paid for this. In the first place, tasks must go in strict alternate sequence (the 'lockstep synchronization' problem). This is usually inefficient, becoming a major problem as the number of tasks increases (like the cyclic scheduling problem). Second, each task may spend considerable time merely checking flag status. During this time no useful work is done, a very inefficient system. Finally, if a task halts within its critical section, it completely blocks access to the shared resource.

So the single flag solution is unacceptable on the grounds of security or efficiency. The inefficiency of the single turn-flag solution is due to use of a **single common** variable. Perhaps a two-variable (two-flag) solution will work?

(c)   The basic two-flag solution

In this approach, each user is given his own flag, located in the appropriate gatehouse. It is used to show access requests for the shared facility ('request to enter the critical area – flag up, no request – flag down'), Fig.9.28. Assume the critical area is free; both flags are down. User 1 enters his gatehouse and **first** raises his flag. He then checks the status of the user 2 flag. Finding this down, he enters the critical area and proceeds to use the resource. When finished he leaves via the gatehouse, lowering the flag as he goes. After this user 2 may access the critical area; alternatively, user 1 may return to re-use the resource.

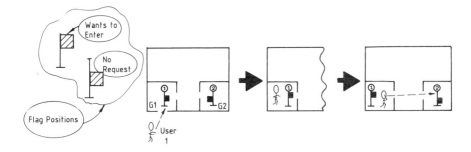

Fig.9.28 The basic two-flag solution

Assume now that, when user 1 is inside its critical area, user 2 wishes to access the shared resource. He first enters his gatehouse and raises his flag. Next he checks user 1 flag; and finds it up. User 2 now waits in the gatehouse, constantly rechecking user 1 flag status. When flag 1 is lowered he knows that it is safe to enter his critical area. User 1, should he return, will find flag 2 raised; therefore he will wait his turn.

This seems very straightforward. Unfortunately it has a subtle flaw, a problem of deadlock (Fig.9.29). Assume that user 1 enters his gatehouse and raises flag 1. Before he has time to check flag 2, user 2 enters **his** gatehouse and raises his flag. Both users check the flag conditions, find the resource unavailable, and go into a permanent wait condition. The system is now deadlocked and comes to a permanent halt.

One way out of this is to make each user periodically lower its flag, wait a short period of time, and then raise it again. This provides an 'access time window' for the other user, thus eliminating permanent deadlock. Flag checking is only carried out by an individual user while it has its own flag raised. It works as follows: suppose that both users are waiting (flags up) in their gatehouses. User 1 lowers its flag; user 2 happens to check during the same period. It sees that the resource is accessible, and so enters it. From this point on, operations are as described above.

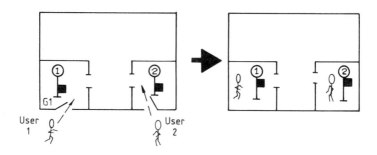

Fig.9.29 Deadlock in a two-flag system

Unfortunately, in solving one problem, we've introduced another one. Both users 1 and 2, while in their gatehouses, may operate at exactly the same speed, doing exactly the same things. Thus the lowering, raising and checking of flags are done in synchronism. Consequently, every time a flag check is carried out, both flags are up. Therefore neither user can get into the critical area!

This problem is called 'indefinite postponement', 'lockout' or 'starvation'. In practice it wouldn't continue forever; some timing jitter will always take the tasks out of step. What it **will** do is introduce an unpredictably long delay which, in critical real-time use, is not acceptable.

(d)   Deadlock and lockout avoidance – Dekkers algorithm

A solution to the deadlock and lockout problems is achieved by adding an extra flag to the system, the 'priority' flag (Fig.9.30). This is called 'Dekkers algorithm', in recognition of its designer. The priority flag is used **only** if there are simultaneous requests for access to the shared resource, its function being to resolve the contention issue. Otherwise operations are as described for the basic two-flag method.

Now examine what happens when both users make simultaneous requests using Dekker's algorithm. The two flags are raised at the same time (Fig.9.30a), each user then checking the status of the other request flag. Each user, on finding a raised flag, now checks the status of the priority flag (Fig.9.30b). Assume the priority flag shows '2', thus giving task 2 priority. Consequently user 2 enters the critical area while user 1 lowers his request flag (Fig.9.30c). User 1 then continually checks the status of the priority flag, waiting for it to change to '1'.

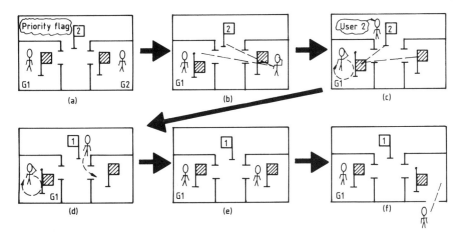

Fig.9.30 Deadlock and lockout avoidance using request and priority flags

When user 2 has finished with the resource he returns to his gatehouse, changing the priority flag setting on the way (Fig.9.30d). User 1, on the next check of the priority flag, finds it set to '1'. He first raises his flag, then checks the user 2 request flag status (Fig.9.30e). As it is still raised user 1 enters a wait–and-check state regarding flag 2. User 2 lowers his request flag (as described earlier) just before exiting the gatehouse (Fig.9.30f). Then, and only then, can user 1 enter the critical area. The contention problem has been eliminated.

Dekker's algorithm provides a safe and secure mutual exclusion mechanism. Unfortunately the method becomes unwieldy as the number of tasks increases. Therefore it isn't usually used in such cases, especially for real-time systems. So, we still have to design a safe, secure and **efficient** mutual exclusion mechanism.

9.5.3   The semaphore

All flag methods considered so far fail for one reason. That is, while one user is testing a flag status, the other may come along and change it **without** the first user seeing this change. How can we prevent this happening? The solution, fairly clearly, is to make testing and setting of flags an indivisible operation.

This problem was tackled by Dijkstra (1965), who developed the concept of the 'semaphore'. This is defined to be a protected variable which can be accessed and altered only by clearly specified operations. There are two semaphore types, the 'binary' and the 'general' or 'counting' semaphore. Both work on the same principles.

(a)   The binary semaphore

The binary semaphore is used as a control mechanism within programs. As described here it functions as a mutual exclusion (contention elimination) device, one semaphore being allocated to each shared resource. It can also be used for other functions, as will be seen later.

The concept of the semaphore is shown in Fig.9.31. The shared resource is housed in a protected area, with access through a single entry point. Located at this point is an access control mechanism which behaves like an automatic barrier in a car park. Like the barrier, its purpose is to limit the number of users having access to the shared facility. With the binary semaphore only one user is allowed past the 'barrier' at any one time.

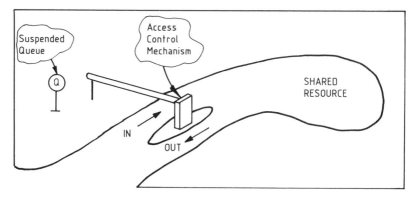

Fig.9.31 The binary semaphore concept

Assume initially that the resource is free. The first operation sets the control mechanism so that it holds the desired system status ('initialization'). When a user wants to use the resource he approaches the barrier, requesting service. In semaphore terminology this is defined to be a 'wait on the semaphore', the WAIT or P operation. As the resource is free the barrier is raised, and the user enters the critical area. On completion of the task he exits, signalling this to the access control mechanism as he goes by. This is defined to be the SIGNAL or V operation. Note that the P and V operations form a pair. Regrettably the basic mechanism **does not** enforce this pairing.

Examine the case where the resource is being used when an access request is made. In response to WAIT? the requesting task is made to wait; it is, in fact, suspended. Once the current user has finished with the resource he leaves the area, generating a SIGNAL as he goes. As a result the barrier control mechanism records that the resource is free. However, the situation is not the same as the previous one; remember there is a task in suspension. **This** should be the next user. And, in normal circumstances, it would be. But another task of higher priority could arrive just as the resource becomes free. This would then pre-empt the waiting (suspended) task, further delaying its execution. To prevent this, the exiting task performs an extra function; it reactivates any suspended tasks. Only when the suspended queue is empty is entry available to other tasks (Fig.9.32).

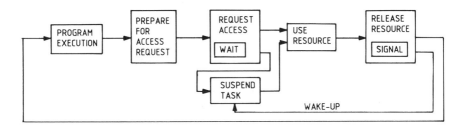

Fig.9.32 State transition diagram using the semaphore

As stated earlier, an individual semaphore is developed for each individual controlled resource. To identify the resource in question its name is given (conceptually) as a parameter of the semaphore operations. For instance, assuming the resource contains the set of control coefficients referred to earlier, we have:

- WAIT(coefficients)
- SIGNAL(coefficients)

A binary semaphore has two values only, '0' or '1'. A '0' shows that the resource is in use, the '1' indicating that it is free. In its original form, the semaphore operations are:

```
(* Part of Procedure 'WAIT' on semaphore 'Coefficients' *)
    IF (Coefficients=1) THEN
        Coefficients:=0;
    ELSE Suspend Task;
    END;

(* Part of Procedure 'SIGNAL' on semaphore 'Coefficients' *)
    IF (TaskWaiting) THEN
        WakeupTask;
    ELSE Coefficients:=1;
    END;
```

Within a program these would be used as and when needed, as follows:

```
        BEGIN
            ProgramStatements;
            WAIT (Coefficients);
            UseSharedResource;
            SIGNAL (Coefficients);
            ProgramStatements;
        END.
```

WAIT and SIGNAL operations are defined to be 'primitive' types, i.e. each one is indivisible. In other words, once the WAIT (SIGNAL) process is started, the sequence of machine instructions cannot be interrupted. This is essential, otherwise we'll just end up with the problems of the single flag exclusion mechanism. Providing indivisibility isn't an easy task; it may pose real implementation difficulties. But they **have** to be overcome for the semaphore to work. Further, these operations must be protected by the operating system, not the programmer.

In practice the binary semaphore can be implemented as a single byte or even a bit within a byte. Some processors support this construct by having a single 'set-and-test bit' instruction. Without this, indivisible ('atomic') operation is attained typically by disabling interrupts before carrying out semaphore actions. In multiprocessor systems this isn't sufficient; a hardware lockout mechanism is needed.

Note in passing that the symbols P and V were devised by Dijkstra, being derived from the Dutch 'Passeren' (to pass) and 'Vrygeven' (to release).

(b)   The general or counting semaphore
Suppose that our single shared resource is restructured so that it now consists of a number of items. Each item is identical, providing a specific service. For instance, it could be a set of data stores, used to store objects for later collection by other users. Given this arrangement it is safe to let more than one user into the controlled area: provided they don't access the **same** store. To support this the semaphore construct is altered so that:

- It has a range of values (say 0 to 5); initially it is set to the maximum value (5).
- Each value corresponds to a specific instance of the provided resource, zero indicating all devices in use.
- When a user wants to access the store it first checks that the resource is available (not a zero value). If access is granted it decrements the semaphore value by 1 (one), and proceeds to use the resource facilities.
- When the user has finished, he increments the semaphore value by 1 and exits the monitor.

```
(* Part of Procedure 'WAIT on semaphore Printer' *)
IF (Printer)>0) THEN
    Printer:= (Printer−1);
ELSE SuspendTask;
END;
```

```
(* Part of Procedure 'SIGNAL on semaphore Printer' *)
IF (TaskWaiting) THEN
    WakeupTask;
ELSE Printer:=(Printer+1);
END;
```

The value of 'Printer' controls access to the resource and defines the item which can be used; it's never allowed to go negative.

9.5.4   The monitor

The binary semaphore has been widely used to enforce mutual exclusion policies. It is easy to understand, simple to use and straightforward to implement. Fine. But it has one particular weakness, more to do with its use rather than its construction. Most programs which use semaphores implement them as and when they are needed. Consequently they tend to be scattered around the code, often proving to be difficult to find. In a small design this isn't too much of a problem, but the same can't be said of large ones. As a result, the designer **must** keep track of all mutual exclusion activities. Later on, in the maintenance phase, scattered mutual exclusion constructs can make life very difficult indeed. In such circumstances, 'simple' program modifications can produce some very strange side effects.

What we want then is a replacement for the binary semaphore which, in program terms:

- Is highly visible.
- Is easy to use.
- Is difficult to misuse.
- Simplifies the task of proving the correctness of a program.

The most important and widely-used construct meeting these criteria is the **monitor**. This owes its origins to Dijkstra (1971), then Brinch Hansen (1972), the final definitive paper coming from Hoare (1974). Fundamentally it functions as a system policeman, keeping order in the use of shared resources. Contact between program processes and shared resources isn't done directly; instead it goes through the monitor. This, as we'll see, allows us to meet the criteria laid out above.

Let's start by looking at the concepts and implementation of the monitor, using a very simple analogy. The essential elements of the construct are shown in Fig.9.33. First we have the resource which is to be shared out. This can be used only by the holder of the resource 'door key'; the key itself is managed by the monitor. By having one key, only one user can access the resource at any one time. This, fundamentally, is how mutual exclusion is imposed. Requests to use the resource are made to the monitor; no direct approach can be made to the resource itself. The function of the queue will become clear later.

A change of situation: the resource is free (depicted by 'key in', Fig.9.34) and a process wishes to use it. The user requests access to the resource from the monitor; this responds by giving him the resource key. He now enters the resource, knowing there will be no interference from other users (it can be seen that the resource is busy because the key is out). When the user finishes he returns the key to the monitor – who hangs it up – and then vacates the area.

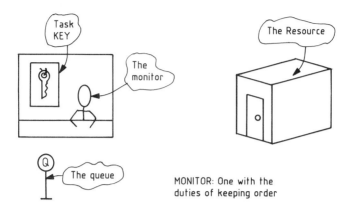

Fig.9.33 Essential elements of the monitor

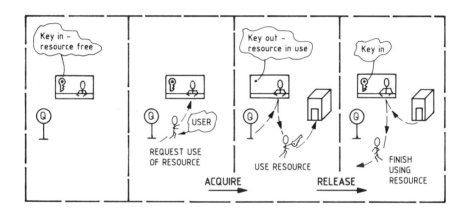

Fig.9.34 Resource access via the monitor

Now visualize the case where a requester (user 2) arrives when user 1 is using the resource (Fig.9.35). The monitor checks the key status. Finding it out, he instructs user 2 to WAIT at the queue sign (this is called the 'external' queue). No further action occurs until user 1 returns the key, releasing the resource. With the key 'in', the monitor SIGNALs user 2 to take it and enter the resource. Thus user 2 gains the key, knowing that the monitor will handle resource contention problems. Any further requesters arriving during this period are lined up in the external queue, generally being serviced on a first-in first-out basis.

So far, so good. What we've described are the basics of the monitor, incorporating a single resource. But practical systems contain more than just one shared item. In such cases separate monitors **could** be provided for each distinct facility. But this would only be mimicking the semaphore, with its attendant disadvantages. Instead, a single monitor controls all shared facilities. Alternatively, one monitor is allocated to each logically-related group of functions. Access to the resource bank is made through the appropriate monitor (Fig.9.36), so ensuring visibility and security of operation. Now this raises an interesting point. Suppose a user goes into the controlled area but then finds that the resource isn't available. What should he do? If he waits for it to come free he blocks all other users during the waiting period. This clearly is inefficient, though in some applications it may be acceptable. Hoare's solution is to have a set of queues in the controlled area (loosely, 'inside the monitor'), one for each individual resource. These are called 'condition' queues (Fig.9.36). It also turns out that another queue is needed inside the resource area, the 'priority' queue, PQ (Fig.9.37).

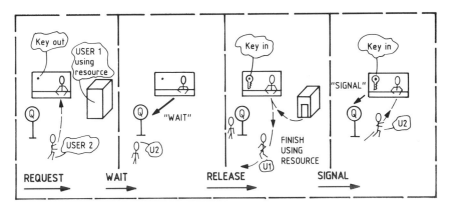

Fig.9.35 Access request – resource in use

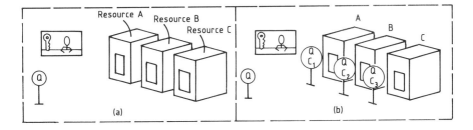

Fig.9.36 Multiple resources and condition queues

How does all this work? Suppose, for instance, user 1 gets the key and accesses resource A, Fig.9.38. He then finds that, for some reason, the resource cannot be used. To free the system he first returns the key and then joins the appropriate condition queue. Now, as the key is 'in', any other user may be granted access to the controlled resource area. A number of outcomes are possible, depending on the following conditions :

- No additional request.
- A new external request.
- Two users waiting on conditions.

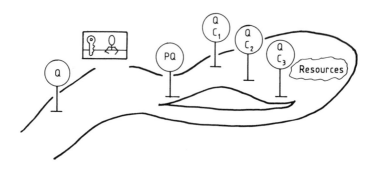

Fig.9.37 Condition and priority queues

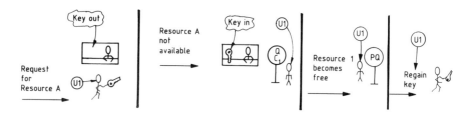

Fig.9.38 Use of condition and priority queues

(a) No additional request

Assume that no other user arrives begging service from the monitor. User 1 remains in his queue, continually checking the availability of resource A. When this becomes free he moves to the priority queue, at its head. From here he can request re-use of the resource from the monitor, which, as the key is in, the monitor will grant. User 1 then regains the key and carries on with its task.

(b) A new external request

Suppose a second user (user 2) arrives while 1 is waiting in his condition queue. This user wishes to enter resource B, not A. User 1 isn't active at this moment, so the monitor gives the key to 2, who now proceeds to use the resource. During this period, 1 continues to check the status of resource A. Once it becomes available, user 1 goes to the priority queue (as before). It then signals the monitor that it is ready to resume its task. However, as the key is out, the monitor merely notes the signal; no action is carried out. What does result, though, is a change in the consequential behaviour of the system. When user 2 vacates the controlled area the monitor doesn't check the external queue;

it gives the key directly to user 1. That is, the internal queue is given priority over the external one (hence its name). This arrangement guarantees that tasks waiting inside cannot be blocked out by the arrival of new requests.

(c) Two users waiting on conditions

It still isn't obvious why we need a priority queue. But consider what happens if two users end up waiting inside the monitor (in different condition queues, of course). Let's further suppose that both resources become free while a third user has the key. How is the monitor supposed to decide which of the waiting users should next receive the key? This question is resolved by the priority queue. Users move into the queue as resources becomes available; they are then served in the order in which they arrived.

Clearly the monitor is more complex than the semaphore. In practice it would normally be implemented using a number of procedures, as follows:

```
PROCEDURE InitializeMonitor(VAR SharedResource :Monitor);
(* This allocates memory for the monitor *)
PROCEDURE InitializeMonitorSignal (VAR Condition :MonitorSignal);
(* This initializes a monitor signal *)
PROCEDURE GainControl(VAR SharedResource :Monitor);
(* This allows a task to gain control of the monitor *)
PROCEDURE ReleaseControl(VAR SharedResource :Monitor);
(* This defines that a task has finished with the shared resource *)
PROCEDURE WaitInMonitor (VAR SharedResource :Monitor;
                         VAR Condition :MonitorSignal);
(* This controls operation of the condition and priority queues *)
```

9.5.5   Mutual exclusion —a comment on practical solutions

The primary purpose of mutual exclusion mechanisms is to control access to shared resources; including both hardware and software (data areas), Fig.9.39.

Many solutions to resource contention have been proposed; few are used in practice. For small programs, or those with little parallelism, low-level direct methods are quite suitable. This also applies to designs which don't use formal operating systems (typical of most small embedded functions). In real-time systems, access control of hardware is usually done via the binary semaphore; the general semaphore is rarely used. There's nothing fundamental about this. It's just that, for the monitoring and control of external devices, the binary semaphore does the job quite well. Even so, semaphores have features which can make them unsafe in use, especially where:

- Programs are large.
- The software is structured as a number of co-operating parallel tasks.

In such instances the monitor should be used.

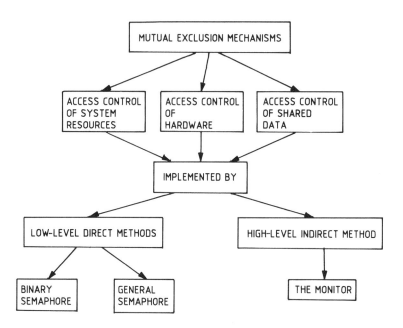

Fig.9.39 Practical mutual exclusion mechanisms

9.6   INTERTASK COMMUNICATION

9.6.1   Introduction

Where a design functions as a set of concurrent co-operating activities we need to support intertask communication, for three reasons. First, tasks may need to synchronize their activities. Consider, for instance, the JPT system of Fig.9.3. Here data might be sent to the serial output line **only** when a command is received from the serial input handling task. No data exchange takes place, merely event signalling.

Second, tasks may have to exchange data but without needing to synchronize operations. In the JPT example, crew information is controlled by a display output task, the data being obtained from other tasks. Now there is no reason why these should all work in synchronism. They can very well proceed as asynchronous functions, merely transferring data as required.

Third, tasks may have to exchange data, but at carefully synchronized times. For example, the output from the measurement task is also the input to the computation task – a data transfer requirement. But it is also important that the computation task acts only on the latest information. Thus it works in step with the measurement process – task synchronization.

Separate mechanisms have been developed for each of the three functions – summarized in Fig.9.40 – to provide safe and efficient operation. Their details are given in the following sections.

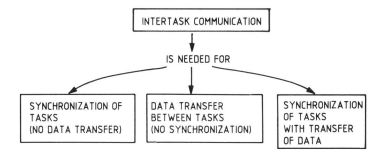

Fig.9.40 Intertask communication features

9.6.2   Task synchronization without data transfer

This generally arises where tasks are linked by events, not data. Such events include time-related factors such as time delays, elapsed time and calendar time. Synchronization is achieved by using signals, these being 'wait', 'send' and 'check' (Fig.9.41a). Signalling activities are the responsibility of the executive; to the user such operations (described below) are transparent.

First consider the 'send' action (Fig.9.41b). Here task A executes its program and reaches a point where it sends a signal (effectively to the executive). At that instant no tasks are waiting to receive this signal; consequently task A is suspended. Some time later task B generates a wait request for the signal sent by A. It (task B) picks up the signal and carries on executing. The wait request also restarts Task A.

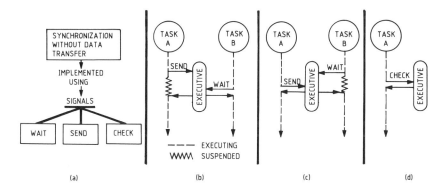

Fig.9.41 Task synchronization using signals

What happens if B generates the wait before A has sent the signal (Fig.9.41c)? The result is that task B is suspended until A sends the signal. Task A never suspends since it finds a task waiting for its signal. B resumes task execution on receipt of the signal.

In many instances a task may wish to invoke suspension as a conditional feature. That is, it maintains synchronization, but either suspends or continues depending on the signal check (Fig.9.41d). The check surveys the status of the signal but doesn't, in itself, halt task execution. Such decisions are taken by the checking task. Conditional checking can be used very effectively for polling operations.

In practice, signals are usually realized using procedures, as follows:

PROCEDURE Send (VAR SyncSignal :Signal);
(* Sends a signal. Suspends if no tasks are waiting for the signal *)
PROCEDURE Wait (VAR SyncSignal :Signal);
(* Waits for a signal. If the signal isn't present when the request is generated, the task suspends. Otherwise the sender is reactivated and the system rescheduled *)
PROCEDURE Check(VAR SyncSignal :Signal):BOOLEAN;
(* Checks to see if a task is waiting to send a signal. Returns TRUE if a signal is present *)

Two important points should be noted. First, there isn't a one-to-one link between senders and waiters; recipients aren't specified in these constructs. Second, signals look remarkably like binary semaphores, something which causes great confusion. In fact their implementations are very similar. The fundamental difference is in **how** they are used, **not** their construction. Semaphores are used as mutual exclusion mechanisms, signals for synchronization (note that you can bend semaphores to use them as signals; such practices are not recommended).

9.6.3   Data transfer without task synchronization

There are many occasions when asynchronous tasks exchange information, either randomly or periodically, without any need for synchronization. This can be supported by using a straightforward data store which incorporates mutual exclusion features. In practice, two data storage mechanisms are used, 'pools' and 'buffers' (Fig.9.42a), the buffer being constructed as a 'channel'.

(a)   Pools
Pools (Fig.9.42b) hold items which are common to a number of processes, such as coefficient values, system tables, alarm settings, etc. The notation used here shows tasks A and C depositing data into the pool, with B reading information out. This is not a destructive read-out, i.e. information within the pool is unchanged by the read action. The pools are usually composed of sections of read-write memory, i.e. RAM.

In a practical system it makes sense to use numerous pools, as and when desired. This restricts access to information, so avoiding problems related to using global data. Even so, it is still essential to control pool usage via a mutual exclusion mechanism like the monitor. Note that the monitor is used to support data transfer activities; it is not **itself** a communication mechanism.

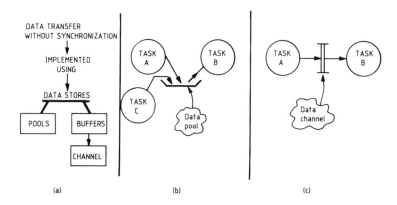

Fig.9.42 Data transfer mechanism – no synchronization

(b) Channels
Channels are used as communication pipes between processes, normally on a one-to-one basis (Fig.9.42c). Here, task A deposits information into the channel, task B extracting it in first-in first-out style. The channel is usually made large enough to carry a number of data words, not just a single data item. As such it acts as a buffer or temporary storage device, providing elasticity in the pipe. Its advantage is that insertion and extraction functions can proceed asynchronously (as long as the pipe doesn't fill up). It is implemented in RAM. The information passed between processes may be the data itself; in other cases it could be a pointer to the data. Pointers are normally used for handling large amounts of data where RAM store is limited.

Two techniques are used to implement channels, the queue and the circular buffer. Queue structures have been discussed under scheduling; no further description is needed. The main advantage of the queue concerns its size. This isn't fixed, but can be expanded or contracted as desired. Further, very large queues can be built, limited only by the available memory space. Yet for embedded systems these aren't particular benefits. First, if RAM is limited, it is impossible to construct large queues at all. Second, large queues organized as FIFO stores have a long transport delay from data-in to data-out. The resulting performance may be too slow for many real-time applications.

A circular buffer is normally assembled using a fixed amount of memory space (Fig.9.43a), being designed to hold multiple data units. Buffer size is defined at creation time, but is fixed thereafter. Under normal circumstances tasks A and B proceed asynchronously, inserting and removing data from the channel as required. Task suspension only occurs under two conditions, channel full and channel empty. Should the channel fill up **and** task A tries to load another data unit then A is suspended. Alternatively, if the channel empties and task B tries to remove a data unit, then B is suspended.

Fig.9.43 shows how the data is stored in a cyclic manner. The basic concept (Fig.9.43a) defines the physical and logical constructs of circular buffers. Fig.9.43b shows how pointers are used to identify the start and finish locations of the stored data ('FirstOut' and 'NextIn'). By using these we don't have to shift data through the buffer. Inserted data units always stay in the same memory locations; only the pointers change value – as explained in Figs.9.43c,d,e. These pointers can also be used to define the 'channel full' and 'channel empty' conditions – they become equal.

There is a conceptual difference between the pool and the channel. In the first, reading of data doesn't affect the contents. In the second, though, channel data is 'consumed' by a read operation.

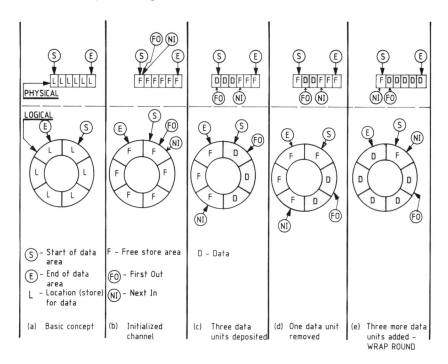

Fig.9.43 The circular buffer – cyclic storage for the channel

9.6.4   Task synchronization with data transfer

As shown earlier, situations arise where tasks not only wait for events, but also use data associated with those events. To support this we need both a synchronization mechanism **and** a data storage area. The structure used is the 'mailbox', this unit incorporating signals for synchronization and storage for data (Fig.9.44).

When a task wishes to send information to another one it 'posts' the data to the mailbox. Correspondingly, when a task looks for data in the mailbox, it 'pends' on it. In reality, post and pend are signals. Moreover, the data itself isn't normally passed through the mailbox; a data pointer is used. Even so, no matter how large the data contents are, the data is treated as a single unit. Thus, conceptually, we have a single-store item. Task synchronization is achieved by suspending or halting tasks until the required conditions are met (Fig.9.44c,d). Any task posting to a mailbox which hasn't got a pending task gets suspended. It resumes when the receiver pends for the information. Conversely, should pending take place first, the task suspends until the post operation occurs.

Frequently the mailbox is used as a many-to-many communication pipe. This is much less secure than a one-to-one structure, and may be undesirable in critical applications.

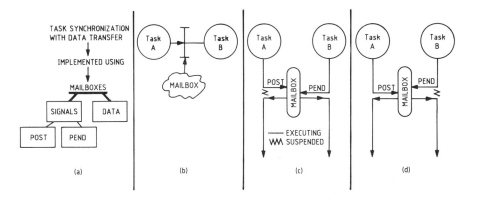

Fig.9.44 Data transfer with task synchronization

9.7 MEMORY MANAGEMENT

In diskless systems memory management forms only a small part of the operating system. Primarily it deals with allocation and deallocation of volatile store (RAM) for use by process descriptors. Its secondary use is to provide extra – temporary – RAM space as requested by tasks. For instance, consider a data monitoring system which measures system parameters, processes the information, and then outputs the results to a remote unit. This process may use a large amount of RAM store; yet it is needed only for a short period of time. It is wasteful to tie up permanently a resource which is used only intermittently. However, by releasing RAM store when required by the data acquisition task and then retrieving it later, the resource can be used more efficiently.

In disk-based systems tasks run from RAM-based primary store. The task programs themselves are held on disk (the backing store), being switched into primary store for execution. Therefore, when a task is switched in, its code may replace that of a task which has been switched out ('overlaying'). Switching control is handled by the executive. The executive also implements 'policing' functions to prevent tasks making accesses outside their allotted memory space. As the majority of embedded systems don't use disk storage this aspect is relatively unimportant. And even those that do include disks normally use them only for the storage of information, not programs.

These memory manipulations are truly dynamic in operation. By contrast, setting up the process descriptors is essentially a static function, even though they are located in RAM. The reasoning for this is that, generally, tasks are not deleted (killed-off) in embedded designs. Apart from initialization, all other tasks reside permanently once the processor is active. Thus the number and location of process descriptors stay fixed during this period.

Dynamic memory manipulation should be avoided wherever possible in real-time systems. It should **never** be used in critical applications.

9.8   STANDARD EXECUTIVES — SOFTWARE IN SILICON

A reliable, robust real-time executive is a complex device. Designing, developing and producing such software is both costly and lengthy. As a result, many designers of real-time systems choose to use off-the-shelf executives (or even full operating systems) for their applications. What makes these different from large operating systems is that they need to reside in PROM, i.e. software in silicon.

This raises some interesting problems. First, the executive code must be position independent. That is, it should work correctly no matter where it is placed in the memory of the processor system. Second, it must be configuration independent, i.e. no assumptions can be made about the RAM, ROM, I/O and device structuring in the target micro. Finally its design must be such that, when the executive itself is updated, no changes need to be made to the target. This is sometimes called 'stepping independence'. What **cannot** be achieved is processor independence because many executive operations directly control processor registers.

Position and configuration independence is attained by providing programmable interfaces between the executive and the rest of the system (Fig.9.45). Here the interfaces are the bootstrap monitor program and the system configuration table. Both are programmed by the user to define the set-up and configuration of the target.

The bootstrap program, activated on power-up, initializes and checks out the target system. It then sets up the interrupt vector table as required by the design. Following this it transfers control to the executive. From this point on, the executive oversees the complete system, interfacing to it via the configuration table. As shown here it uses interrupts to access the table.

The configuration table usually carries a combination of pointers – addresses of tasks, for instance – and system information, e.g. RAM size. Such information is target system dependent and therefore has to be provided by the user. It is usually located in EPROM (as is the bootstrap monitor program). The executive itself is normally supplied in a single ROM chip.

Listed below are some commercial executives typical of those used in embedded systems. Two approaches are used. First there are those specifically

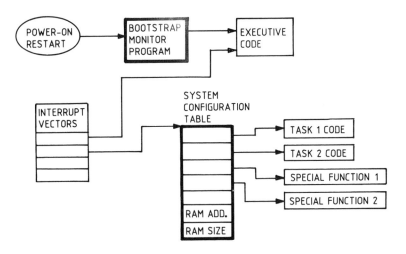

Fig.9.45 Typical system configuration using a silicon executive

produced for embedded applications. Then there are sub-sets of more general purpose operating systems, stripped down for embedded designs. Such sub-sets should be very carefully analysed before using them in a real-time environment. All real-time executives have one common feature, a small size, typically occupying about 5 Kbyte of ROM space. The upper limit is in the region of 10 Kbyte. Large systems such as the Intel iRMX 286 – requiring an absolute minimum of 30 Kbyte – have been excluded from this list.

PDOS
Eyring Research Institute, Inc.
 1450 West 820 North, Provo, Utah 84601, USA.

Professional OS-9
 Microware Systems Corporation
 186 N.W. 114th Street, Des Moines, IA 50322, USA.

REALTIME CRAFT
 GSI-TECSI
 6 Cours Michelet, 92064 Paris la Defense Cedex 52, France.

REX 186
 REX Systems
 18 Brooklyn Rd., London, UK.

RMOS 2
 Siemens AG
 Bereich Baülemente, Vertrieb, Produktinformation
 Balanstrasse 73, D-8000 Munchen 80, West Germany

Tripos
  Metacomco PLC
  26 Portland Square, Bristol, UK.

USX
  Creative Data Systems GmbH
  Bahnhofstrasse 103–8032 Grafelfing/Munchen, West Germany.

VRTX32 – Versatile Real-Time Executive
  Ready Systems
  P.O. Box 61029, Palo Alto, CA 94306–9991, USA.

VRTX32 has had extensive use in high technology applications, and is certified for use in aircraft systems.

VxWORKS
  Wind River Systems
  UK Distributor – GMT Electronic Systems,
  Unit 7, Mole Business Park, Leatherhead, Surrey, UK.

9.9   CLOSING COMMENTS

Two factors have profoundly influenced the use of operating systems in embedded application – processor performance and memory density. Without doubt the increase in memory density, both RAM and EPROM, has been the most significant. But recent processor designs make it much easier to design real-time executives due to built-in functions. These enhancements include single instruction 'test and set' operations and on-chip memory management functions.

Real-time operating systems are gradually being accepted as the norm, not the exception, in embedded applications. Whether one is designed in-house or bought-in, it should provide a set of operations (or 'primitives') relating to:

(a) **System set-up**
- Initialize the executive.
- Start execution of the application programs.

(b) **Task control**
- Declare a task.
- Start a task.
- Stop a task.
- Destroy a task.
- Set task priorities.
- Lock-out task (make it non-pre-emptive).
- Unlock a task.

- Delay a task.
- Resume a task.

(c) Mutual exclusion
- Gain control using semaphores (entry to critical region).
- Release control using semaphores (exit from critical region).
- Gain control using monitors.
- Release control using monitors.
- Wait in a monitor.

(d) Synchronization functions – no data transfer
- Initialize a signal.
- Send a signal.
- Wait for a signal.
- Check for a signal.

(e) Data transfer without synchronization
- Initialize a channel/pool.
- Send to a channel/write to a pool.
- Receive from a channel/read from a pool.

(f) Synchronization with data transfer
- Set up a mailbox.
- Post to a mailbox.
- Pend on a mailbox.
- Check on a mailbox.

(g) Dynamic memory allocation
- Allocate a block of memory.
- Deallocate a block of memory.

Some commercial systems augment the executive with I/O and file handlers. The I/O may be extremely useful in some circumstances, particularly when the application code is written in assembly language. However, the use of a modern high-level language such as Modula-2 obviates this need. The second item, the file handler, is only used in conjunction with disk systems. As the majority of embedded designs are diskless this is a less relevant topic. However, a full-blooded operating system **should** offer this function.

So far no mention has been made of Ada, which may seem surprising. The language, after all, was designed with operating systems features as an integral part of it. However, at the present time, it hasn't lived up to expectations for embedded applications. The code size tends to be large, complex and, in some cases, extremely slow. This perhaps explains why, at the moment, some embedded designers use Ada for their application code only. Operating system features are provided by a standard executive such as VRTX32.

REFERENCES

Allworth, S.T. (1981), *Introduction to Real-time Software Design*, Macmillan Press Ltd., London, ISBN 0–333–27137–8.

Brinch Hansen, P. (1972), Structured multiprogramming, *Communications of the ACM*, **Vol.15**, No.7, July, pp574–577.

Deitel, H.M. (1984), *An Introduction to Operating Systems*, Addison-Wesley Publishing Co., ISBN 0–201–14502.

Dijkstra, E.W. (1965), Cooperating sequential processes, Technological University, Eindhoven, Netherlands (reprinted in *Programming Languages*, ed F. Genuys, Academic Press, New York, 1968).

Dijkstra, E.W. (1971), Hierarchical ordering of sequential processes, *Acta Informatica*, **Vol.1**, pp115–138.

Hoare, C.A.R. (1974), Monitors: an operating system structuring concept, *Communications of the ACM*, **Vol.17**, No.10, October, pp549–557.

Leigh, A.W. (1988), *Real Time Software for Small Systems*, Sigma Press, Cheshire, UK, ISBN 0–905104–98–6.

Chapter Ten

Software analysis and design – methods, methodologies and tools

Finally we've arrived at a state where theory and ideas can be turned into practice. The starting point for this? When a customer arrives on our doorstep, asking us to develop a software system for his application. It finishes when the delivered software runs reliably, correctly and safely in the target system (cynics may argue that by this definition, most jobs are never finished). However, what concerns us here is the piece that fits between the two end states, the design and development phases. Just how do we go about this process? What methods should we use? What tools are available? How can we best use these tools? These, and others, are the questions tackled in the next two chapters.

There are two major steps in the development process. The first involves translating the customer's requirements into source code. The second concerns the transformation of this source code into fully functional target system object code. An ideal software development toolset supports both stages. Unfortunately, this is a rare item, particularly for the support of 'bare-board' original designs. Either tools are intended for front-end use, frequently assuming that the second stage is trivial. Or else they are aimed at the back end of the development, neglecting software design aspects entirely. Chapter 11 deals with development methods and tools designed for use in the second-stage processes. However, in this chapter we look at:

- What the overall specification-to-coding process involves.
- What it means to execute the various steps within this.
- How different techniques achieve the same ends in quite different ways.
- What the unifying themes are within the various techniques.
- What the important factors are when selecting toolsets.

Specifically, the methods of CORE, YSM, JSD, MASCOT and HOOD are described here.

10.1 THE DEVELOPMENT PROCESS

10.1.1 General description

In this chapter the complete development process is viewed as a series of distinct steps, consisting of:

- Requirements analysis.
- Requirements specification.
- Architectural design.
- Physical design.
- Implementation – to source code level.
- Test, integration and debug.

(a) Requirements analysis
Here the purpose is to establish precisely what the system is supposed to do. In small systems it tends to get merged with other parts of the development process; in large systems it is an essential, separate activity.

(b) Requirements specification
This describes what the software must do to meet the customer's requirements. It is based on information obtained during the analysis phase.

(c) Architectural design
This stage is concerned with identifying and modelling the software structure, using information supplied in the requirements specification. It defines the essential software components of the system, how these fit together and how they communicate.

(d) Physical design
Here the architectural structure arrived at in the previous stage is partitioned to fit onto hardware. In a small, simple system this is a trivial task. But, in multiprocessor designs, distributed systems, and designs using 'intelligent' interfacing devices, it is a critical activity.

(e) Implementation
Ultimately the software tasks are expressed as a set of sequential single-thread program structures. The function of the implementation stage is to take these design structures and translate them into source code.

(f) Test, integration and debug
The purpose here is to show that the finished code performs as specified. It involves testing of individual software modules, combined modules (subsystems) and finally the complete system. This topic is covered in chapters 11 and 12.

10.1.2 Methods, methodologies and tools

Method – a special form of procedure
Methodology – an orderly arrangement of ideas
Tool – thing used in an occupation or pursuit
(*Concise Oxford Dictionary*).

In this chapter the following software development and design techniques are described in some detail:

- Controlled Requirements Expression (CORE).
- Yourdon Structured Method (YSM).
- Jackson System Development (JSD).
- Modular Approach to Software Construction, Operation and Test (MASCOT).
- Hierarchical Object-Oriented Design (HOOD).

The purpose is to show what these can do, how they do it, and what the results are. Fig.10.1 shows the methods in question and how they fit into the overall development process. CORE is the only systems requirements **analysis** technique discussed here. It is claimed that YSM and JSD can be applied successfully to the requirements analysis phase. This is open to question. However, both YSM and JSD, together with MASCOT and HOOD, are widely used in the design and implementation phases. The methods used are very different; surprisingly their methodologies are quite similar.

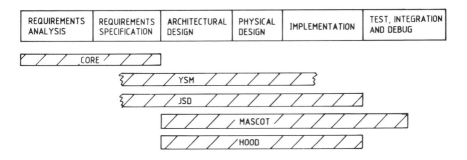

Fig.10.1 Software techniques – coverage of the development process

10.2 CONTROLLED REQUIREMENTS EXPRESSION — CORE

10.2.1 Introduction

CORE is both a method and a tool designed specifically for the requirements analysis phase of the software life cycle. It has been under development since 1979, both by British Aerospace plc and Systems Designers plc. Since then it has been widely applied to UK and European avionics projects and in UK defence systems. The reasons for describing it are threefold. It:

- Is a requirements analysis tool only (thus avoiding confusion with multi-purpose tool implementations).
- Has been applied extensively to the analysis of real-time systems.
- Is a proven practical method.

As a 'front-end' method its role is to:

- Establish the **actual** problem to be solved (as opposed to perceived variations on this).
- Eliminate ambiguities and inconsistencies in the customer's requirements.
- Increase knowledge and understanding of the problem.
- Highlight effects produced by changing system specifications.
- Formalize system specifications so that they are understood and agreed by all involved in the project.

But, most importantly, it does not define **how** to solve requirements problems; it attempts to describe **what** has to be solved. In practice it includes, within the functional requirements, design decisions applicable to lower levels of the system. This usually occurs when dealing with very large real-time projects.

10.2.2 Design fundamentals

CORE is a prescriptive method, consisting of a set of defined steps, for the development of systems requirements models. Information is produced in both text and graphical form, being held in a single data base. This 'single-source' approach ensures documentation consistency, both in the initial analysis phase and, later, when modifications are made.

Central to CORE is the concept of 'viewpoints'. Put simply, they describe the nature and content of the problem as seen from particular points of view. This includes both people and 'things'. Each viewpoint looks at the problem in terms of:

- Information acquired.
- Processing of this information ('actions').
- Generation of output results.

An overview of the CORE analysis method is shown in Fig.10.2.

First the analyst collects information and, using this, builds a descriptive model based on the different viewpoints. He then combines the information, picking out loose ends, inconsistencies and conflicts (or, in some cases, unrealistic objectives). This information describes the behaviour of the system (or so we hope); it can then be used as the requirements document for the systems, hardware and software design teams.

Fig.10.2 is self-explanatory except for 'thread' diagrams; they are described later.

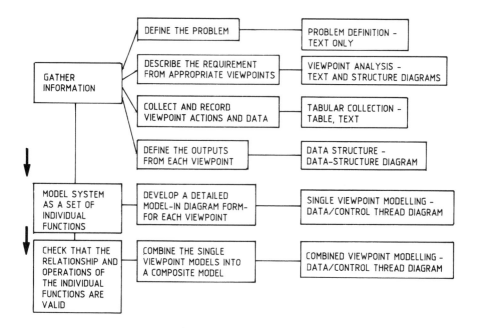

Fig.10.2 The core analysis method

10.2.3 Detailed aspects and notation

One of the first tasks in analysing customer requirements is to form an overall viewpoint structure model. What this contains varies considerably from system to system; that of Fig.10.3 describes (in simple terms) many real-time avionic and marine applications.

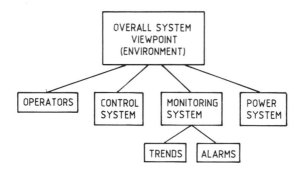

Fig.10.3 Formal viewpoint structure

For each viewpoint a tabular dataflow diagram is formed ('tabular entries' or 'tabular collections'). Fig.10.4 is typical of these, being developed for the alarm monitoring viewpoint of Fig.10.3. This defines:

- Where input data comes from.
- The input information to a viewpoint.
- What happens within a viewpoint (the actions).
- What information is put out by actions.
- Where output data goes to.

In this particular diagram there is only one level of decomposition; in a large system many levels (typically 3 to 7) may be required.

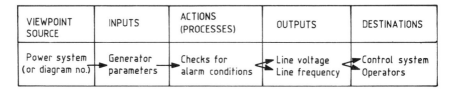

VIEWPOINT SOURCE	INPUTS	ACTIONS (PROCESSES)	OUTPUTS	DESTINATIONS
Power system (or diagram no.)	Generator parameters	Checks for alarm conditions	Line voltage Line frequency	Control system Operators

Fig.10.4 Viewpoint diagram (part)

When all the viewpoint diagrams are produced the complete system can be checked for consistency, loose ends, missing data sources, etc. A more detailed analysis of data structuring may also be done, using data structure diagrams, Fig.10.5. This shows three important factors:

- What data is produced by a viewpoint.
- The order in which data is produced.
- Repeated or optional data groups.

The structure and notation used are similar to those found in Jackson structured diagrams.

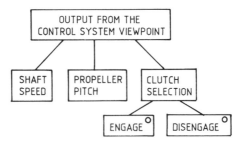

Fig.10.5 CORE – data structure diagram

Viewpoint tabular diagrams completely describe the dataflow of each viewpoint. They are fairly straightforward to construct; unfortunately they aren't all that easy to use when reviewing system requirements and behaviour. To help us here, dataflows and actions are also shown in diagram form – 'thread' diagrams. The basic constructs of the thread diagram are action boxes and data flowlines (Fig.10.6).

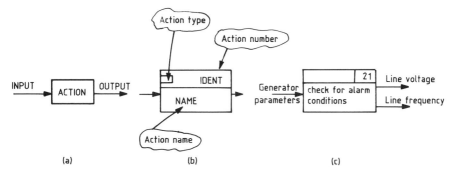

Fig.10.6 Basic constructs of thread diagrams

Various forms of dataflow can be shown using the notation of Fig.10.7.

Actions frequently involve repetition or selection. Such operations are described using the symbols of Fig.10.8. In (a) the label 'CONTROL' controls the extent of the iteration operation. In (b) 'CONTROL' determines whether action A1 or A2 is selected.

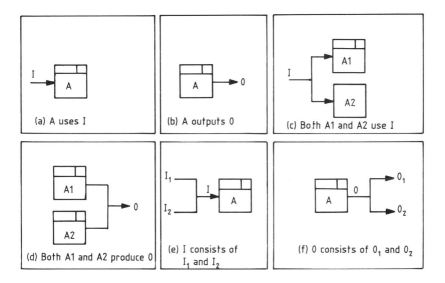

Fig.10.7 Thread diagram – dataflow constructs

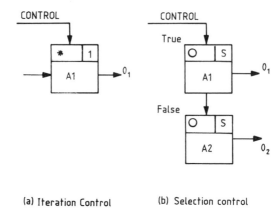

(a) Iteration Control   (b) Selection control

Fig.10.8 Control of iteration and selection

10.2.4 Example design — the steam propulsion system

The purpose of this section is to show how CORE can be used in a practical situation. Clearly, in a text like this, only a small problem can be tackled. It is, though, a realistic one, being based on a control system requirement in a steam propulsion plant.

The starting point, as with all real systems, is the SOR. For this example the relevant parts read as follows:

STATEMENT OF REQUIREMENTS – STEAM PROPULSION SYSTEM

(a) **General functional description**
The purpose of the steam propulsion system is to provide propeller power using a steam turbine as the mechanical power source. Control of turbine speed and power is achieved by varying the steam feed to it, Fig.10.9, using a steam throttle valve.

The valve is motorized, being driven by an electrical actuator. It is fitted with a position sensor. When the valve is closed, steam flow is shut off. With the valve fully open maximum power is delivered by the turbine.

Exhaust steam is fed to a condensing well, where it changes state to water. From here it is pumped out as feed water to the system heat exchanger. Level control of the water is maintained by recirculating some of the output water back into the well, using a motorized water valve (the level control valve). This valve is also fitted with a position sensor.

It is required to automate control of:

- The input steam flow to the turbine.
- The water level in the condenser well.

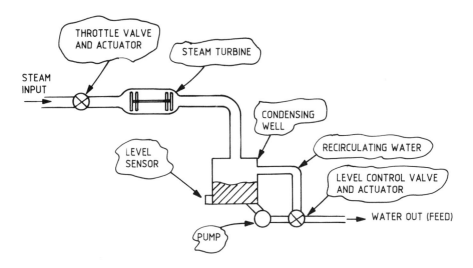

Fig.10.9 Design example – steam propulsion system

(b)   Steam flow control system
The input steam flow is determined by the position of the throttle valve. This is set by the control system in accordance with the input demand set by the propulsion system power lever. It is required to do this automatically under closed-loop control. Static and dynamic performance requirements are defined elsewhere. Valve position data is to be shown on an operator display.

(c)   Level control system
Level is to be controlled to the value set by the operator on a level-setting dial. This is to be done automatically, using a closed-loop control system. Preliminary stability analysis shows that an inner loop is needed to control the position of the level actuator. The input signal for this loop is to be derived from within the level control system. To improve loop dynamics a cross (bias) feed is to be provided by the throttle controller for the level controller. Water level data is to be shown on an operator display.

(d)   Special points
Sampling rates

Throttle actuator loop sample rate: 30 Hz.
Level actuator loop sample rate: 30 Hz.
Level loop sample rate: 10Hz.

Safety
If during system operation the level rises excessively (defined elsewhere) the operator is to immediately close the power lever.

END – STATEMENT OF REQUIREMENTS

From this information an overall viewpoint diagram is produced, Fig.10.10. This shows that the total system is described from five viewpoints, labelled 1 to 5. For each one an individual viewpoint diagram is produced, the following being shown here:

- Fig.10.11, for the operator (reference V01E01).
- Fig.10.12, for the interface devices (reference V02E01).
- Fig.10.13, for the control logic (reference V05E01).

To appreciate these they must be studied carefully; this is left to the reader. Two particular points need stressing. First, across all viewpoint diagrams, there must be a balance between source and destination information. Second, attention must be paid to missing inputs and outputs.

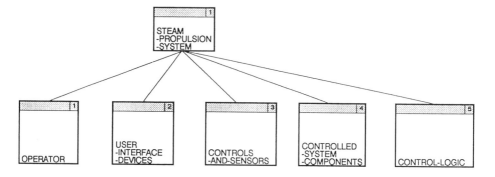

Fig.10.10 Example system – viewpoint hierarchy diagram (VPH)

The first point is fairly obvious, but not so the second one. Consider Fig.10.11. On this the action 'monitor-throttle-position' has no output. One may well ask why this function is required at all. From the diagram it appears that the operator monitors the display but does nothing about what he sees. Questioning like this helps us eliminate pointless or redundant operations. However, it isn't always obvious when operations **are** redundant. For instance, in the case here, the operator functions may be defined at a higher system level. But at our level we are concerned only with providing information. In this case a no-output action is perfectly valid (similar arguments apply to inputs).

Using this information individual viewpoint thread diagrams are produced. Fig.10.14 (ref.V01T01) is a simple example showing part of the operator viewpoint thread diagram.

In the final stage of analysis – not shown here – the separate thread diagrams are first matched up, then they're combined into composite diagrams. This has two objectives. First, it confirms that the composed system (built from the low-level items) describes the model that we started with. Remember, we began with a top-level view, decomposing as required. Unfortunately, during this process, it's all too easy to make mistakes which don't break decomposition rules – but are logically wrong. Second, it highlights actions

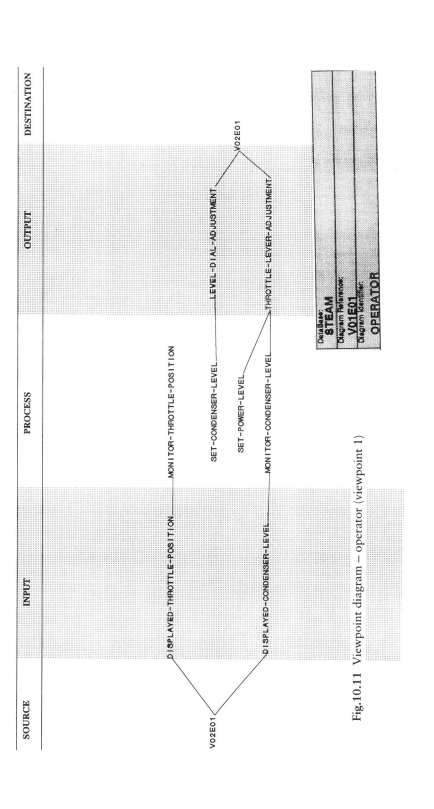

Fig.10.11 Viewpoint diagram – operator (viewpoint 1)

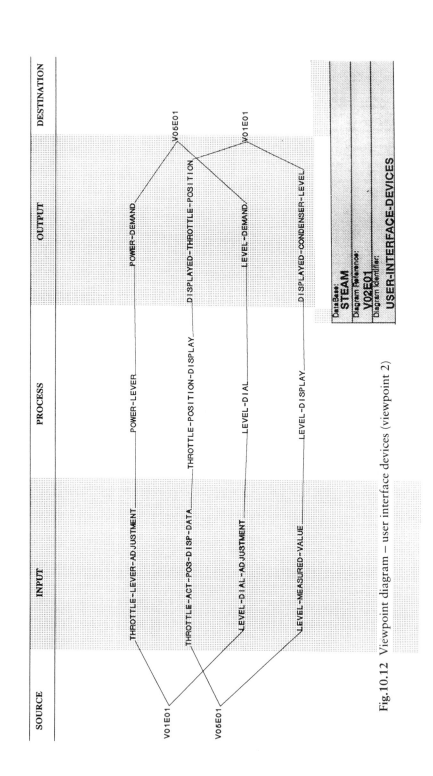

Fig.10.12 Viewpoint diagram – user interface devices (viewpoint 2)

SOURCE   INPUT   PROCESS   OUTPUT   DESTINATION

THROTTLE-LEVER-ADJUSTMENT — POWER-LEVER — POWER-DEMAND — V06E01

THROTTLE-ACT-POS-DISP-DATA — THROTTLE-POSITION-DISPLAY — DISPLAYED-THROTTLE-POSITION

LEVEL-DIAL-ADJUSTMENT — LEVEL-DIAL — LEVEL-DEMAND — V01E01

LEVEL-MEASURED-VALUE — LEVEL-DISPLAY — DISPLAYED-CONDENSER-LEVEL

V01E01

V06E01

Data Base:
STEAM
Diagram Reference:
V02E01
Diagram Identifier:
USER-INTERFACE-DEVICES

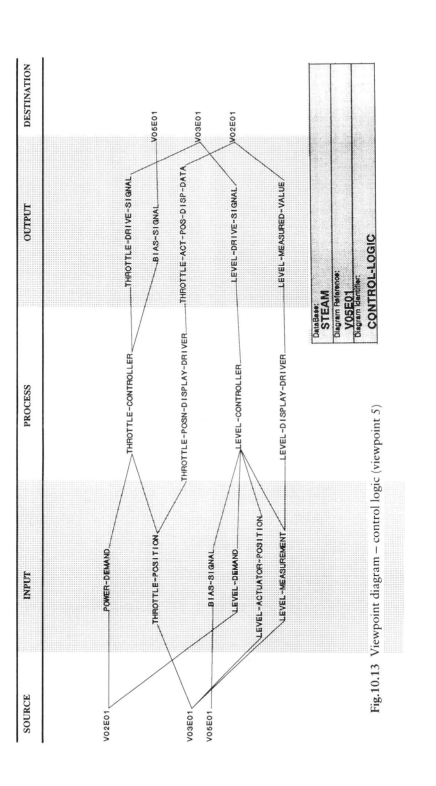

Fig.10.13 Viewpoint diagram – control logic (viewpoint 5)

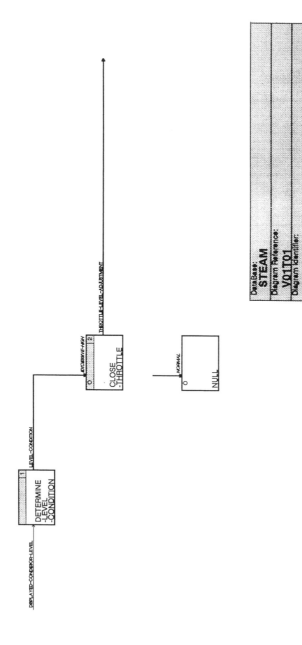

Fig.10.14 Thread diagram – operator (viewpoint 1)

which involve many viewpoints. These are usually the most important ones in the system; therefore it's important to identify them early on, before design begins.

The output from the analysis phase forms the specification for the software design phase. Data produced by CORE is likely to be augmented by new – system – information resulting from the analysis process itself: Figs.10.15 and 10.16 for example.

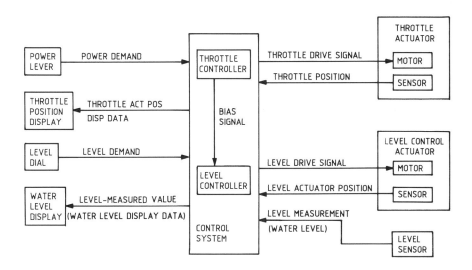

Fig.10.15 Example system – block diagram

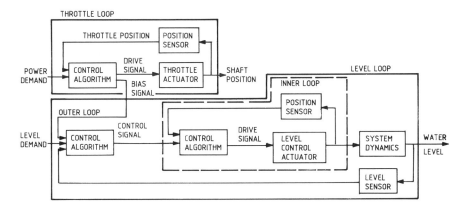

Fig.10.16 Example system – control loop diagram (part)

10.2.5 A comment on analysis tools

To do analysis work manually is, at the best, tedious. This is true even of the small example system given here. Moreover, it's very easy to make mistakes with manually-controlled methods. In large systems the situation is much worse; errors are likely to be the normal state of affairs. The only practical way to attain high productivity and minimize mistakes is to use automated tools.

10.3 YOURDON STRUCTURED METHOD —YSM

10.3.1 Introduction

The Yourdon Structured Method (YSM) deserves special mention because:

- It is based on quite specific analysis and design methods – functional structuring.
- It has been developed and refined over many years so that it meets the **actual** needs of software designers.
- Two embedded design methodologies which have proved to be very successful – Ward–Mellor (1985) and Hatley–Pirbhai (1988) – have been derived from the basic Yourdon techniques.
- It is applicable both to small and large projects.
- The basic ideas are used within many design toolsets.
- Yourdon tools are beginning to be widely used by the real-time systems community.

The original ideas were proposed in the mid 1970s, all design activities being manual tasks. In 1985, or thereabouts, Yourdon Inc. introduced the first automated tool for the methodology, now known as the 'Analyst/Designer Toolkit'. A more comprehensive toolset, CRADLE, has recently been released.

10.3.2 Design fundamentals

The Yourdon method provides support for the analysis and design of software-based systems (Fig.10.17). Using this the designer first explicitly defines what a system is supposed to do – then implements these requirements. Here, analysis and design are two distinct stages, the output from the analysis stage forming the input to the design phase. In practice, though, they are likely to be used in a cyclic (iterative) manner.

  Analysis is concerned with identifying the properties (attributes) of a system and then building a model based on this information. This, in Yourdon terminology, describes the 'essential' model of the system. The essential model itself is composed of two parts, an 'environmental' and a 'behavioural' model; these aren't tied to specific implementations.

  Design is concerned with implementing the derived (essential) model on the hardware and software structures available to the designer. In essence it:

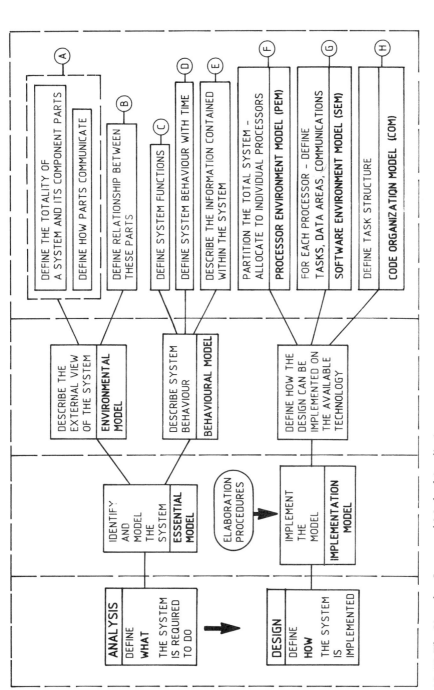

Fig.10.17 The Yourdon Structured Method (outline)

- Takes information from the analysis stage.
- Expands and refines this data ('elaboration').
- Maps system structure onto the hardware configuration.
- Identifies task and data aspects.
- Builds program structures for these tasks.

This forms the 'implementation' model, being composed of three separate parts, the 'processor environment' model (PEM), the 'software environment' model (SEM) and the 'code organization' model (COM).

The relationship between the different models, and between the models and various diagram types, is shown in Fig.10.18; further details are given below. The general structure, content and application of these diagrams were covered in chapters 5 and 6. Here their features and uses are described specifically in the context of YSM.

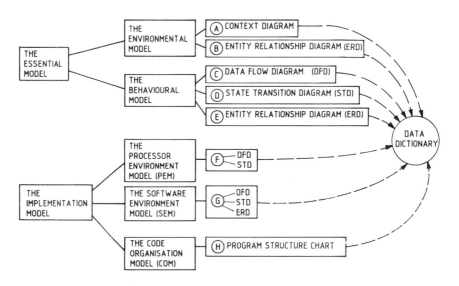

Fig.10.18 Yourdon method – relationship between models and diagrams

10.3.3 The environmental model

In the analysis phase the system being investigated is described in abstract terms. That is, we set out its functions and operations without considering hardware or software. The first part of this phase consists of forming an external view of the system, using the environmental model. This defines:

- What the system consists of.
- How individual external items communicate with the system.
- How the system responds (relates) to events in the real world.

A context diagram shows the first two aspects, an entity relationship diagram

(ERD) the third one.

A context diagram (Fig.10.19) consists of the system itself, surrounded by sinks and sources of data (terminators). The system is described using a named circle (you don't get much more abstract than that), being connected to the terminators using named connectors. Terminators, which may be items of hardware, people, or other systems, define the boundary between the system and the real world.

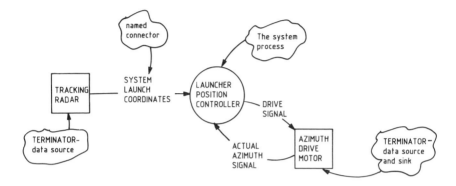

Fig.10.19 YSM context diagram

Within the overall system anything real or abstract about which we hold data is defined to be an 'entity'. Clearly, by this definition, terminators are entities. Frequently entities have interdependent links ('functional connections'), these being shown on an entity relationship diagram (Fig.10.20). Note though that ERDs essentially describe passive relationships, not dynamic ones.

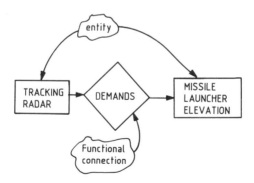

Fig.10.20 YSM entity relationship diagram

There are text support features for the environmental model, including a statement of purpose, a data dictionary and an external event list (Fig.10.21). This last item is used to describe how the system responds to external actions and incidents ('the events'). Such events, which can be time, data or control related, trigger preprogrammed responses.

AGENT	ACTION	SUBJECT	INSTRUMENT	CLASSIFICATION
TRACKING RADAR	DEMANDS ELEVATION	ELEVATION DRIVE MOTOR	——	Data
MISSILE OPERATOR	ACTIVATES	SYSTEM	——	Control
MISSILE MAINTAINER	LUBRICATES	SERVO GEARBOX	WITH OIL	Data

Fig.10.21 YSM event list

10.3.4 The behavioural model

System behaviour is described in three ways: functions, dynamics and relationships. This is shown in the behavioural model using dataflow, state transition and entity relationship diagrams. Information needed to construct these diagrams is derived from the environmental model.

(a)   System function

The overall system function is expressed as a series of transformations acting on the data which flows through the system. These transformations ('processes'), and their interfaces, are shown using data flow diagrams (DFDs), Fig.10.22. In this example the data is continuous. However, YSM also allows discrete data to be shown on DFDs.

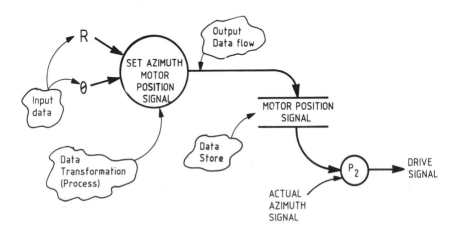

Fig.10.22 YSM dataflow diagram – data transformation (DT)

(b) System dynamics

The behaviour of a system depends not only on data; it relates to time and – especially in embedded designs – to control and event signals. In YSM design the resulting actions are called 'responses'. Dataflow and transformations are unable to describe such operations; control information must be added to the model. Specifically, both control flow and control transformations are used.

The basic function of a control flow is to control one or more data transformations, Fig.10.23. In this example the data transformation ('set azimuth motor drive signal') is forbidden to calculate the motor drive signal unless it is enabled by the control flow 'enable azimuth servo'. Generally, to 'enable' a data transformation means to activate it; 'disable' is the reverse process.

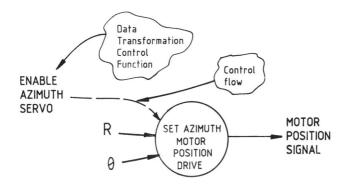

Fig.10.23 YSM dataflow diagram – controlling data transformations

Events don't always **directly** produce control flows; the effect may be indirect. Also, the status of an enable/disable control flow may be determined by more than one event. To express these (and similar) actions, the 'control transformation' is used, Fig.10.24.

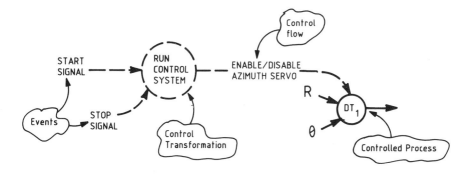

Fig.10.24 YSM dataflow diagram – control transformation (CT)

More generally, control transformations are used to organize, order and explain control flows within the system – in particular those coming from the external environment. A variety of flow–transformation relationships have to be catered for, Fig.10.25.

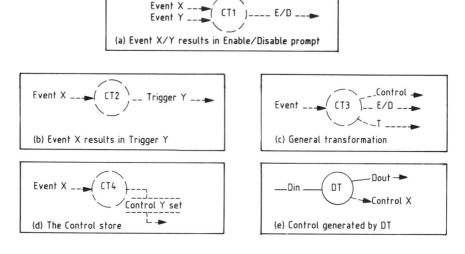

Fig.10.25 YSM control flow–transformation relationships

In (a), CT1 generates enable and disable signals in response to events X and Y. For instance, when X occurs, the enable control (or 'prompt') is generated; when Y occurs, disable is generated. As shown here the separate prompts are combined into one flow line. This can be done when both control flows stem from the same CT.

There are many instances when a process needs to be activated by a momentary event. In other situations an event may be required to produce an activating signal, independent of the event duration. To cater for these situations a 'trigger' control flow (also defined to be a 'prompt') is used, (b). The trigger prompt, when applied to a transformation, activates the process until some specified function is completed (it is a single-shot operation).

The general operation of a CT is shown in (c). Both E/D and T, the prompts, can be input to data transformations. In contrast, the control flow can only be input to another CT or to a control store, (d). Finally, a data transformation can itself generate a control flow, (e).

Thus any real system exhibits a particular behaviour pattern (the 'states'), with periods of time (the 'modes') between such states. A change of state is caused by one or more events. This event-dependent behaviour is modelled using a state transition diagram (STD), Fig.10.26. On this diagram the condition which causes a state change is shown, together with its corresponding action.

In expressing dynamic behaviour, the starting point is the event list. From this the STD is generated, thus providing the information for constructing control transformations (each control bubble should correspond to an STD transition).

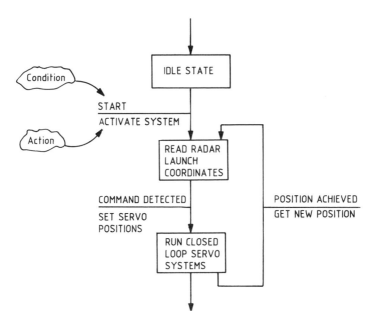

Fig.10.26 YSM State transition diagram

(c) System relationships
Information relating to the model entities (their 'attributes') together with relationships between entities are shown on entity relationship diagrams. But to form a complete view of any system more information is needed. This requirement is shown – conceptually – in Fig.10.27a. Observe how different applications produce quite different system footprints, (b), (c).

10.3.5 The processor environment model (PEM)

The highest level design decision concerns the allocation of computing functions to processor hardware (Fig.10.28). Where more than one processor is used the functions of the essential model have to be spread across these. Precisely how this is done is described using the PEM. The resulting interface connections are also described in this model. This is an elaboration of the required system behaviour; thus it's not surprising that DFDs, STDs and ERDs are used to describe it.

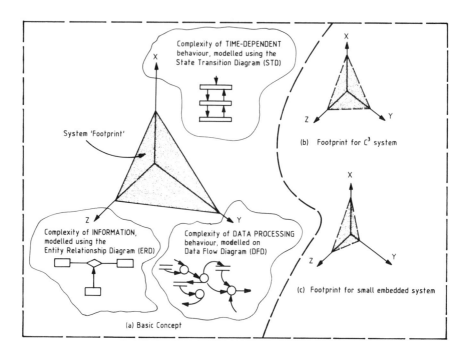

Fig.10.27 The Yourdon models of system behaviour (courtesy of Yourdon International Ltd.)

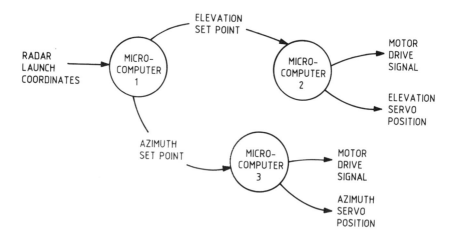

Fig.10.28 YSM processor environment model – allocation of functions

10.3.6 The software environmental model (SEM)

Within each processor it is necessary to define the software architecture and its effect on:

- Task allocation.
- Task functions (transforms) and states.
- Interfaces (internal and external).
- Data area structuring.
- Services and resources provided.

This last item includes support for concurrency, task activation and deactivation, task synchronization, and intertask communication. For that reason an operating system can be viewed as a specific instance of a generalized software architecture.

DFDs, STDs and ERDs are used to build the SEM, Fig.10.29.

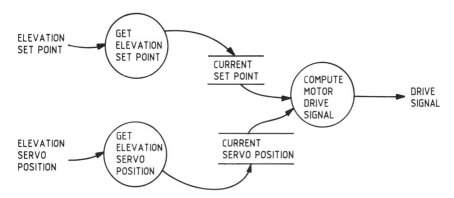

Fig.10.29 YSM software environment model

10.3.7 The code organizational model (COM)

The modular structure of each task, built in a functional manner, is described in the code organizational model. Where appropriate the module interfaces are defined. A program structure diagram ('chart'), Fig.10.30, is used to implement the COM.

10.3.8 Design example

The implementation (in part) of the software design for the steam propulsion system using the Yourdon Structured Method is shown below. This concentrates on the essence of the method; for clarity many detailed items are omitted. Figs.10.31 to 10.37 illustrate the process. In the first place a context diagram is produced (Fig.10.31).

Note here the introduction of a 'virtual' terminator named TIME. It is necessary to use such a construct to incorporate time-driven events in the system.

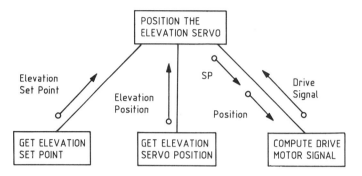

Fig.10.30 YSM program structure chart

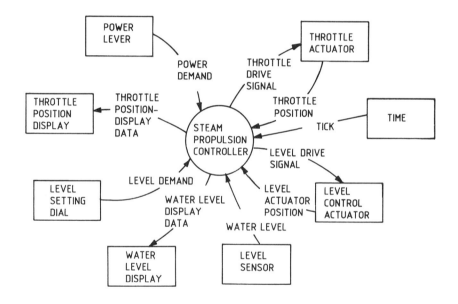

Fig.10.31 Example system – YSM context diagram

There now follows the event list, Fig.10.32, which has been slightly modified to include a list of external responses. Using this information, preliminary design diagrams are produced, Fig.10.33. The behavioural model is now developed, its DFD being shown in Fig.10.34. Note that control flows (trigger prompts) have now been introduced to activate the various timed data transformations (processes). These originate in the control transformation 'schedule control loops', responding to the input control flow 'tick'.

At this stage the system is partitioned onto processor hardware as shown in

AGENT	ACTION	SUBJECT	INSTRUMENT	CLASSIFICATION	EXTERNAL RESPONSES
Power Lever	Sets power demand	Throttle controller	—	Data	Throttle drive signal
Level Setting Dial	Sets level	Level controller	—	Data	Level actuator drive signal
Throttle Actuator	Gives throttle position information	Throttle and level controllers	—	Data	Throttle position display
Level Control Actuator	Gives level actuator position information	Level Actuator Controller	—	Data	—
Level Sensor	Gives level information	Level controller		Data	Water level display
Time	Activates control loops	Actuator and level controllers	Real time Clock	Control	—

Fig.10.32 Example system – YSM event list

the PEM, Fig.10.35. Now the SEM is developed for each processor, the relevant DFD for micro 1 being that of Fig.10.36. Finally the program structure charts are generated. In this case processes are run consecutively – not concurrently – to simplify the design, Fig.10.37. Handling the documentation for even this relatively simple design is a major task. Thus implementing the Yourdon Structured Method without tool support is daunting; design maintenance even more so. But with the appropriate toolset, software design moves onto another plane.

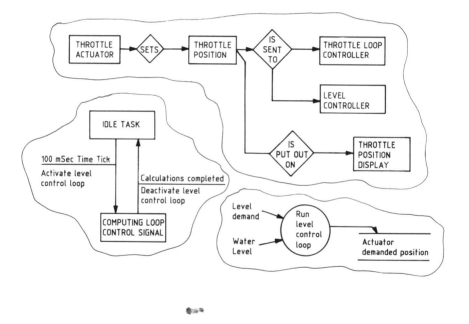

Fig.10.33 Example system – YSM preliminary design diagrams (part)

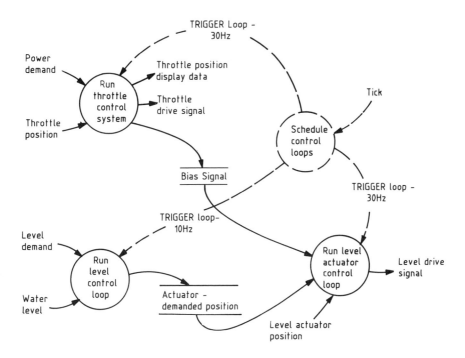

Fig.10.34 Example system – YSM behavioural model DFD

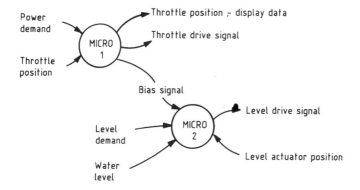

Fig.10.35 Example system – YSM processor environment model DFD

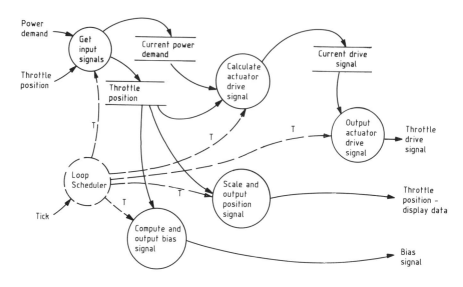

Fig.10.36 Example system – YSM software environment model DFD for micro 1

10.4 JACKSON SYSTEM DEVELOPMENT —JSD

10.4.1 Introduction

During the 1970s a number of program design methods were proposed and developed, one major strand being the data-driven approach. Within this area, the ideas of Michael Jackson (1975) have been highly significant. These concepts, formalized as Jackson Structured Programming (JSP), had their roots in the DP field. Over the next 10 years JSP became a leading design method for this area of work, but had little impact on the real-time community. Fundamentally, real-time systems are not data-driven, being quite different from DP applications (this view is not shared by Michael Jackson, 1988). In the early 1980s Jackson developed a new methodology for use in the complete software design process (not just the program design stage), Jackson System Development (JSD). Its concepts and use are described in various papers by one of its co-developers, John Cameron (1983). Subsequent papers (Cameron, 1986, 1988) show that the method is still evolving, using experience gained from practical applications. In recent years it has been applied to a number of real-time systems, including naval control and surveillance (Davies, 1987) and torpedo systems (Cameron and Butcher, 1988). Originally design was very much a manual process. Now design work is performed using the 'Program Design Facility', 'Speedbuilder' and 'Network Builder' packages provided by Michael Jackson Systems Ltd.

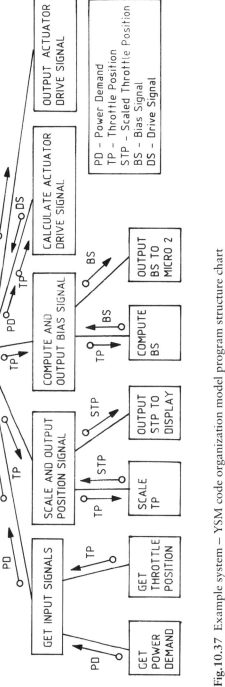

Fig.10.37 Example system – YSM code organization model program structure chart

10.4.2 Design fundamentals

JSD sets out to achieve the same ends as YSM. But the way it does it is very different; in fact it is quite unlike all other design methods. Unfortunately, a brief description of the technique doesn't bring out the essential aspects of the approach. Therefore it is described here in some detail.

In general terms system design using JSD is carried out as shown in Fig.10.38. There are three distinct stages: analysis, specification and implementation. The purpose of the analysis (modelling) stage is to generate a description of the system, based on events which occur within the system. This formal description embraces all relevant real-world aspects of the system under analysis. To provide this description we must identify:

- Objects (entities) within the model.
- Actions carried out by objects.
- Actions suffered by objects.
- Attributes of objects and actions.
- Time ordering of actions.
- Action updating mechanisms.

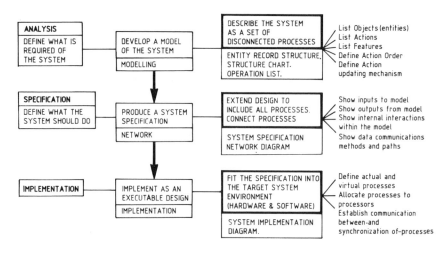

Fig.10.38 The Jackson System Design (JSD) method – outline

This resulting system description consists of a set of individual unconnected processes, each process being a single sequential thread of activity. These single-thread operations define the behaviour of the object within the real world. The documentation used to describe the model consists of entity-record structures, structure charts and operations lists.

Model processes describe what the system does, but this doesn't include inputs and outputs to the real world. Also excluded are processes which act on model output information to modify subsequent model behaviour.

The specification stage extends the design to include **all** processes, and then connects them. Specifically, it defines the:

- Inputs to the model.
- Outputs from the model.
- Internal interactions within model processes.
- Data communications methods and paths.

These are shown on a system specification network diagram (note: this is often referred to as a system network diagram or a system specification diagram).

At this point we have an abstract description of the system. It is based entirely on the application for which the design is intended. How this is supposed to work as a practical system is not considered within the specification stage – thus decoupling specification from implementation. For any one specification there are many possible implementations – provided by the implementation stage.

In this final stage of design we 'map' the specification into a target system environment. To do this we need to:

- Define actual and virtual processes.
- Allocate processes to physical processors.
- Establish communication between processes.
- Establish synchronization of processes (where required).

This target system structure is shown on a system implementation diagram.

10.4.3 The modelling stage

The JSD model consists of three major components: entities (objects), actions and attributes (Fig.10.39). The general relationship of these parts is shown in Fig.10.40. When devising a model structure the designer must answer the following questions:

- What objects (entities) exist in the system? (Entities are real-world objects which our system manipulates.)
- What events (actions) take place in the system? (Actions are operations which cause the system to modify its state; these must be observable.)
- How do these actions relate to entities?
- What are the sequential and concurrent aspects of the actions?
- What qualifying features (attributes) do the entities and actions have?

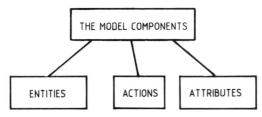

Fig.10.39 JSD model – component parts

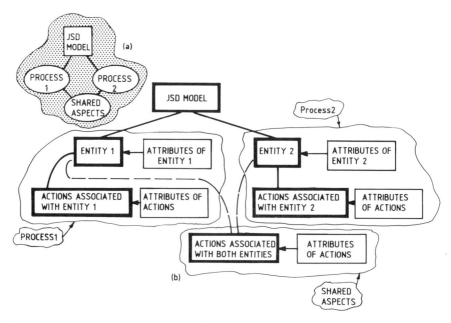

Fig.10.40 JSD model – relationship of component parts

The first step is to set up a record for each entity, its attributes, its associated actions, and **their** particular attributes (Fig.10.41). Each record describes a single process within the software structure. Next the ordering of actions for each particular entity is defined, using a JSP structure diagram, Fig.10.42 (and chapter 6).

```
                    Record Identifier Process


   ENTITY :  Name Of Entity            ENTITY ATTRIBUTES :

  ┌─ ── ── ── ── ──┐
  │Informal description of│            Attribute  1 : TYPE
  │the entity        │                 Attribute  2 : TYPE
  └─ ── ── ── ── ──┘                    etc.

   ACTION : Name Of Action             ACTION ATTRIBUTES :

  ┌─ ── ── ── ──┐
  │Description of action│              Attribute 1 : TYPE
  └─ ── ── ── ──┘                      Attribute 2 : TYPE
                                       etc.

   ACTION : Name Of Action             ACTION ATTRIBUTES :

  ┌─ ── ── ── ──┐
  │Description of action│              Attribute 1 :  TYPE
  └─ ── ── ── ──┘                      Attribute 2 : TYPE
```

Fig.10.41 The entity record structure

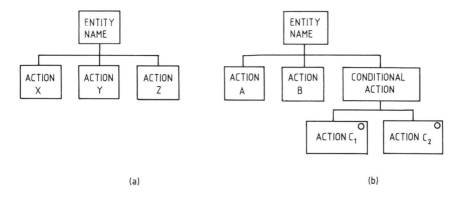

(a)   (b)

Fig.10.42 Ordering actions

Fig.10.42a shows a simple sequential ordering of actions: X followed by Y followed by Z. In (b) the final action is conditional; either Z1 or Z2 is executed. Operations which cause a change of state (updating) are detailed in an operations list (Fig.10.43); these are appended to the structure diagram. This relationship describes a single-thread (time ordered) sequence of actions. But it may also be found from the analysis stage that a single entity displays concurrent behaviour. In such situations the entity is first decomposed into a set of parallel actions, called roles (Fig.10.44). Each role is then treated in the same way as an entity as far as modelling is concerned. Note that where concurrency is involved, roles may well be shared between entities (Fig.10.45).

At the end of the modelling stage we end up with a set of distinct processes, each one having its own structure diagram (Fig.10.46).

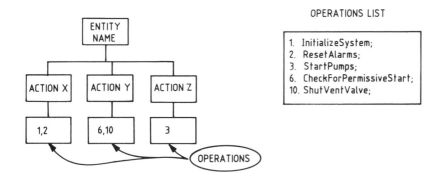

Fig.10.43 Updating actions via the operations list

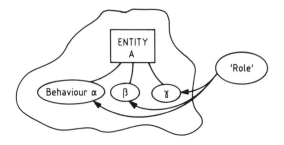

Fig.10.44 Modelling concurrent behaviour – 'roles'

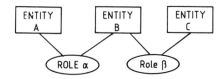

Fig.10.45 Sharing roles

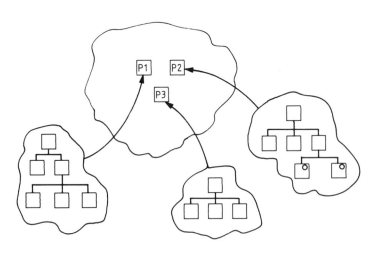

Fig.10.46 The JSD model and its processes

10.4.4 The specification (network) stage

So far we've derived the model processes. But the total system also includes input, output and interactive functions, Fig.10.47. These functions are defined to the model by adding processes to the specification network. Their relationship with the model processes is shown in Fig.10.48. As described by Cameron (1986), output processes 'extract information from the model, perform calculations and summaries, and produce the system outputs'. This is quite a different view from that of YSM, for instance; there the overall software system is seen as a form of 'black box'.

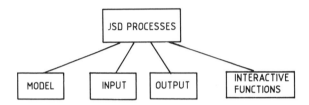

Fig.10.47 JSD process types

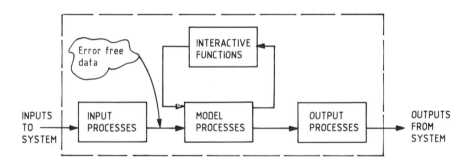

Fig.10.48 JSD system overview diagram

The input processes collect data from the outside world, check it for errors and pass on the information to the model. Interactive functions, like output processes, extract data from the model, but then feed back into the model. Processes communicate by transferring data.

The system overview diagram is a very general one; detail is shown on a system specification (network) diagram. Three symbols are used, Fig.10.49. Communication is implemented using data stores (streams) and state vectors as shown in Fig.10.50. In (a) and (b) true storage is required. In (c) this isn't necessarily the case; the information, for instance, could be passed as parameters of a procedure.

A state vector is a data store which holds local variables and state information relating to an individual process. In some ways it is like the process descriptor of a system executive. It can be written to **only** by its controlling process; as far as other processes are concerned it is a read-only store. Hence, in (d), SV1 is the state vector associated with process P1; thus it can be written to and read by P1. But P2 can only read the contents of SV1. Finally, the situation where a process acquires data from two other processes is shown in (e).

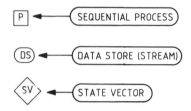

Fig.10.49 Notation used on JSD system specification (network) diagrams

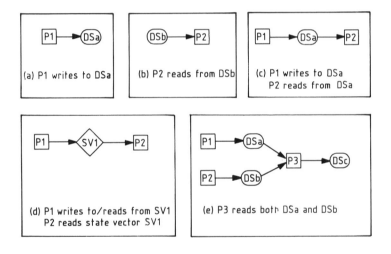

Fig.10.50 Process communication mechanisms

A small (but complete) system specification diagram (also called a network level diagram) is shown in Fig.10.51. In summary then:

- A network diagram consists of a number of individual sequential processes.
- Each process has its own internal structure.
- Processes communicate by reading and writing messages.
- Model processes define what the system does, together with its updating rules.
- Non-model processes are either the interfaces to the real-world or else are generators of system actions.

It now remains to turn this abstract description into reality.

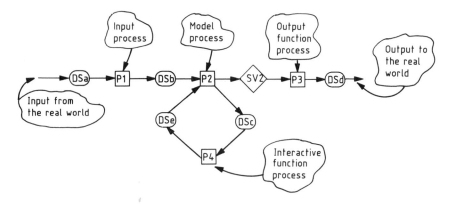

Fig.10.51 JSD system specification (network) diagram

10.4.5 The implementation stage

This final stage uses a set of transformation rules to turn the specification processes into implementation processes, Fig.10.52. This is where programs and data base information are created for a particular target system. Two broad functions have to be carried out. First, the abstract processes have to be allocated to real processors. Second, communication links have to be set up between the various processes.

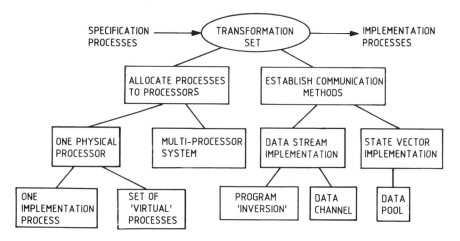

Fig.10.52 JSD implementation strategy

The implementation may use one processor only – or it may require a multiprocessor solution. When using multiprocessors the design can be tackled as a set of single processors. For both structures the simplest software design implementation uses only one process. More generally though, a number of processes have to be implemented on each machine. These, identified as 'virtual' processes, operate in a quasi-concurrent (multitasking) way. Such designs can be effected, at the very minimum, by using interrupts: more generally a real-time executive is needed.

Both data streams and state vectors, together with appropriate communication mechanisms, must be provided as part of the implementation. Two mechanisms can be used for data stream communication, program inversion and data channels. The state vector can be readily built using data pools.

Channels and pools have been described earlier (chapter 9) but program inversion is a new concept (very much a JSP one). Its primary function is to turn two (or more) specification processes into a single implementation process. In concept (Fig.10.53) it is similar to the co-routine of Modula-2. Here, two tasks (processes) are executed by a single processor, though obviously only one can run at any one time. Task-swapping takes place as in the co-routine structure. That is, as a task suspends, it stores information concerning its current status, then activates the other one. On reactivation it picks up from where it left off, suspension being invisible (transparent) to the system. However, program inversion differs from the co-routine in that tasks do not have equal status. One is designated the master, the others being subordinate to this. The master can invoke any subordinate process; control must be returned to it when the called process suspends.

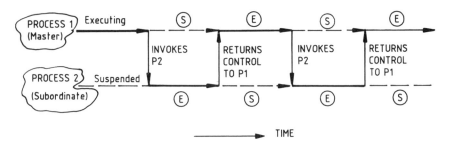

Fig.10.53 JSD program inversion

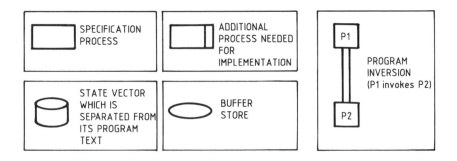

Fig.10.54 JSD implementation diagram symbols

Implementation processes are shown on a system implementation diagram, using the symbols of Fig.10.54. Note: this implies that extra processes may be needed to make the design work (typically schedulers and the like). Transformation from a system specification to an implementation is shown in Fig.10.55. Here a top-level process ('control') has been introduced, responsible for activating subordinate processes P1, P2 and P4. Both P1 and P2 can, in turn, activate P3 for the purpose of passing data to it. The rest of the diagram is self-explanatory.

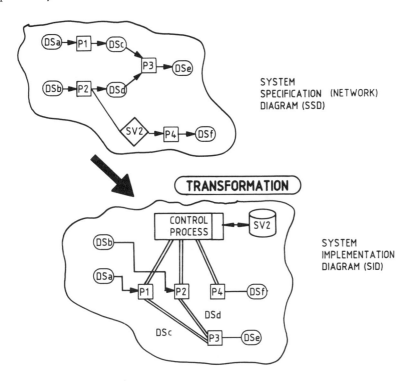

SYSTEM SPECIFICATION (NETWORK) DIAGRAM (SSD)

SYSTEM IMPLEMENTATION DIAGRAM (SID)

Fig.10.55 Transformation from specification to implementation

10.4.6 Design example

The system specification (network) diagram for our example system is shown in Fig.10.56. It consists of three model processes ('throttle loop,' 'level loop' and 'level actuator loop') and four non-model processes ('throttle sensors', 'level sensors', 'throttle outputs' and 'level outputs'). Communication and data storage are implemented using data streams and state vectors.

The system is split into two parts, the throttle control and the level control sub-systems. Each part is allocated to a separate microcomputer. Now the system implementation diagrams are developed for each sub-system, that for the throttle being shown in Fig.10.57. It can be seen that two extra processes have been added: an overall control process and a communication controller. The need for the first one is clear enough; it provides correct timing and sequencing of operations. The need for the second arises from the physical split of the network across two processors; communication between them must be supported.

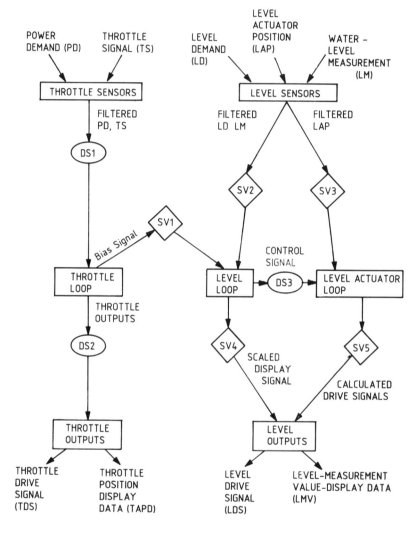

Fig.10.56 Example system – JSD system specification (network) diagram

A program structure chart is produced for each process, the one for the throttle loop being shown in Fig.10.58. This is usually produced using the Jackson program development facility (PDF) tool. Each line of the operations list is a single program statement, being written in the appropriate programming language. Statements can be made in any order; the allocation of numbers to the structure chart fixes the execution sequence (though in this example lines are ordered correctly).

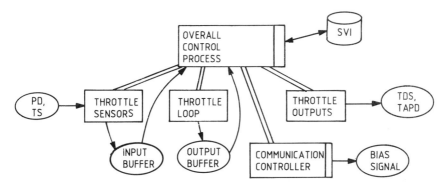

Fig.10.57 Example system – JSD system implementation diagram – throttle control sub-system

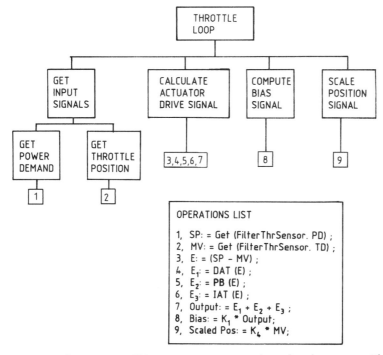

Fig.10.58 Example system – JSD program structure chart for the process 'throttle loop'

Using this information the PDF package can automatically generate source code for submission to the compiler or assembler.

One last point concerning processes needs highlighting. Strictly speaking, the rectangle symbol represents a process **type**; an 'instance' of the type performs actions. For each type it is permitted to have numerous instances ('instantiation') within the system. In simple terms it's rather like dealing with the variables and variable types of programming languages. However, in the design example given here, only **one** instance of each process type is assumed. This keeps the explanation simple.

10.5   MASCOT

10.5.1   Introduction

MASCOT – Modular Approach to Software Construction, Operation and Test – is a development methodology for designing and building real-time embedded systems. It was originally developed at the Royal Signals and Radar Establishment (RSRE) in the 1970s, aimed mainly at fast, complex and highly interactive software applications.

What functions, as a software tool, does MASCOT perform? The following abstract from the MASCOT-defining document (MASCOT, 1983, 1987) gives a clear view of its purpose and application. 'MASCOT incorporates:

- A means of design representation.
- A method for deriving the design.
- A way of constructing software so that it is consistent with the design.
- A means of executing the constructed software so that the design structure remains visible at run time.
- Facilities for testing the software in terms of the design structure.

It is neither a language nor an operating system, although it includes elements related to both aspects.'

MASCOT isn't restricted only to defence work though, in practice, this has been its main application area. It hasn't had significant use outside the UK defence community. The small number of support tools and their high cost have been restricting factors. Further, its take-up in the microcomputer field has been fairly slow, due mainly to the limited performance of microprocessors (in the 1970s the applications MASCOT was devised to handle typically ran on minicomputers, such as the Ferranti Argus). However, there are good reasons to assess MASCOT here. First, much of the professional level software in the UK is developed using this tool. Second, it is a sound, practical and proven method, incorporating the principles of modularization, decomposition, information hiding, decoupling and cohesion. Third, its need for operating system support is no longer the barrier it used to be. Fourth, more (and cheaper) tools are coming into the marketplace. Finally, modern microcomputers have the power, speed and memory features to handle MASCOT designs for embedded applications.

MASCOT, as a design methodology, has two major features. First, it's specifically devised for use in real-time systems. Second, its structure allows designers to implement concurrent solutions fairly easily. This is a very important point; most real-time systems operate naturally as a series of co-operating parallel processes. The newest version, MASCOT 3 (1987), is designed with very large real-time systems in mind, especially those using multiprocessors. It supports a variety of target system configurations, typified by those of Fig.10.59(a); a single-processor design, is typical of most MASCOT designs at the present time; (b), (c) and (d) are typical of multiprocessor structures which are now beginning to be fairly widely used within the real-time community.

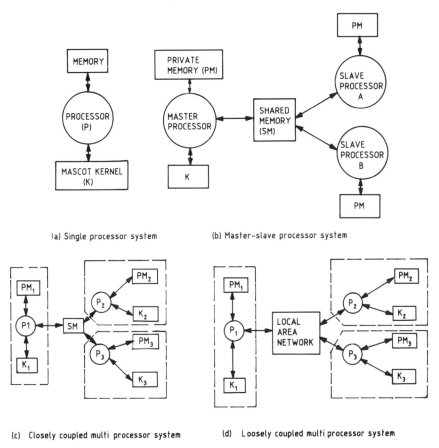

Fig.10.59 Typical MASCOT target system configurations

Concurrency is supported by a set of functions provided in the system kernel. Previously these facilities were defined as part of a conceptual machine designed to execute application programs. Now, because newer languages (e.g. Ada, Modula-2) include concurrent constructs, this is no longer the case. Instead, concurrent features are described using a reference model. This model may be

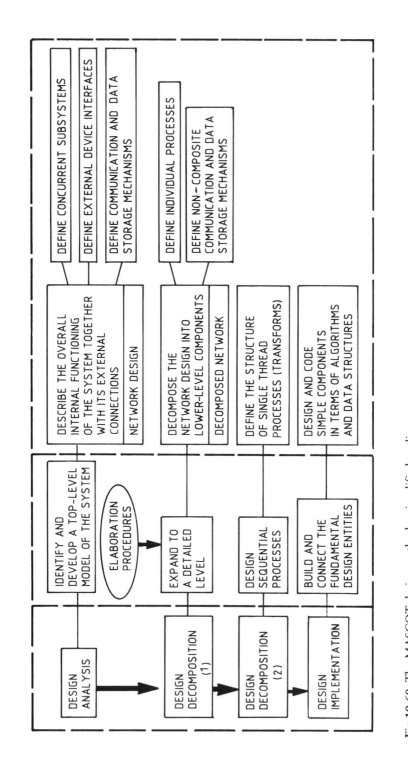

Fig.10.60 The MASCOT design method – simplified outline

implemented (as previously) using languages devoid of concurrent constructs – Coral66 for instance. Alternatively, the software developer may use the equivalent features of a concurrent language.

Specific features of the kernel depend somewhat on the target system configuration. Such aspects are beyond the scope of this book; interested readers can find detailed information in the defining document.

10.5.2 Design fundamentals

A simplified description of the MASCOT method is shown in Fig.10.60, integration and test aspects being ignored. MASCOT does not support requirements analysis work. Therefore it is assumed that, before starting the design, the requirements have already been established.

The opening phase is network design. Here the overall software requirements are analysed in order to define a simplified model of the system. This network model describes the internal functioning of the system, emphasizing concurrent processes (transforms), communication links and data storage requirements. It also shows interactions between external devices and the software system itself, these being described using dataflow diagrams.

The information is now expanded (decomposed) hierarchically into lower-level components – the 'decomposed network'. Decomposition ('elaboration') is continued until all items are shown in their simplest form, the so-called 'simple elements'. At this point each transform represents an individual sequential single-thread process. The program structure of each process is now defined.

The final stage, design implementation, involves design and coding of the elementary building blocks to produce executable software.

An alternative description of this design method is shown in Fig.10.61, revealing its hierarchical structuring. At the top level the structure is portrayed as a set of external devices connected to the software system. The software entity is expanded down to the network level, defined in terms of active sub-systems and internal communication links. Each sub-system is further elaborated until the component level view is reached. This consists of data transforms ('activities') and internal/external data communication links. Now, from a concurrent point of view, each item is described in its simplest form.

The individual items listed above, both simple and composite, are fundamental MASCOT design entities – the 'elements'.

In the following sections emphasis is placed on the design and diagramming aspects of the method. Development tool requirements, build and configuration control, data base aspects and system testing are not covered.

10.5.3 Network design

The primary aim of the network design phase is to develop and validate the overall software structure – before getting down to design details. Prior to this an initial design diagram should have been produced (a necessity for large systems). This, Fig.10.62, shows interactions between the software itself and the external devices connected to it (similar to the context diagram of YSM). From this a network diagram is produced, showing data flow, transformations (processes), and communication links. It is structured using three basic entities, Fig.10.63, which themselves may consist of composite or single components. In large systems initial network diagrams usually contain composite components only.

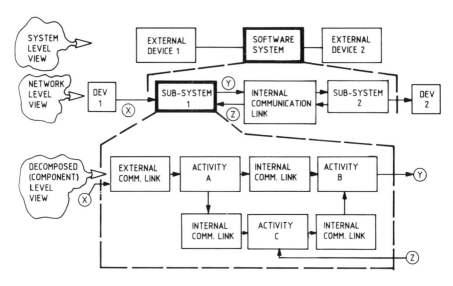

Fig.10.61 MASCOT – hierarchical design structure

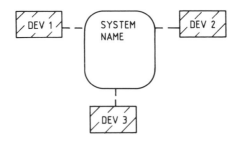

Fig.10.62 Initial design diagram

The first entity, the sub-system, is a composite item which performs processing of system data. Each sub-system represents a major concurrent activity; it generally houses further sub-systems, interconnection data areas (IDAs) and servers within it. IDAs are data storage devices; but are used specifically (and **only**) to implement communication between concurrent processes. They are passive devices, though they may contain executable code. However, such code cannot be called up by the IDA itself; it is invoked by external active entities (or by an IDA which itself has been invoked by an active entity). Servers are used to interface the system to the outside world, one server per device. They hold the software needed for controlling and acquiring data from these external hardware items. Consequently they must be tailored to meet the interfacing needs of these devices.

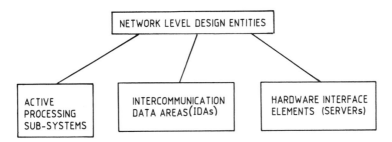

Fig.10.63 System entities – the network level view

The network diagram is decomposed through a series of levels until the process can't be continued any further. At this point – the component level – the diagram consists of processing units (activities) and intercommunication data stores (Fig.10.64). Two types of store are used, the channel and the pool (chapter 9).

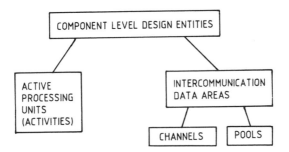

Fig.10.64 System entities – the component level view

10.5.4 Communication between entities

In large systems the software design effort is too great to be handled by one person; a team is needed. Therefore the total design then has to be split up, each part being developed separately. To ensure that the complete system works correctly when the parts are integrated, rigorous control methods must be enforced. One factor is essential here; correct, formal communication between the separate sub-systems. This is a fundamental aspect of the MASCOT methodology.

Mascot entities communicate through the use of PATHS, Fig.10.65a, along which flows information. Path connections are made at access points, Fig.10.65b, consisting of ports and windows. A port is used to invoke (REQUIRE) operations: these are implemented outside the component which houses the port. At the other end of the path is a window, specifying a set of operations PROVIDED by the component which houses it. Normally windows are located in communication components (or in components which include communication elements). Ports are held both by activities **and** communication components. It is clear why activities use ports; but why put them in IDAs? The answer is quite simple. This arrangement enables IDAs to be connected so that data can be sent directly between them.

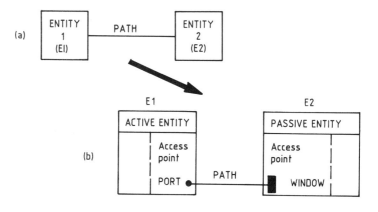

Fig.10.65 The basic communication model

To fulfil the operations demanded by a port, code must be executed. This code is located in a passive communication element: but is run only when invoked (commanded) by an active processing element.

The name given to a path is that of an ACCESS INTERFACE type (see later). On a network diagram the direction of dataflow is defined by arrowheads (Fig.10.66a).

Ports are shown as filled circles connected to paths (b), usually being labelled with unique identifiers. They may act either as sinks or sources of data, the arrowhead direction defining the type. Where paths cross a number of boundaries on the network diagram, the port symbol is placed at each boundary, (c). In cases where activities share operations provided by a common source, paths may be merged, (d).

The symbol used for a window is a thin filled rectangle, (e). Like the port it may be either a source or sink of data, this also being identified using arrowheads. The rest of the diagram is self-explanatory, but note one important point; windows are passive devices.

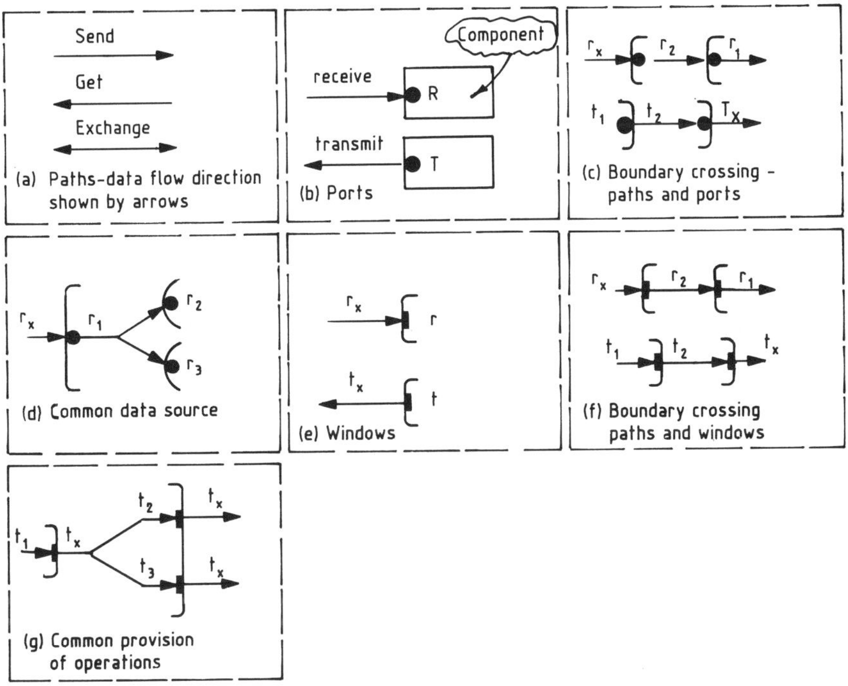

Fig.10.66 Paths, ports and windows – diagram representation

In the MASCOT methodology these diagramming items (Fig.10.67a) are described textually, in 'modules'. An access interface module, (b), specifies the interactions which may take place along a path. Note here that the path name – 'Send3' – is the same as that of the access interface class name. Each access interface defines procedures (and other items) available from this class of interface. The ports and windows are specified in their own particular modules, the general form being that of Fig.10.67c. Here the statement 'REQUIRES sp:Send3' means that port sp requires use of the facilities defined in the access interface Send3. Likewise, 'PROVIDES sw:Send3' in (c) means that the window sw provides the facilities defined in Send3.

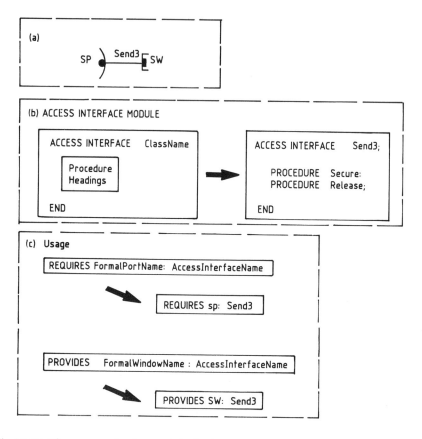

Fig.10.67 The communication model – basic text representation

10.5.5 MASCOT entities — specifications and templates

MASCOT entities are grouped into specification and template classes, Fig. 10.68. Only the ones discussed so far are shown, though others are provided. There is only one specification type, the access interface; no more need be said concerning this. However, the concept of templates **does** need some discussion.

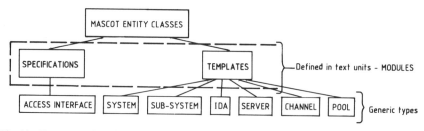

Fig.10.68 Entity classification (part)

A template can be likened to the specifications of a standard integrated circuit; it defines the function provided by the component. When designing equipment the electronic engineer selects appropriate devices using the specification manual (the template description) as a guide. Placing a specific component into a circuit can be seen as implementing a particular instance of the generic device. In MASCOT the template plays a similar role, being a software component pattern. Each generic type has its own template, which defines the:

- Functions provided.
- Connection methods used.

These are described in text form, called template modules. Using the templates the designer can realize specific instances of the component type.

10.5.6 Network diagrams

Top-level network diagrams are built using interconnected sub-systems, IDAs and servers. Sub-systems provide and require services; thus they include ports and windows (Fig.10.69). Their details are defined in text form, a simplified description being given here. Note: Send, Signal and Get refer to particular access interfaces.

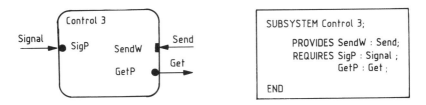

Fig.10.69 Sub-system representation

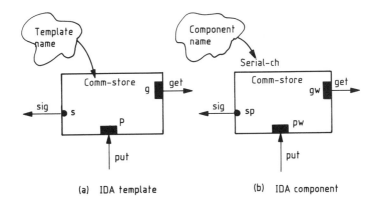

Fig.10.70 IDA diagram

IDAs are shown as in Fig.10.70, where the template 'Comms store' acts as a generic defining unit. A specific instance of this template is the IDA component named 'Serial-Ch'.

The third diagram type, the server (Fig.10.71), is self-explanatory. One important feature of servers concerns interrupt routines invoked by external devices. Such routines are located in the servers connected to the interrupting devices, not in the body of the program.

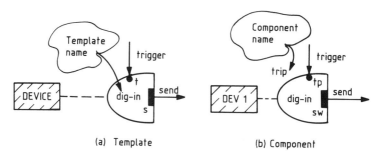

Fig.10.71 Server diagram

Top-level network diagrams, like those of Fig.10.72, are described in terms of these components. The corresponding system template module is shown in Listing 10.1. This may seem complex at first reading; in fact it is fairly easy to follow. The reason for including it here is to show that, at this top level, the system is completely and unambiguously described. This demonstrates a fundamental rule of MASCOT; a description at any level must be complete.

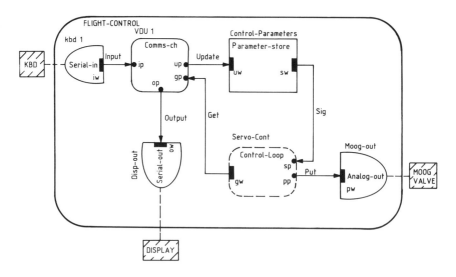

Fig.10.72 Top-level system network diagram

```
**************************************************************************
SYSTEM FLIGHT_CONTROL
   USES Serial_in, Comms_ch, Serial_out,
        Parameter_store, Control_loop, Analog_out;

      IDA Control_parameters:Parameter_store (uw=VDU1.up,
                                              sw=Servo_cont.sp);
      SERVER Kbd1:Serial_in (mw=VDU1.ip);
      SERVER Moog_out:Analog_out (pw=Servo_cont.pp);
      SERVER Disp_out:Serial_out (ow=VDU1.op);

      SUBSYSTEM VDU1:Comms_ch (ip=Kbd1.mw, up=Control_parameters.uw,
                               gp=Servo_cont.gw, op=Disp_out.ow);
      SUBSYSTEM Servo_control:Control_loop (sp=Control_parameters.sw,
                               pp=Moog_out, gw=VDU1.gp);
**************************************************************************
```

Listing 10.1 System template for Fig.10.72

As the diagram is decomposed individual sub-systems are elaborated. Finally they consist only of elementary processing elements (activities), channels and pools, Fig.10.73.

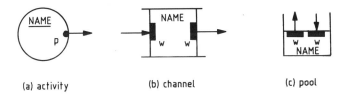

(a) activity   (b) channel   (c) pool

Fig.10.73 Activity, channel and pool templates

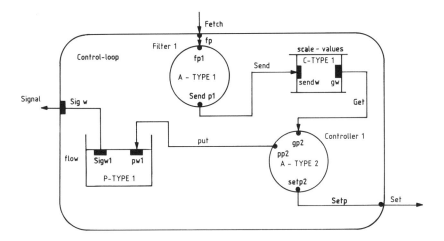

Fig.10.74 Decomposed sub-system diagram

A specimen decomposed sub-system diagram is that of Fig.10.74. Further decomposition is still necessary to show operations which define the program structure. Remember, each activity represents a concurrent task, built as a set of sequential actions. To model these single-thread actions another stage of elaboration is needed, Fig.10.75. Activity A_Type 1 is decomposed into three modules, mainroot, subroot1 and subroot2, connected by 'links'. One, and only one, module within an activity is defined as a 'root' component. This contains the initial entry coding for the activity, calling on services provided by the other components – the 'subroots'. Subroots consist of collections of procedures, being designed (usually) using structured methods (in effect a hierarchical abstract machine structure).

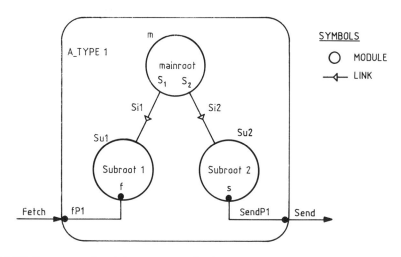

Fig.10.75 Decomposed activity – roots and subroots

Part of the text structure for this example – including specification and template modules – is shown in listing 10.2. In MASCOT these form the formal description of systems: **not** the diagrams. Some designers may consider this to be a major weakness of the method (contrast this with YSM and JSD where diagrams are an integral part of the design process).

10.5.7 Run-time support

In the MASCOT method two distinct classes of software are defined: application and support. Application software is that specifically written to carry out particular tasks; thus it varies from system to system. Support ('context') software is designed to provide service to the application software, mainly for executive functions and device handling (Fig.10.76). The design environment is similar to that provided by standard commercial operating systems. This is defined in full in the MASCOT design handbook; consult this for further information. The important point to note, however, is the provision of such support within the design method. This removes a burden from the shoulders of the application software developer.

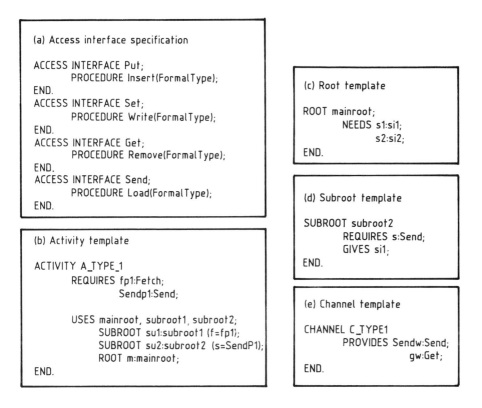

Listing 10.2 Decomposed sub-system – text modules (part)

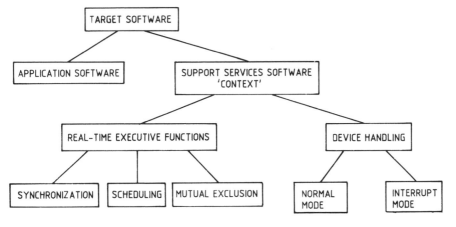

Fig.10.76 Target software structure

10.5.8 Design example

The MASCOT implementation – in part – of the steam propulsion system is described in Figs.10.77,10.78 and 10.79. Only two comments need to be made about this example. The first concerns component templates and implementations. MASCOT assumes that a general set of templates is devised; from these, particular instances are created. In practice it may be more sensible to make templates application specific – especially for smaller systems. In such cases only one instance is created from the template. The second comment relates to task scheduling. In this example we have three tasks which must be run at preset regular intervals. Nowhere is this information shown on the design diagrams or text descriptions. It is, in fact, implemented via the run-time support facilities of MASCOT.

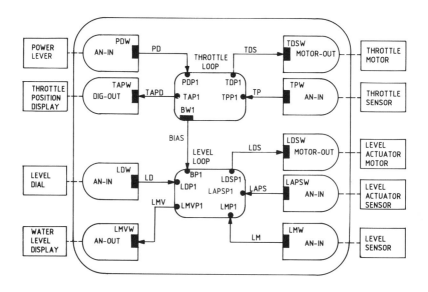

Fig.10.77 Example system – MASCOT network level diagram

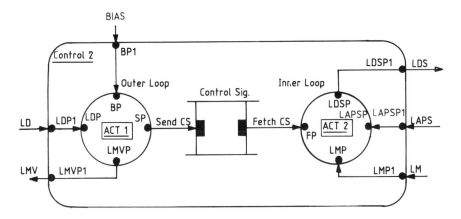

Fig.10.78 Example system – MASCOT decomposed subsystem

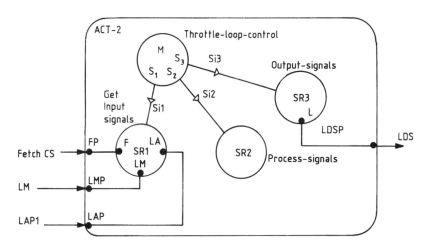

Fig.10.79 Example system – MASCOT activity decomposition – program level description

10.6 HOOD — HIERARCHICAL OBJECT-ORIENTED DESIGN

10.6.1 Introduction

Object-oriented design methods are now receiving serious attention by the real-time community. Both YSM and JSD are likely to incorporate OOD within their toolsets, some work having already been done in this area (Hull *et al.*, 1989). But, at the moment, the only available European real-time OOD tool is HOOD, developed by CISI Ingénierie, CRA A/S and Matra Aerospace. It can be used without regard to programming language support though currently it is targeted at Ada implementations. So far it has been used on projects for the

European Space Agency. Even so, because it is still evolving only an outline of the design process is given here.

10.6.2 Design fundamentals

HOOD covers the same parts of the life-cycle as JSD, the implementation part being Ada specific. Conceptually, though, it is very different. The method takes the output from the requirements analysis stage – and then expresses this information as a set of related objects. The basic design strategy (Fig.10.80) is based on hierarchical structuring; but seen from two distinct – yet complementary – points of view. In the first, (a), a conventional senior–junior abstract machine structure is formed. Senior machines (parent objects) use the operations provided by junior machines (also parent objects). However, any parent object may itself be broken down into lower level ('child') component objects, (b). These child objects, taken together, implement the function defined by the parent. In this way each top-level object can be described using a design process tree (DPT), Fig.10.81. At each stage a formal 'design step' is applied to the problem, its aim being to:

- Define and analyse the problem tackled by the object.
- Describe an informal high-level solution of the problem.
- Formalize the high-level informal description.
- Produce a formal solution to the problem.

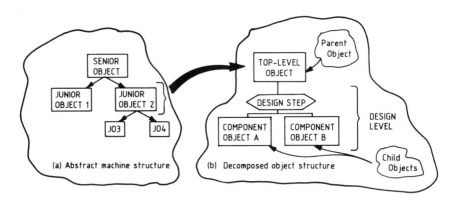

Fig.10.80 HOOD basic design strategy

This is shown in more detail in Fig.10.82. Note well: this process is carried out for **each** and **every** design step. Thus, at any level of decomposition, the description is complete and correct (although, as with MASCOT sub-systems, detailed information is omitted at higher levels). In Ada, a parent object is implemented in a Package Interface, child objects being contained in the corresponding Package Body.

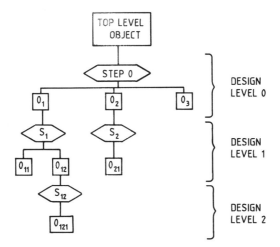

Fig.10.81 HOOD design process tree (DPT)

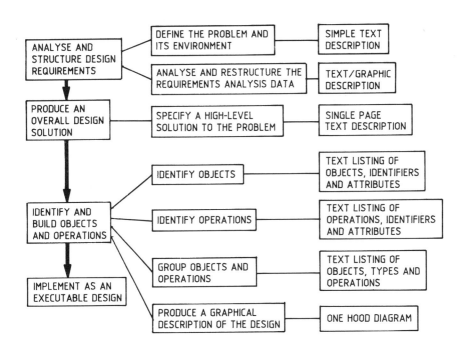

Fig.10.82 HOOD – structure of a basic design step

10.6.3 HOOD objects

An object is a model of 'something' in the real world. It contains both data relating to this real-world entity and operations which act on that data, Fig.10.83. It is characterized by what it does – its static properties – and how it does it – the dynamic features. The execution of an object operation can be done either passively or actively (chapter 4). Looked at from the point of view of the object user, passive execution involves:

- Transfer from the caller to the called object.
- Execution of the called operation.
- Return of control to the caller.

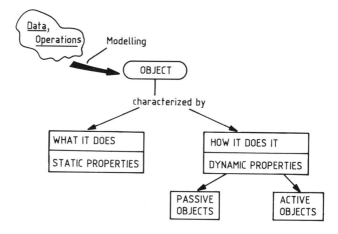

Fig.10.83 HOOD objects

This internal action within the callee is described in its operation control structure (OPCS). Each object 'provides' operations; it may or may not 'require' operations from other objects (Fig.10.84). All provided operations are defined in the object interface.

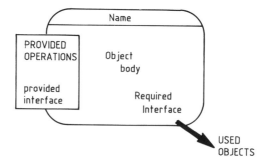

Fig.10.84 HOOD object symbol

Different symbols are used for passive and active objects, Fig.10.85. Moreover, external interrupt events can be described on the object diagram.

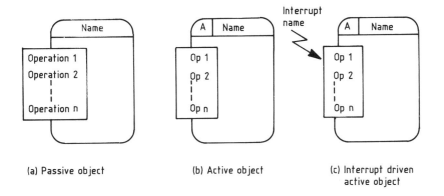

(a) Passive object   (b) Active object   (c) Interrupt driven
                                                           active object

Fig.10.85 Active and passive objects

10.6.4 Use of objects —control and dataflows

When an object (1) uses operations provided by a second object (2), then 1 is said to **use** 2. The relationship thus set up describes the control flow between these elements. HOOD imposes a set of rules governing the control flows in a system. An active type can freely use other objects, but passive ones may only use passive objects. Further, control flow between passive types must take place in a 'linear' manner, Fig.10.86; cyclic flows are forbidden (e.g. 3 cannot use 1).

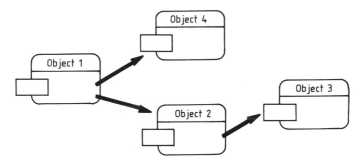

Fig.10.86 Control flow between passive objects

These rules set up a senior–junior hierarchy of elements. Active objects, because they can use all other ones, are at the top level. Passive types are located at lower levels.

For low coupling and high cohesion objects should:

- Use as few other objects as possible (low 'fan-out').
- Be used as much as possible (high 'fan-in').

Objects may use other objects without exchanging information. But where they do, this must be shown on the HOOD diagram as in Fig.10.87 (the word 'data' includes both data and event information). For this the symbol used is an arrow with a circled end, dataflow being in the direction of the arrow. The name of the data item is written alongside the arrow. In this example object X uses object Y – but data flow can be from X to Y (Fig.10.87a) or from Y to X (Fig.10.87b). More generally, two-way data transfer may be invoked. Note that the diagram itself doesn't distinguish between data and events – hence meaningful naming is important. In (a) the item, 'speed', represents a true data value, whereas 'running' in (b) is an event signal. Dataflows are implemented as parameters of the provided operations of the USED objects.

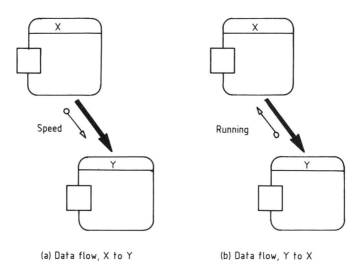

(a) Data flow, X to Y   (b) Data flow, Y to X

Fig.10.87 Dataflow between objects

10.6.5 Decomposition —the include relationship

As shown earlier, the complete structure of an object is derived in a top-down manner using object decomposition. That is, a parent object is divided into a number of child objects, where each child may be further decomposed. This can be shown informally on a DPT diagram. More formally it is described using an INCLUDE relationship, using both text and graphic notation, Fig.10.88. Here an include relationship is depicted by drawing children inside the parent. Operations at the parent level are set out in the parent operations list box. Operations provided by children are listed in **their** boxes. Operations listed at the parent level are actually implemented by those of the child; mapping between them is expressed using dashed arrows. As shown, when operation

OP2 is invoked by a user, operation ChildB.OP3 is that which is activated.

A child may use other children within the same parent; it may also use objects at the parent level, the so-called 'uncle object'.

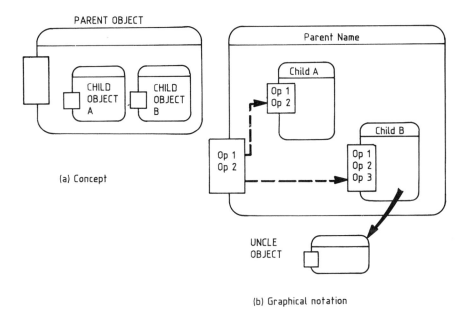

(a) Concept

(b) Graphical notation

Fig.10.88 Top-down decomposition – the include relationship

10.6.6 Object relationships and decomposition

There are different rules concerning the relationship and decomposition of passive and active objects.

(a) Passive objects
Passive types may be implemented in three ways, Fig.10.89. In the first case, (a), no decomposition is involved: there aren't any child operations. In (b), a parent operation at a senior level calls another parent operation at a lower level. For case (c), a parent function is provided by using a number of child objects.

In Ada, passive objects are implemented using packages (for Modula-2 the module would be used).

(b) Active objects
Active objects are primary building blocks of concurrent structures (which includes interrupt-driven activities). Fig.10.90 shows a number of different active task structures; each is best suited to particular system requirements.

In practice these aren't mutually exclusive; combinations are likely to be used. The Ada task is used for active object implementation; in Modula-2 the process would be used.

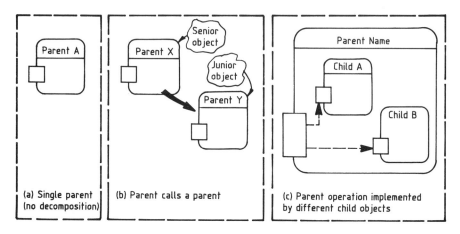

Fig.10.89 Passive object implementations

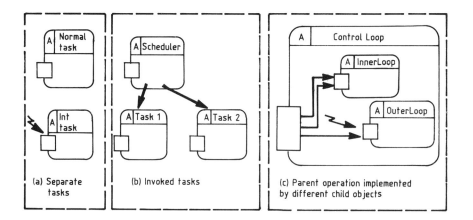

Fig.10.90 Active object implementations

For these designs communication and synchronization operations are intrinsic features. Therefore they should be described explicitly in the design documents. For HOOD designs this is done within a text unit called the 'object control structure'.

10.6.7 Exception handling

HOOD recognizes that exception handling is an essential part of real-time operations. It therefore includes graphical notation to describe the raising of an exception by used objects (Fig.10.91). HOOD assumes that Ada is the target language; thus it also assumes that exceptions are handled using the Ada 'raise exception' facility.

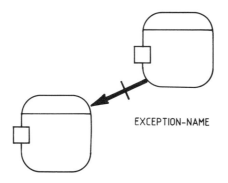

Fig.10.91 Raising exceptions

10.6.8 Formal text descriptions — the Object Definition Skeleton

So far diagrams have been used to describe design methods and solutions using HOOD. But, like MASCOT, the methodology is formalized using a text description of the design. This description is defined in a text document called the Object Definition Skeleton (ODS), written using the HOOD program design language (HOOD-PDL). The contents of an ODS are as follows:

- OBJECT name.
- DESCRIPTION of the object.
- PROVIDED INTERFACES – resources provided to other objects.
- REQUIRED INTERFACES – resources required from other objects.
- INTERNALS – description of the interface implementation.
- OBJECT CONTROL STRUCTURE – for active objects only.
- OPERATION CONTROL STRUCTURE – both exported and internal operations.
- EXCEPTION HANDLER.

The object described formally in HOOD-PDL is now transformed into Ada code, using the following relationships:

- Passive object → Package.
- Active object, no children → Task, declared in package body.
- Active object with children → Package with possibly embedded task body.
- Procedural operation → Procedure or function.
- Parallel operation → Task entry, or package entry linked to task entry.
- Exception → Exception.
- Class definition → Abstract data type (package) or generic package.
- Class-object instances → Type of package instantiation.
- Use and include actions → WITH clause.

10.6.9 Design example

The first HOOD diagram shows the top-most view of the system. But precisely what that view is depends on the level at which the analyst or designer is working. Like the CORE method it could well include people, real objects and combinations of hardware and software entities. Here, to keep things simple, we'll start at a fairly low level, as shown in Fig.10.92.

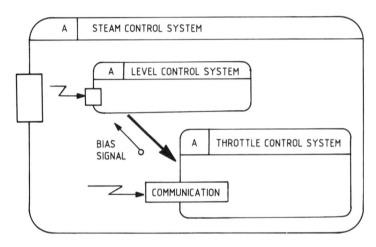

Fig.10.92 Example system – top-level HOOD diagram

At this stage a decision has already been made to partition the design using two processors, one for each control system. The objects within the throttle control system are now informally identified, as follows:

OBJECT: Power lever.
FUNCTION: Sets the demanded power for the throttle control system.
OPERATION PERFORMED: Measure power lever position.
OPERATION DEMANDED: Send position data (MEASURE DATA).

OBJECT: Throttle Position display.
FUNCTION: Displays the throttle position to the system operator.
OPERATION PERFORMED: Display throttle position.
OPERATION DEMANDED: Scale and set display data (DISPLAY DATA).

OBJECT: Throttle actuator.
FUNCTION: Drive and monitoring of the main steam throttle valve.
OPERATION PERFORMED: Drive actuator.
                    Measure actuator position.
OPERATION DEMANDED: Set actuator motor direction and speed
                    (SET DRIVE).
                    Send throttle valve position data
                    (MEASURE DATA).

OBJECT: Throttle controller.
FUNCTION: Control throttle actuator position.
OPERATION PERFORMED: Compute actuator drive signal
                    compute level loop bias signal.
OPERATION DEMANDED: Execute control loop calculations
                    (CONTROL).

OBJECT: Communication controller.
FUNCTION: Implement and support inter-processor communications.
OPERATION PERFORMED: Establish two-way communications with
                    processor 2.
OPERATION DEMANDED: Send bias signal (TRANSMIT/RECEIVE).

Their interaction is shown in Fig.10.93. To turn this into a full HOOD design
much detailed – and mainly textual – design work has to be done. Such detail
is beyond the scope of this text.

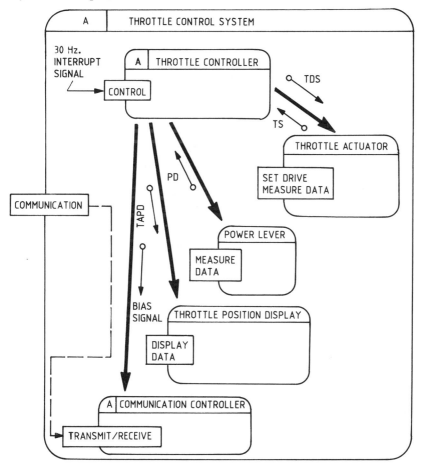

Fig.10.93 Example system – HOOD diagram for throttle controller

10.7   SOFTWARE TOOLS — AN OVERVIEW

10.7.1   The ideal tool

By now it should be clear that to achieve quality software we must use effective analysis and design techniques. Even so, this in itself is not enough. We also need proper tool support for such techniques. With these we can automate many stages of the process, minimize errors, increase productivity and provide good documentation. What then are the features and facilities of this ideal tool? Fundamentally they can be described in three ways:

- Basic facilities.
- Coverage provided for the development (and maintenance) process.
- Management of the tool facilities.

(a)   Basic facilities
Every computer-based system should have a good man–machine interface. Therefore our tool would have a large, high-resolution colour display screen, with both keyboard and mouse input devices. Text work would be implemented using a good word processor. Output devices would include both a laser printer and a colour printer. The system should be a multiuser one.

(b)   Coverage
Here the coverage is concerned mainly with the phases defined in Fig.10.1. Our tool must at least provide an integrated set of functions to deal with these. But it should also enable us to generate software prototypes, perform system simulation and formally prove software correctness. It should also provide reverse engineering for the maintenance of existing systems (that is, from source code back to design and specification documents).

   Note that for large systems, project management is often more important than design and development. However, as this is beyond the scope of the text, no more will be said on the subject.

(c)   Management of the tool facilities
The system should ensure, when creating documents and diagrams, that:

- The correct rules are followed.
- All the required steps are implemented.
- The end result is both complete and consistent.

Moreover, when items are modified it should impose a formal change control procedure. It must also keep track of the different versions when changes are made (version control).

   Our ideal tool doesn't exist at the present time, though some are getting very close to it. From an academic point of view such tools are a vital part of the software development process. Unfortunately, it ignores one major factor –

cost. These tools are extremely expensive, typically costing between £100,000 and £250,000. In reality only large companies can afford investments of this size (and they would only be justified for large software projects). No single solution exists to meet the diverse needs of the market place. In practice there is a range of options, varying in capability, coverage and cost. Each one fits onto a particular rung of the software tool ladder, Fig.10.94. These, known as Computer-Aided Software Engineering (CASE) tools, are discussed in general terms below. When reading this, bear one thing in mind; this subject is a rapidly moving target.

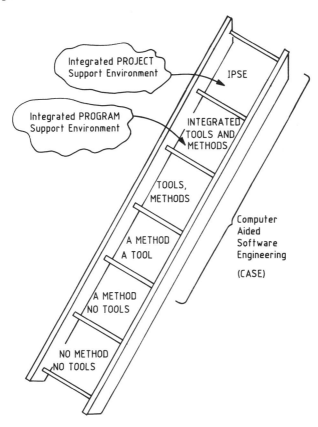

Fig.10.94 The ladder to better software

10.7.2 A method and a tool

The simplest form of tool is one that supports diagram production (we've already seen how important diagrams are to the design process). Drawing packages such as Digital Research's GEM are quite powerful and flexible. These are usually hosted on a PC or a Macintosh, costing typically between £200 and £500. The cost of the machine **should** also be taken into account, but as most users already have personal computers, this would merely be an exercise in creative accounting.

Tools like these unfortunately have one major drawback; they **are** only drawing packages. The user can draw exactly what he wants to, with no need to follow design rules or procedures. No discipline or control is imposed on the designer.

One step up from this are drawing packages specifically designed for software diagramming – which have inbuilt knowledge of design rules and text syntax. An example of this is 'MacCadd', developed by Logica Space and Defence Systems Ltd. It supports:

- Dataflow diagrams.
- Finite state machine diagrams.
- MASCOT (activity, channel, pool) diagrams.
- Structure diagrams.
- Generic network diagrams (i.e. those without any specific rules).

It enables the designer to decompose a single diagram in a top-down fashion into a series of diagram sheets. Any part of the diagram may be drawn in more detail on separate sheets, the tool ensuring automatic inheritance of information by the lower-level sheets. Consistency checks are performed across the diagrams, as also are checks for 'loose ends' (incomplete designs). Packages such as this cost much the same as general purpose drawing tools.

10.7.3 A combination of methods and tools

Quite frequently we find designers using a combination of different tools in the software development process. Generally there are two reasons for this: lack of tool coverage and/or piecemeal growth.

The first situation doesn't need explaining, it's clear enough. The second one occurs for a number of reasons. For instance, consider where a firm has invested in a low-cost tool for their first use of CASE technology. Naturally enough, such tools only apply to part of the development procedure. Suppose now that a decision is made to increase the use of CASE tools. It may turn out that the suppliers of the original tool don't have one to meet the new (extended) requirements. So any addition to the toolset must come from a different source – which usually turns out to be incompatible with the first one. It's not that the methodologies are incompatible: just that the tools aren't able to handle each other's files automatically. As a result individual parts of the total process are well controlled; but it's quite difficult to maintain consistency and version control across the complete design.

Diagrams are an essential part of modern design methods. But it should always be remembered that the really important factor is the **meaning** behind the diagram. With the tools described so far there isn't any automatic way of accessing this information. More powerful tools allow the designer to describe his problem in graphical terms, and then extract meaning from this. One such tool is the Program Development Facility (PDF) from Michael Jackson Systems Ltd. The basic input to it is a Jackson structure diagram of a single-thread program, the final output being source code. Program behaviour is described graphically in terms of sequence, selection and iteration operations. This could, of course, be drawn using MacCadd, but PDF is significantly more powerful. Its major feature is that information embedded in the structure diagram is used automatically in later design phases – so enforcing order, correctness and consistency.

10.7.4 Integrated program support environments

The integrated program support environment is a set of compatible software tools designed to automate the overall development process. Its purpose is to provide development support from requirements analysis through to physical design of the software. Quite specifically this excludes project management aspects of the task.

These toolsets come in two forms: those designed to support one specific design method and those which support a number of methods. Evaluating these isn't easy because many products provide only partial coverage; it's rarely a case of comparing like with like. Let's consider the first group first.

Typical of these are the tools provided by Yourdon International Ltd. and Michael Jackson Systems Ltd. The Yourdon Analyst/Designer Toolkit is a powerful, single-user, integrated toolset designed to run on a personal computer. The cost is approximately £2000. The roughly equivalent Jackson tool is the Speedbuilder/Network Builder combination, also designed to run on a PC. In its basic form it costs £3500, but many extensions are available. Using all these takes the tool cost to £13,000 (approximately).

There are many commercial toolkits available. Some support standard design methods such as DeMarco, Gane and Sarson, Yourdon, etc. Others have their own particular methods, though frequently these are based on well-known design techniques. Host machines frequently include the IBM PC (and compatibles), Apollo and Sun workstations and VAX minicomputers. The cost variation is very wide, from about £3000 to £50,000 (this is only a rough guide).

10.7.5 Integrated project support environments (IPSEs)

At the top of the ladder is the IPSE, designed to support and integrate the total software development process. This includes:

- General project management.
- Requirements analysis.
- Requirements specification.
- Architectural design.
- Implementation.

- Coding, debugging and testing.
- Verification and validation (using formal methods).
- Configuration control.
- Maintenance support.

For Ada environments these are usually called APSEs (Ada project support environments).

It is likely that similar toolkits have been developed for in-house use by firms such as IBM, DEC and Hewlett-Packard. However, few tools sold as IPSEs give complete coverage of all these items. Most concentrate on particular parts of the problem, often as a result of tool evolution to meet customer needs. As an example, the upgrade from the Yourdon Analyst/Designer Toolkit is to their advanced CASE toolset, 'CRADLE'. It is hosted on a much more powerful machine (typically an Apollo workstation), designed to support multiple users and multiple projects. Interaction between machines (for large projects) is done using network techniques and distributed data bases. A single-user installation is likely to cost in the region of £20,000 (allowing for the hardware needed for the toolkit). This represents the bottom end of the market (in terms of price, not performance). At the other extreme are installations costing over £250,000.

10.8 A LAST REVIEW

The primary aim of this chapter has been to describe techniques which translate theoretical ideas into practice. The need for, and use of, automated tools for the development of quality software should by now be obvious. Furthermore, it should be clear that while design methods may be different, their methodologies are much the same. Once the reader appreciates this he can make a better assessment of the various CASE tools on the market. It should also be clear from this chapter that there is no such thing as the perfect tool – it all depends on project size, complexity and the costs involved.

To give a comprehensive assessment of CASE tools is an enormous task, well beyond the scope of this book. And, because it's a rapidly changing subject, information quickly goes out of date. To obtain the current state of the subject the reader is advised to consult the National Computing Centre, Manchester. Their STARTS Guide (NCC, 1987) is an extremely useful data source, giving a reasonably unbiased view of the situation.

The closing message here is that there is only one real way to understand what's involved in the software design process: get out and do it. Taking just one project to completion using just one software tool provides significant insight and understanding – which can never be obtained from trawling through countless chapters like this.

REFERENCES

Cameron, J.R. (1983), The Jackson approach to software development, IEEE tutorial 516.

Cameron, J.R. (1986), An overview of JSD, *IEEE Transactions on Software Engineering*, Vol. SE-12, No.2, February, pp222–240.

Cameron, J.R. (1988), The modelling phase of JSD, *Software and Information Technology*, Vol.30, No.6, July/August, pp373–383.

Cameron, J.R. and Butcher, J.M.(1988), The use of JSD on the Spearfish system, second IEE/BCS Conference *Software Engineering 88*, University of Liverpool, 11–15 July, pp143–148.

Davies, J.A. and Scott-Gatty, S. (1987), Systems software for digital control and surveillance, 8th Ship Control Systems Symposium, October, The Hague, pp2.298–2.323.

Jackson, M.A. (1975), *Principles of Program Design*, Academic Press, London.

Jackson, M.A. (1988), Real-time embedded systems v commercial DP – never the twain shall meet: against. All systems are the same, second IEE/BCS Conference *Software Engineering 88*, University of Liverpool, 11–15 July, pp185–186.

Hatley, D. and Pirbhai, E. (1988), *Strategies for Real-time System Specification*, Dorset Publishing House, ISBN 0–932653–04–8.

Hull, M.E.C., *et al.*, (1989), Object-oriented design, Jackson system development (JSD) specifications and concurrency, *Software Engineering Journal*, March, pp79–86.

MASCOT (1983), *The Official Handbook of MASCOT, MASCOT II*, Issue 2, issued by the Joint IECCA (Inter-Establishment Committee on Computer Applications) and MUF (MASCOT Users' Forum) Committee on MASCOT (JIMCOM).

MASCOT (1987), *The Official Handbook of MASCOT, Version 3.1*, Issue 1, issued by JIMCOM, June.

NCC (1987), *The STARTS Guide – A Guide to Methods and Software Tools for the Construction of Large Real-time Systems*, NCC Publications, Manchester, ISBN 0–85012–619–3.

Ward, P.T. and Mellor, S.J. (1985), *Structured Development for Real-time Systems*, Vols.1, 2 and 3, Yourdon Press.

FURTHER READING

CORE – *Controlled Requirements Expression* (1986), Systems Designers plc, Fleet, Hampshire, GU13 8PD, UK, document no.1986/0786/500/PR/0158.

Fisher, A.S. (1988), *CASE: Using Software Development Tools*, John Wiley & Sons, New York.

HOOD, (1989), *HOOD Reference Manual*, Issue 3.0, Document no. WME/89–173/JB, European Space Research and Technology Centre.

Woodman, M. (1988), Yourdon dataflow diagrams: a tool for disciplined requirements analysis, *Information and Software Technology*, Vol.30, No.9, November, pp515–533.

Chapter Eleven

Development tools

The culminating point in embedded system design is the installation of correct, reliable and safe software into the target system. To use a well-known cliché, this is easier said than done. Even assuming that system specifications are clear, precise and agreed, many problems still have to be overcome. The final design and development phase can (no, will) be one of graft, perspiration and frustration. Any help at this stage is gratefully received. The early designers of microprocessor systems soon realized that existing instruments were inadequate. As a result, many tools have been developed over the years specifically to support this task. Such developments have been driven by the needs and demands of the user.

During this time microprocessor software became increasingly more complex. This complexity is mirrored by the facilities of the development support tools. Not surprisingly, the newcomer to the subject can easily be confused by the variety and features of such tools. So, this chapter sets out to show the need for and use of software development tools. Specifically it covers:

- Development environments.
- Host/target debugging facilities.
- Software debuggers.
- Hardware debuggers.
- In-circuit emulators.
- Logic analysers.
- PROM programmers and emulators.
- Performance analysis tools.

First, a definition. A 'bug' in this chapter means 'a localized implementation error rather than, say, an error introduced at the requirements or system-design stage' (Illingworth *et al.*, 1983).

11.1 THE DEVELOPMENT PROCESS

11.1.1 A preamble

Let's be very clear concerning the task of developing software for real-time systems. The end result of this process is to have correct, safe and reliable software running in a target system. In many cases the target will be a 'bare board' unit, having little or no support software. Frequently the board will be a new, untested, hardware design. Mass storage devices such as floppy/Winchester disks are rarely available for use in the target. True, these are occasionally designed into embedded systems. However, they are usually integrated into the design only after the processor board itself has been proven. Similar comments apply to display terminals. Given these conditions, it isn't surprising that the target software cannot be developed on the target itself. Instead we use a separate machine, the so-called 'host' system.

11.1.2 The host-target environment

What facilities should the host provide, and how should it interact with the target? Fig.11.1 lays out the basic software development production cycle which has evolved with time and experience. The process starts with the typing in of the source program itself. Thus keyboard and display facilities are needed, together with text-handling software. Such a software package is called an editor. The source program or 'source code' is assembled or compiled into a linkable file. In a small system this would be the complete target program. For most systems, though, we develop software using program building blocks. In their simplest form these are libraries of commonly-used functions. The linker software allows us to integrate our program with such libraries. But even more importantly, we don't have to consider the internal details of such programs, only their interfaces. This feature enables us to design programs in a truly modular fashion.

At this stage the complete program is held in storage in the host system. All relative addressing has been sorted out. Next, the actual or 'absolute' addresses have to be set using the locator program. This must be done to allow for differing memory usage of RAM and ROM in target systems. After this the 'object' file is set up by the loader software so that it can be executed by the PROM programming utility program. The final operation in the host is to run the programming utility software. Once the EPROM is programmed it is removed from the programmer, inserted into the target board, and the target unit checked out.

This forms the basis of current and future software techniques (Fig.11.2). Major changes from earlier systems are that:

- The link-locate-load actions are usually invoked as a single operation, the so-called 'absolute linker'.
- PROM programmers are mainly stand-alone, separate, units. They communicate with the host using serial and/or parallel interfaces.
- PROM emulators are often used to eliminate the actual device programming stage.
- The source program can be executed on the host (but with many limitations, see later).

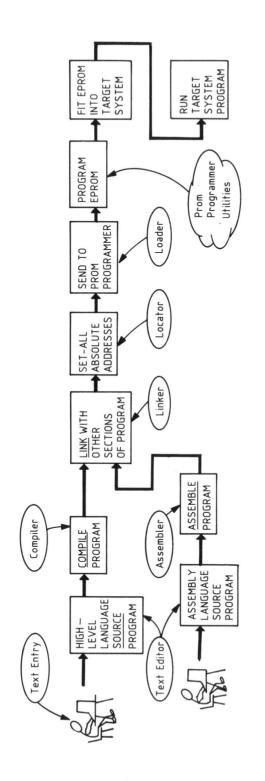

Fig.11.1 Microprocessor software development process – past/current methods

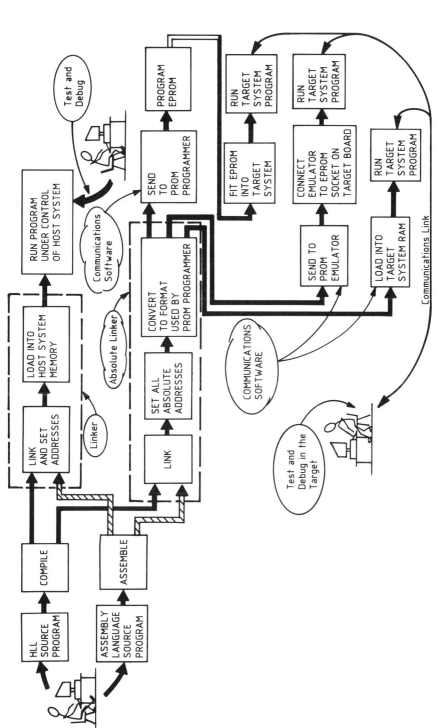

Fig.11.2 Microprocessor software development process – current/future methods

To repeat, Fig.11.2 describes the **basis** of modern development systems. But many more facilities, both hardware and software, are needed to meet the needs of current microprocessor designs.

11.1.3 Causes and effects of run-time malfunctions

If we could always produce error-free software and hardware then the facilities of Fig.11.2 are all that we need. Unfortunately, this is a mythical situation. New hardware never works correctly and almost any target code contains bugs. Tracking down these faults frequently reduces normally sane and balanced engineers to a demented state. Even when software does what it's supposed to do it may run too slowly.

No single tool can analyse and solve these problems. As a result a number of types have been developed (Fig.11.3). System run-time errors are due both to hardware faults and software bugs. Such errors can be made in a number of ways (Fig.11.4), as described in chapter 2. Notice that certain syntactic mistakes and those due to misunderstandings of system requirements are not included. The reasons for this are that:

- These syntax errors are those which are picked up by the compiler or assembler. Therefore they can't produce run-time faults.
- Misunderstandings of task requirements (task-semantic errors) do not cause run-time faults. Programs will run exactly as designed; unfortunately the designs are wrong. Tools devised as program development aids cannot possibly recognize such mistakes.

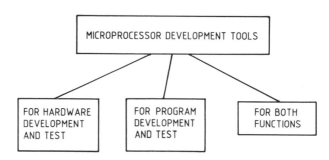

Fig.11.3 Development tool requirements

What are the effects of software bugs? First (and fairly obviously) the target program won't do what it's supposed to do. The resulting behaviour is wide-ranging and unpredictable. Time and effort spent in tracking down such bugs ('debugging') can seriously affect development timescales. Ultimately these lead to commercial and financial problems such as late delivery and project overspends. As a result, commercial factors have greatly influenced the evolution of development tools. Success comes to those who can deliver good software and systems in the shortest possible time. Never forget that economics is one of the strongest driving forces in our cultural system.

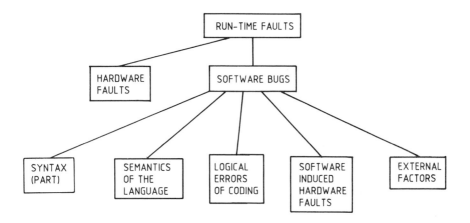

Fig.11.4 Causes of run-time faults

11.1.4 The modern development process

In early microprocessor developments, hardware and software design was treated very much as an integrated activity. Little or no software proving was carried out prior to running it in the target. Most code was written in assembly language, requiring a high level of expertise to analyse and correct mistakes. Further, debugging tools were fairly primitive. Hence coping with simultaneous hardware and software problems was an uphill task. So it's not surprising that it could take a long time to finalize even small programs.

Economic pressures have resulted in a convergence towards a particular development process (Fig.11.5). First, hardware is treated as a separate design and development action. On new and specialized designs such work is carried out concurrent with the software design. The myth that hardware cannot be developed separately from software has been well laid to rest. Many designers now use standard hardware such as VME, STE and Multibus (Cooling, 1986), installing their own application software as required. The process outlined here has the same purpose; to enable the designer to embed his software in fully tested and operational hardware.

If software is checked out by loading code into EPROM, fitting this into the target, running the system, then re-doing the source code, loading into EPROM . . . debugging becomes a long and tedious task. How many changes to source code can be made in a day? This is rather like 'how long is a piece of string?'; it depends on many factors. But we **can** give a sort of ball-park figure. Working with a program size of 10–20 kByte, and using fairly fast EPROM programming methods, we are unlikely to exceed 20 change cycles per day. This productivity level speaks for itself. As a result great emphasis is now placed on tools which enable us to develop and test software on the host machine. Practical experience has shown that major productivity gains are made in this way.

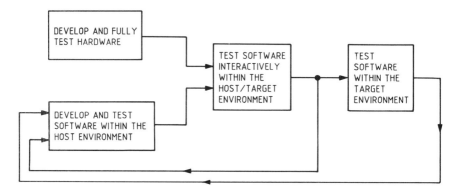

Fig.11.5 The modern microprocessor development process

Unfortunately, for a number of reasons, this can validate only part of the complete software task. For instance:

- The hardware configuration (memory, I/O, special devices) of host and target are very unlikely to be the same.
- It is doubtful if real-time interfacing and signalling can be accommodated on the host.
- The host clock rate may not be the same as that of the target.
- The host CPU may not even be the same as that of the target.
- It is doubtful whether hardware interrupts specific to the target system can be handled within the host.

The next stage is to test the software when it is actually located in the target. This validates it in its design environment. By doing this interactively with the host, however, high productivity levels can be maintained. We have access to and use of all host facilities. These include large-volume disk storage, graphics displays, hard-copy printouts, program disassembly and performance monitoring and evaluation.

A number of methods and tools have been developed for such work. In general, they avoid using on-board EPROM during this phase. Sometimes the program runs in the target RAM. Such testing usually involves disturbing the normal operation of the program; hence it cannot be regarded as the ultimate test. More complex tools minimize such restrictions. They provide the memory elements (and sometimes the CPU itself) needed for the task. However, until programs run entirely within the target system, testing is incomplete.

What do we do when bugs are found at this final stage? If we've followed the process described above then the errors are likely to be very subtle ones. At this point there really aren't quick and easy solutions. It's rather like a war of attrition, slogging through the problems one by one. Fortunately, they should be few in number. Experience has shown that, in this situation, tools oriented towards hardware debugging are the most useful. There is now, in fact, quite an overlap between hardware and software debuggers for this level of work.

Microprocessor debugging tools were developed simultaneously from two directions. At one end of the spectrum were the pure hardware items; at the other the host software tools. Initially these were simple and basic. With improvements and refinements they have become complex and extremely powerful (and often very expensive). At the same time the boundaries have blurred between the two areas. The move is towards an integrated workstation which supports all aspects of the development work. This is typified by the modern PC-based microprocessor development system (MDS).

Debugging tools tell us much about the embedded software. But what they don't do is produce information concerning the run-time performance of the code. For instance, how fast does a section of code run? How many times are particular procedures called? True, we can get at such data, but it's not usually an easy process. And, for real-time systems, run-time performance is the bottom line of the design process. In response to these needs, performance analysis tools are being produced for integration within the MDS environment. These represent the latest stage of software and hardware developments for MDSs.

In the following sections the points discussed above are covered in detail.

11.2 SOFTWARE DEBUGGING —AN OVERVIEW

One point must be clearly understood. Software debugging is concerned with error detection in the software, not in the hardware. We assume that the hardware is fault-free. Hardware faults induced by software are here regarded as software errors; so they are included in the listing of software bugs.

A simplistic view of program execution ('journey into the unknown') is depicted in Fig.11.6. The complete program consists of the instructions and data needed to get from A to B. Along the way many actions are carried out. Data is collected, deposited and modified, output devices activated and input devices interrogated. When B is reached and all actions correctly performed we can be pretty sure that the program is correct.

Now, how do we test this program? The simplest way is to install it in the target system and run it. In fact, unless special test tools are available, this is our only option. If the program executes as predicted, that's fine. But what if we arrive at C instead of B, carrying the wrong baggage? Or, even more confusing, what if this happens only occasionally, the program running correctly most times? Further, it isn't just enough to arrive at the destination clutching the correct information. All intermediate activities and data changes must also have been done exactly as desired.

Let's assume that errors exist. How can these be tracked down? The most basic method is to print out a source code listing and carefully analyse its operation. This is a time-consuming and tedious task. And it doesn't necessarily provide the answer. For instance, suppose that the mistake is caused by wrongly using an assembler instruction; for some reason we've misunderstood its operation. In this situation no amount of searching through the program listing is going to help. The only option now is to work through the program bit by bit to find the bug. As pointed out earlier, this is a very lengthy, dispiriting and expensive task. What we really need are tools which allow us to search for bugs much more directly.

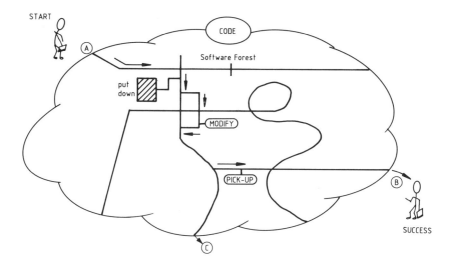

Fig.11.6 The program – journey into the unknown

What are the primary requirements of such tools? These must be able to elicit three fundamental aspects of the program under test (Fig.11.7):

- What happened within the program as it executed?
- What objects were changed by the program along the way, and how was this done?
- What did the program pick up along the way, and how was this done?

From the debugging point of view it is extremely helpful to use a heuristic approach (i.e. the 'what if'). Thus the ability to change the original program while interrogating it is also a basic requirement.

In response to these needs a wide range of tools has been developed, Fig.11.8; study this figure carefully. Three distinct debugging environments have been identified:

- On the host only.
- In the target system.

● In the host when this itself is also the target.

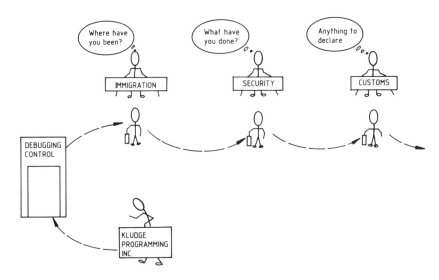

Fig.11.7 Debriefing a bugged program

(a) Host-only debugging

For host-only methods the simplest development tool is a utility package supplied with the operating system. This is the cheapest solution of all. However, it normally only supports debugging at assembly language level. More comprehensive features are available from specialist debugging packages; moreover, these normally allow the user to interact with high-level language source code. Naturally these cost more than the utility package. An alternative at this stage is to use debugging tools supplied as part of a language development package. This last item is possibly one of the most significant developments in recent times.

(b) In the target

For reasons discussed later, host system software debuggers are unable to test target system software fully. Such software can only be fully validated in their final settings. Two methods can be used in the target: software-based or hardware-assisted techniques.

To use software methods some form of target debugger support package must be installed into the target system. In its simplest form it may be an elementary monitor package developed by the user. Interaction with the target board is normally done using a dumb terminal connected via a serial communication link. Commercial packages are available which do much the same job; these eliminate the need to produce a home-grown variety. The more powerful ones enable the tester to work using high-level language source operations. Further, these usually replace the dumb terminal with some form

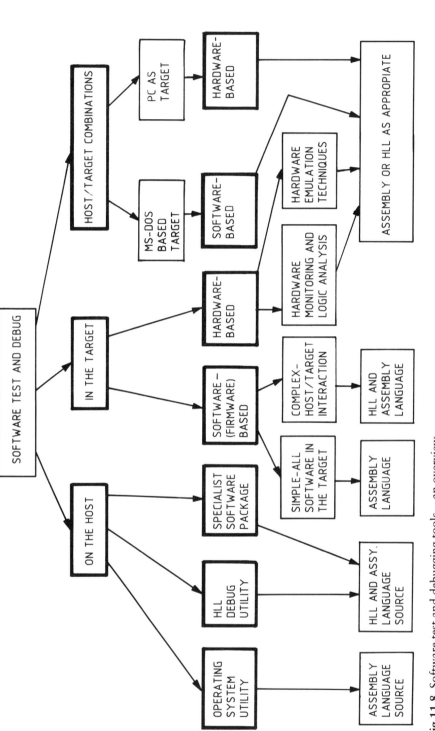

Fig.11.8 Software test and debugging tools – an overview

of host machine (typically a PC). The result is a much more powerful and comprehensive debugging system. Similar facilities are also provided in some modern language support packages; this approach is expected to be the norm in future.

No matter how good software-based tools are, they suffer from one fundamental limitation. Using these methods, debugging is essentially an invasive process. That is, we interfere with the execution of the program. As a result, program behaviour during debugging just isn't the same as that on a normal run. Other restrictions exist (discussed later), but this is the primary one. To overcome this we have to resort to hardware test tools designed for debugging purposes. These allow us to run and observe program execution at full speed with proper isolation between the debugger and target programs. The simpler hardware tools are designed specifically for this purpose. However, more advanced hardware tools such as the In-Circuit Emulator (ICE) do much more than support simple software debugging. These features are described later.

(c) Host as target
In microprocessor systems, it isn't often the case that the host is also the target. Some manufacturers **do** supply microprocessor development systems based on the target hardware. These are usually augmented by disk and terminal facilities. The target software is debugged on this system using disk-based software. Once proven, the programs are blown into EPROM and loaded into the target proper. So even here the host and the target are distinct machines. However, in the last few years a whole industry has grown up around the ubiquitous PC. The number of specialized software packages and plug-in boards developed for the IBM PC (and clones) is immense. Here, software can be developed on the host (the PC), destined to run on the PC itself (the target). As a result a market has been generated for debugging tools specifically for PC development. Hardware debugging tools used for this particular function are generally termed 'hardware-aided (or -assisted) software debugging tools'. ICE is a general purpose tool. In contrast, hardware-aided debuggers can be used only with software which runs on the host machine.

11.3 SOFTWARE DEBUGGING ON THE HOST

11.3.1 Dynamic debugging tool —the operating system utility

Dynamic debugging tools (DDTs) have been around for a long time (DEC, 1974). Originally they were developed for assembly language operations on mainframe and mini-computers. So it's not surprising that DDT concepts were introduced at an early stage into microprocessor systems. One of the first (possibly even **the** first) was DDT from Digital Research for the CP/M (Control Program/Microcomputer) operating system. The most recent form is

```
                    ;LISTING 11.1
                    ;FileName: Demo.A86
                    CSEG

                    ;Software interrupt 250 is used to allow transfer
                    ;of control from the bootstrap program to the
                    ;Modula-2 one.
     00FA           StartModula EQU 250      ;interrupt 250
     03E8           StartModulaInt EQU  (250*4)

                    ;Here are the vector interrupt settings in EPROM.
                    ;These are transfered to RAM during
                    ;initialisation.
                    ORG StartModulaInt
     03E8 0000      StartIntOffset DW 0H
     03EA 0098      StartIntSegment DW 9800H


                    ;********************************************************
                    ;********************************************************

                    ;Here is the start of the bootstrap program.
                    ORG 100H;
                    StartBootstrap:

                    ;Set up the Data segment register so that it
                    ;points to the bottom of the bootstrap ROM.
     0100 B800FE    MOV AX,0FE00H
     0103 8ED8      MOV DS,AX


                    ;This sets up the jump to the start of the
                    ;Modula-2 program.
     0105 2EA1E803  MOV AX,StartIntOffset
     0109 26A3E803  MOV ES:StartIntOffset, AX
     010D 2EA1EA03  MOV AX,StartIntSegment
     0111 26A3EA03  MOV ES:StartIntSegment, AX

                    ;Set up the Data segment registor so that it
                    ;points to the bottom of RAM.
     0115 B80000    MOV AX,0H;
     0118 8ED8      MOV DS,AX;
     011A FB        STI
     011B CDFA      INT StartModula

     END OF ASSEMBLY. NUMBER OF ERRORS:   0.  USE FACTOR   0%
```

LISTING 11.1

DDT-86, used with CP/M-86 and Concurrent DOS (Digital Research, 1983). Its equivalent for MS-DOS (Microsoft DOS) is 'Debug'. Below are described the overall features of dynamic debugging tools, illustrated by examples using DDT-86.

Consider that the programmer has written the following code so as to set up a particular interrupt in his system (Listing 11.1). Suppose that this failed to run correctly in the target system. The first question is 'what happened?', the second being 'why?' Let's start by verifying whether the code executes as intended. This, at least, will indicate whether or not the error is a logical one. DDT-86 is the selected debugging tool.

What functions (at a minimum) must DDT contain? Fig.11.9 shows the overall features of the debugger. These requirements will be explained by working through the faulty program.

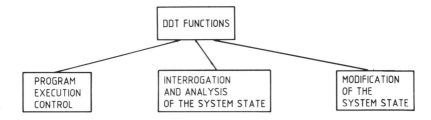

Fig.11.9 DDT – Basic functions

The purpose of this piece of code is to load up information at defined addresses for use by the interrupt system. After execution we should have the following situation:

address	0:3E8H	0:3E9H	0:3EAH	0:3EBH
data	00H	00H	00H	98H

A first check can be done quickly by:

● Presetting the address contents (a modification function).
● Running the program to a defined point (control).
● Examining the resulting state of the address contents (interrogation).

Using the DDT utility functions, the program is loaded into host RAM and its location is obtained. As a further check, the actual memory contents can be listed in assembler form (Listing 11.2). This seems correct. Now the memory contents at the above noted addresses are set ('filled' – F) to FFH. These values (now called the 'vector values' for simplicity) are then displayed (D) to ensure that the command was properly executed (Listing 11.3). The program can now be executed at full speed up to the required point, the so-called 'breakpoint'. The command is 'G', the breakpoint being at memory address 2F98:011B.

After execution the vector values are displayed (Listing 11.4). It can be seen that these have not been changed by the program.

```
L2F98:100,11B

2F98:0100 MOV   AX,FE00
2F98:0103 MOV   DS,AX
2F98:0105 CS:   MOV   AX,[03E8]
2F98:0109 ES:   MOV   [03E8],AX
2F98:010D CS:   MOV   AX,[03EA]
2F98:0111 ES:   MOV   [03EA],AX
2F98:0115 MOV   AX,000
2F98:0118 MOV   DS,AX
2F98:011A STI
2F98:011B INT   FA
```

LISTING 11.2

```
F0:3E8,3EB,FF


-D0:3E8,3EB
0000:03EB FF FF FF FF
```

LISTING 11.3

```
G2F98:100,11B
*2F98:011B

-D0:3E8,3EB
0000:03EB FF FF FF FF.....
```

LISTING 11.4

It's been established that the program doesn't do what it should. To find out what actually happens it is necessary to follow the program through step by step, the so-called 'Trace' facility. At each step the state of the system can be examined. Listing 11.5 is representative of the trace function in action. Careful examination of this shows that the ES register value is 2F98. However, ES is used as the segment register in the instructions.

Clearly the problem is due to failing to set this register correctly. The source file **could** be amended to take this into account, then assembled and checked. It is quicker, however, if direct modifications can be made to code within the debug activity. Such modifications are called 'patching'. In this case the new assembly language statements are entered ('assemble' – A), the program executed and the vector values examined (Listing 11.6). This modification has achieved its desired result. Now the source code can be modified and a final check carried out using DDT.

```
T2F98:100,11A
?
-TS8
               AX   BX   CX   DX   SP   BP   SI   DI   CS   DS   SS   ES   IP
--1-----     0000 0000 0000 0000 005C 0000 0000 0000 2F98 2F98 2C1A 2F98 0100
MOV  AX,FE00
--1-----     FE00 0000 0000 0000 005C 0000 0000 0000 2F98 2F98 2C1A 2F98 0103
MOV  DS,AX
--1-----     FE00 0000 0000 0000 005C 0000 0000 0000 2F98 FE00 2C1A 2F98 0105
CS:  MOV AX,[03E8]
--1-----     0000 0000 0000 0000 005C 0000 0000 0000 2F98 FE00 2C1A 2F98 0109
ES:  MOV [03E8],AX
--1-----     0000 0000 0000 0000 005C 0000 0000 0000 2F98 FE00 2C1A 2F98 010D
CS:  MOV AX,[03EA]
--1-----     9800 0000 0000 0000 005C 0000 0000 0000 2F98 FE00 2C1A 2F98 0111
ES:  MOV [03EA],AX
--1-----     9800 0000 0000 0000 005C 0000 0000 0000 2F98 FE00 2C1A 2F98 0115
MOV  AX,0000
--1-----     0000 0000 0000 0000 005C 0000 0000 0000 2F98 FE00 2C1A 2F98 0118
MOV  DS,AX
--1-----     0000 0000 0000 0000 005C 0000 0000 0000 2F98 0000 2C1A 2F98 011B
```

LISTING 11.5

```
A2F98:FB,
2F98:00FB MOV AX,0
2F98:00FE MOV ES,AX
2F98:0100

L2F98:FB,11A
2F98:00FB MOV    AX,0000
2F98:00FE MOV    ES,AX
2F98:0100 MOV    AX,FE00
2F98:0103 MOV    DS,AX
2F98:0105 CS:    MOV  AX,[03E8]
2F98:0109 ES:    MOV  [03E8],AX
2F98:010D CS:    MOV  AX,[03EA]
2F98:0111 ES:    MOV  [03EA],AX
2F98:0115 MOV    AX,0000
2F98:0118 MOV    DS,AX
2F98:011A STI

G2F98:FB,11B
*2F98:011B

-DO:3E8,3EB
0000:03E8 00 00 00 98.....
```

LISTING 11.6

This is not intended to be a tutorial on DDT. What it does though, is introduce the basic features of all software debugging tools. These are to:

- List the program, as loaded for debugging, in assembler mnemonics.

- Execute the program under debugger control.
- Set program breakpoints as required.
- Trace the program as it executes.
- Single-step through the program.
- Modify processor and program status during trace and step.
- Modify memory contents.
- Patch the program without the need to re-assemble it.

The above example is only a fragment of a program. When DDT is applied to code of any sensible size it becomes awkward to use. Consequently, software debugging tools have been produced to meet the demands of frustrated DDT users.

11.3.2 Assembly level language debuggers —specialist packages

Specialist packages have been developed mainly to extend the facilities of DDT. To appreciate these extensions we must understand the limitations of early debugging tools.

In the previous example, when the bug was found, new instructions were added to correct the mistake. Notice that these were placed before the ones produced by the assembler. Trying to insert statements within the existing code using the simpler dynamic debuggers can be very difficult (or impossible). This comes about because DDT usually works in terms of absolute addresses and numbers. Changing these at debug time is not the easiest of tasks.

A further restriction met in low-cost debuggers can be seen by comparing Listings 11.1 and 11.2. The first contains program symbol names; the second doesn't. All references are again given in terms of absolute addresses and values.

A third important feature in any debugger is the amount of information given during the trace operation.

Major improvements to DDT at the assembler level fall into four categories (Fig.11.10):

- Symbolic debugging.
- Interactive patching.

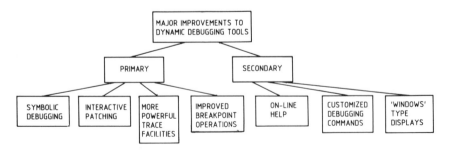

Fig.11.10 Major improvements to DDT at the assembler level

- Trace facilities.
- Breakpoint operations.

(a)   Symbolic level debugging

Symbolic representation of program items is the norm in modern assembly language programming. Symbolic debugging is the ability to reference such symbols instead of using their absolute addresses. Without this feature debugging is time consuming, tedious and error prone. Fig.11.11 shows how symbol manipulation commands can be used in practice, this being done using the Atron software source probe (ATRON, 1989).

(b)   Interactive patching

This leads directly to the second point, interactive patching. By using program symbols, on-line patching can be carried out without having to worry about absolute addresses (Fig.11.12). While on-line patching can speed up the debugging process it cannot be recommended as a routine way of working.

(c)   Trace facilities

The debugging process can be greatly speeded up by providing more and better information during the trace operation. The ATRON debugger facilities include – in addition to that shown in Listing 11.5 – displays of stack, I/O and bus operations, interrupt cycles and data transferred during execution cycles (Fig.11.13).

(d)   Breakpoint operations

With DDT, the number of breakpoints is quite limited; further, their locations are specified in absolute address form. That is, each breakpoint is designated as a point within the program code; the effects due to data values or program operations are not taken into account. Such a breakpoint is termed an 'execution' type. But there is also a need for non-execution breakpoints. A modern tool such as the ATRON supports both execution and non-execution breakpoints, including:

- Unconditional read of memory or I/O.
- Unconditional write to memory or I/O.
- Qualified memory or I/O read or write.
- Complex (multiple) breakpoint sequences.

Other (secondary) improvements are less fundamental in nature. They generally aim to simplify the use of the debugger and improve productivity. That isn't to say that they are less important: far from it. Such enhancements (Fig.11.10) include:

- On-line help, incorporating screen windowing techniques.
- Creation and use of customized debugging commands.
- Data display in clear, understandable form.

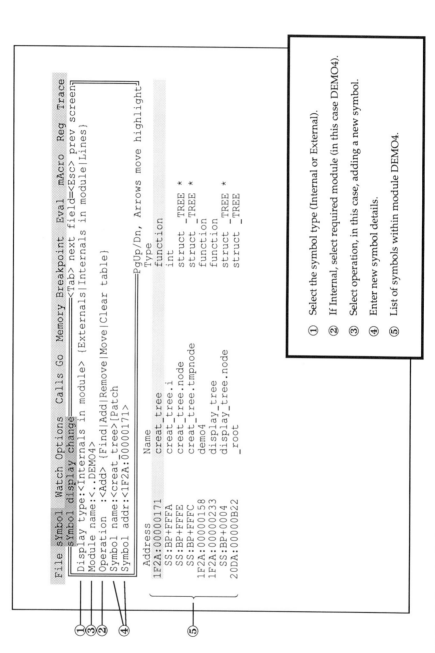

```
File sYmbol Watch Options Calls Go Memory Breakpoint Eval mAcro Reg Trace
       sYmbol display change        <Tab> next field=<Esc> prev screen
Display type:<Internals in module> {Externals|Internals in module|Lines}
Module name:<..DEMO4>
Operation :<Add> {Find|Add|Remove|Move|Clear table}
Symbol name:<creat_tree>[Patch
Symbol addr:<1F2A:00000171>
                                    PgUp/Dn, Arrows move highlight
Address         Name              Type
1F2A:00000171   creat_tree        function
SS:BP+FFFA      creat_tree.i      int
SS:BP+FFFE      creat_tree.node   struct _TREE *
SS:BP+FFFC      creat_tree.tmpnode struct _TREE *
1F2A:00000158   demo4             function
1F2A:00000233   display_tree      function
SS:BP+0004      display_tree.node struct _TREE *
20DA:00000B22   _root             struct _TREE
```

① Select the symbol type (Internal or External).

② If Internal, select required module (in this case DEMO4).

③ Select operation, in this case, adding a new symbol.

④ Enter new symbol details.

⑤ List of symbols within module DEMO4.

Fig.11.11 Symbol manipulation

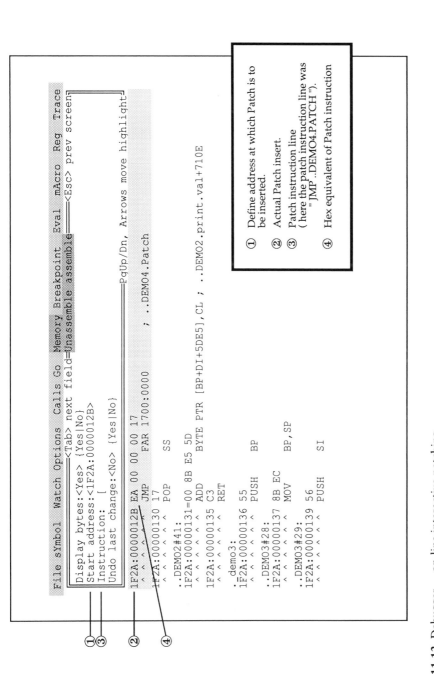

```
  File sYmbol  Watch  Options  Calls Go  Memory Breakpoint  Eval  mAcro  Reg  Trace
                           <Tab> next field=Unassemble assemble====<Esc> prev screen
  Display bytes:<Yes> {Yes|No}
  Start address:<1F2A:0000012B>
  Instruction: [
  Undo last change:<No> {Yes|No}
  ===================================================PgUp/Dn, Arrows move highlight

  1F2A:0000012B EA 00 00 00 17    JMP  FAR 1700:0000    ;   ..DEMO4.Patch
       ^ ^ ^ ^ ^  POP  SS
  1F2A:00000130 17
       ^ ^ ^ ^ ^
  ..DEMO2#41:
  1F2A:00000131=00 8B E5 5D    ADD  BYTE PTR [BP+DI+5DE5],CL ;  ..DEMO2.print.val+710E
  1F2A:00000135 C3            RET
       ^ ^ ^ ^ ^
  .demo3:
  1F2A:00000136 55            PUSH  BP
       ^ ^ ^ ^ ^
  ..DEMO3#28:
  1F2A:00000137 8B EC         MOV   BP,SP
       ^ ^ ^ ^ ^
  ..DEMO3#29:
  1F2A:00000139 56            PUSH  SI
       ^ ^ ^ ^ ^
```

① Define address at which Patch is to be inserted.

② Actual Patch insert.

③ Patch instruction line (here the patch instruction line was "JMP ..DEMO4.PATCH").

④ Hex equivalent of Patch instruction

Fig.11.12 Debugger – on-line interactive patching

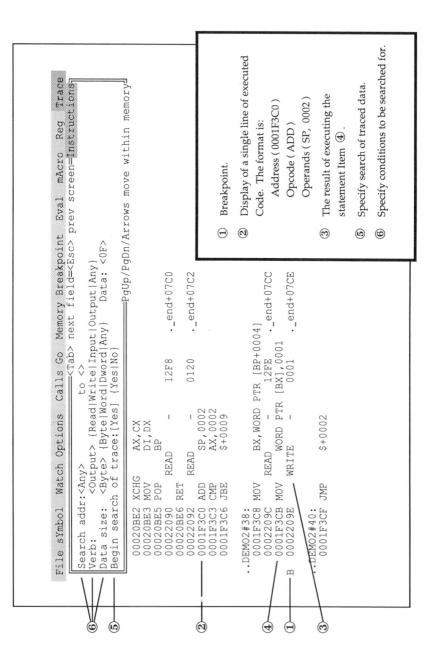

```
File sYmbol Watch Options Calls Go Memory Breakpoint Eval mAcro Reg Trace
                                  <Tab> next field=<Esc> prev screen=Instructions
Search addr:<Any>        to <>
Verb:       <Output> {Read|Write|Input|Output|Any}
Data size:  <Byte> {Byte|Word|Dword|Any}    Data: <0F>
Begin search of trace:[Yes] [Yes|No}          PgUp/PgDn/Arrows move within memory

00020BE2 XCHG    AX,CX
00020BE3 MOV     DI,DX
00020BE5 POP     BP
00022090 READ    -       12F8    ._end+07C0
00020BE6 RET
00022092 READ    -       0120    ._end+07C2
0001F3C0 ADD     SP,0002
0001F3C3 CMP     AX,0002
0001F3C6 JBE     $+0009

..DEMO2#38:
0001F3C8 MOV     BX,WORD PTR [BP+0004]
0002209C READ    -       12FE    ._end+07CC
0001F3CB MOV     WORD PTR [BX],0001
0002209E WRITE   -       0001    ._end+07CE

..DEMO2#40:
0001F3CF JMP     $+0002
```

① Breakpoint.

② Display of a single line of executed Code. The format is:
   Address (0001F3C0)
   Opcode (ADD)
   Operands (SP, 0002)

③ The result of executing the statement Item ④.

⑤ Specify search of traced data.

⑥ Specify conditions to be searched for.

Fig.11.13 ATRON debugger – trace display

11.3.3 High-level language debuggers —general

Why should we want to debug at a high-level language source code level? If we do decide to work at this level, what features and facilities are needed? Finally, what tools are available to us? These are the questions we seek to answer in the following sections. Note in passing that 'source level' debugging is generally understood as debugging the high-level source language.

(a)   Why debug at a high level?
We can best appreciate HLL debugging by looking at developments in this topic from early days onwards. In the 'dark ages' of microcomputers few real-time high-level languages were around. One which became available quite early on was Coral66, targeted at the Intel 8080. The problems faced by software developers using such languages on minicomputers is well covered by Pierce (1974); the problem was much greater on micros. Fig.11.14 shows the Coral code development sequence for the 8080 system. With this method the only aids to debugging were the source code, assembler and Hex listings. Debugging and code analysis using these can be described, at the very best, as primitive. With the arrival of DDT tools an important step forward was made. These could operate on the compiler-generated object code (Fig.11.15), letting the programmer interact directly with his program (as described earlier).

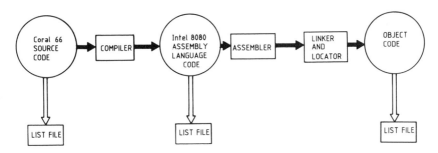

Fig.11.14 Primitive HLL debugging methods

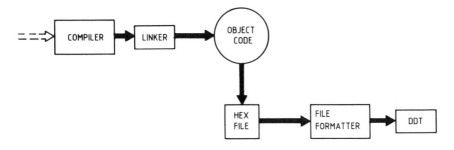

Fig.11.15 The first step – debugging at assembler level

Unfortunately this is not quite as powerful as it first seems. The problems are twofold. First, matching the source statements to the resulting assembler operations must be done manually. Secondly, interrogation of the assembler code is also a manual task. Consider the following listing (Listing 11.7). This relatively small amount of source code is pretty straightforward. Yet the assembler output is much more complex. Further, additional code statements, 'JMPF', 'PUSH BP' and 'INT E4', have been added by the compiler. We are certainly going to need the services of a proficient assembler programmer to make sense of this. Analysis is going to take time, is a tedious affair (Fig.11.16) and requires much effort. And, in one sense, we spend too much time on the wrong job. That is, effort is concentrated on the symptoms of the problem rather than its causes. Further, the difficulty of handling code generated by an optimizing compiler adds another dimension to this task (due to the problems in debugging such code many designers initially turn off the optimizer; the code produced will certainly be longer but at least it can be analysed).

All these factors produce the same effects: increased time, effort and cost. This, in essence, is the answer to the question raised above.

```
MODULE Test;
VAR
     X, Y, Z:INTEGER;

BEGIN
   Z:=X+Y;
END Test.
```

(a) High Level Language Listing

```
3B98:0100 JMPF    0014:0007
-
3B98:0147 PUSH    BP
3B98:0148 MOV     BP,SP
3B98:014A NOP
3B98:014B NOP
3B98:014C NOP
3B98:014D NOP
3B98:014E NOP
3B98:014F CS:     MOV    DS,[0000]
3B98:0154 MOV     AX,[0000]
3B98:0157 ADD     AX,[0002]
3B98:015B JNO     0161
3B98:015D MOV     AL,24
3B98:015F INT     E4
-
```

(b) Compiler Generated Assembly Language Listing

LISTING 11.7

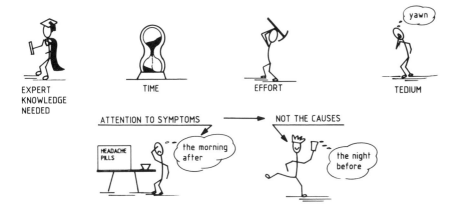

Fig.11.16 Debugging HLLs at the assembler level – the consequences

(b)   What features are needed?

Having now decided that HLL source level debugging is highly desirable, what should such debuggers do for us? All the operations used with assembly language debugging are directly relevant. But because of the more complex language structure of HLLs, much more is needed. This is especially true of the latest generation of languages such as Modula-2 and Ada. HLL constructs which are important in debugging sessions include:

- The need to operate with symbols (symbolic debugging).
- The facility to manipulate procedures and procedure parameters.
- The ability to handle complex data structures such as arrays, records and dynamic data units.
- The ability to work with separately-compilable program units such as Modula-2 modules and Ada packages.
- The capacity to manipulate both local and global variables.

(c)   What tools are available?

Two clear methods have emerged for the provision of HLL debugger tools. In the first, language designers have provided these as part of the total system package ('system resident debuggers'). In the second one, independent software houses have developed general purpose debuggers to meet market demands. As would be expected, these are targeted at the more popular languages, especially C and Pascal.

11.3.4 System resident debuggers

Until recently few language environments provided resident debuggers as part of the system package. This is now changing, particularly with regard to C, Modula-2 and Ada. The following example program is included to highlight the use of such debuggers. It uses the Logitech Modula-2 Symbolic Run-time Debugger (Logitech, 1987). Note that this is **not** a tutorial on either Modula-2 or the run-time debugger. What it shows is how an HLL debugger helps you to see where you are, where you came from and how your results were obtained.

```
MODULE Integral;
(************************************************************)
(* This operation calculates the integral of an input value *)
(* Xnew, outputting the result as Ynew.  The technique used *)
(* is that of trapezoidal integration.                     *)
(************************************************************)

VAR
    Xnew, Ynew, K1:REAL;

PROCEDURE InitialiseAlgorithm;
BEGIN
    Xnew:=1.0;
    K1:= 0.05;
END InitialiseAlgorithm;

PROCEDURE CalcIntegral(Xn, K1:REAL):REAL;
VAR
    n :CARDINAL;
    Yn, Yo, Xo :REAL;
BEGIN
    Yo:=0.0;
    Xo:=0.0;
    n:=1;
    REPEAT
        Yn:=K1*(Xn+Xo) + Yo;
        Yo:=Yn;
        Xo:=Xn;
        INC(n);
    UNTIL n = 20;
    RETURN Yn;
END CalcIntegral;

BEGIN
    InitialiseAlgorithm;
    Ynew:=CalcIntegral(Xnew, K1);
END Integral.
```

LISTING 11.8 Example program

The first question, 'where are we?' is answered by displaying four items of information (Listing 11.9):

- The program text ('text' window).
- The current value of system variables ('data' window).
- The procedure currently being activated, i.e., being called ('call' window).

- A list of separately-compiled units used by the program ('module' window).

The data and module information are shown in Listing 11.9. Note that only data declared at the program level is shown (i.e., that local to procedures is suppressed). Although this feature is a specific implementation feature it follows the concepts of top-down design. That is, only relevant information is given at any stage; further it invokes the concepts of information hiding, decoupling and cohesion.

```
Text   linef   1   Integral.MOD                                      Call

     MODULE Integral;                                                 No call list
     (********************************************************
     (* This operation calculates the integral of an input valu
     (* Xnew, outputting the result as Ynew.   The technique use
     (* is that of trapezoidal integration.
     (********************************************************

     VAR
         Xnew, Ynew, K1:REAL;

   Data   Integral.                                                   Module

     Xnew            -7.8112732336E-145   REAL                        +Integral
     Ynew             3.5840571572E-188   REAL                        RTSMain
     K1              -8.9746499634E+245   REAL                        Reals




   Raw Help   F1      MOD file of  Integral    :  C:Integral.MOD
```

LISTING 11.9 Screen display – Logitech Real-time Debugger

Stepping through the program can be done using the basic methods of single stepping, stepping to breakpoints and stepping to the end. However, two particular features are highly desirable for HLLs. These are, first, stepping on a procedure call basis and second, stepping to breakpoints in different concurrent processes. The first case is important as procedures are an essential part of many structured design techniques. The second is necessary for use with multitasking designs.

Listings 11.10 to 11.12 illustrate a sequence of operations during the debugging process. Specific operations are defined on the listings. The text window information relates to the active procedure. Note also that both program (global) and local variables are now listed.

Observe how this allows us to execute procedure calls as single program statements; it also shows how the details of a procedure may be interrogated. Moreover, it enables us to check the parameter-passing behaviour of the procedure. Finally, the listing of procedure calls and current system status can provide useful information, especially where nested procedures are used. In all of this it is possible to modify program data and so verify particular program operations.

```
Text  linef   12  Integral.MOD                 | Call    PROCEDURE s
                                                |
    Xnew, Ynew, K1:REAL;                        | >InitialiseAlgori
                                                | >initialization
  PROCEDURE InitialiseAlgorithm;                | >PROCESS
 >BEGIN                                          |
     Xnew:=1.0;                                 |
     K1:= 0.05;                                 |
  END InitialiseAlgorithm;                       |
                                                |
  PROCEDURE CalcIntegral(Xn, K1:REAL):REAL;      |
------------------------------------------------|------------------
 Data   Integral.                               | Module
                                                |
  Xnew          -7.8112732336E-145   REAL        | >+Integral
  Ynew           3.5840571572E-188   REAL        | RTSMain
  K1            -8.9746499634E+245   REAL        | Reals
                                                |
                                                |
                                                |
                                                |
------------------------------------------------|------------------
  Raw Help    F1 Reading from REF file
```

LISTING 11.10 Operation: Step into procedure InitialiseAlgorithm, at line statement 'BEGIN'. Data values are random.

```
Text  linef   14  Integral.MOD                 | Call    line step
                                                |
  PROCEDURE InitialiseAlgorithm;                | >InitialiseAlgori
  BEGIN                                          | >initialization
     Xnew:=1.0;                                 | >PROCESS
 >   K1:= 0.05;                                 |
  END InitialiseAlgorithm;                       |
                                                |
  PROCEDURE CalcIntegral(Xn, K1:REAL):REAL;      |
  VAR                                            |
     n :CARDINAL;                               |
------------------------------------------------|------------------
 Data   Integral.                               | Module
                                                |
  Xnew           1.0000000000E-000   REAL        | >+Integral
  Ynew           3.5840571572E-188   REAL        | RTSMain
  K1            -8.9746499634E+245   REAL        | Reals
                                                |
                                                |
                                                |
                                                |
------------------------------------------------|------------------
  Raw Help    F1 Reading from REF file
```

LISTING 11.11 Operation: Step into procedure InitialiseAlgorithm, at line statement 'K1:=0.05;'. Note that Xnew has been initialised.

There are many detailed operations specific to this debugger. Listing these would be pointless. What is important is that this method of interaction allows us to view the program at a symbolic level. Thus we can concentrate on the design and objectives of the software, not its machine operation.

```
┌─────────────────────────────────────────────────────────┬─────────────────────┐
│ Text   line₤   37   Integral.MOD                          │ Call                │
│                                                           ├─────────────────────┤
│          INC(n);                                          │ No call list        │
│       UNTIL n = 20;                                       │                     │
│       RETURN Yn;                                          │                     │
│    END CalcIntegral;                                      │                     │
│                                                           │                     │
│    BEGIN                                                  │                     │
│       InitialiseAlgorithm;                                │                     │
│       Ynew:=CalcIntegral(Xnew, K1);                       │                     │
│    END Integral.                                          │                     │
├─────────────────────────────────────────────────────────┼─────────────────────┤
│ Data    Integral.                                         │ Module              │
│                                                           ├─────────────────────┤
│   Xnew           1.0000000000E-000    REAL                │ +Integral           │
│   Ynew           1.8500000000E-000    REAL                │  RTSMain            │
│   K1             5.0000000000E-002    REAL                │  Reals              │
│                                                           │                     │
│                                                           │                     │
│                                                           │                     │
│                                                           │                     │
│                                                           │                     │
├─────────────────────────────────────────────────────────┴─────────────────────┤
│  Raw Help    F1        MOD file of  Integral      :  C:Integral.MOD             │
└─────────────────────────────────────────────────────────────────────────────┘
```

LISTING 11.12 Operation: Program executed to completion. Note the data values.

11.3.5 General purpose debugging packages

A number of software suppliers have developed debugging packages which are general purpose in design. These normally support a range of high-level languages, together with assembly operation. In contrast the system resident debuggers operate with one specific high-level language (and the assembler output from this). One important point should be noted at this stage. A debugger may allow the use of a number of HLLs, but it can only test software destined for a specific target processor. Thus, for instance, separate packages would be needed for the Intel 386 and the Motorola 68030 processors.

In selecting a general purpose debugger it is important to check its real-time capability. One package which is representative of such debuggers is SoftProbe II (Creative Systems Ltd., 1987). Its organization is shown in Fig.11.17. Many of its features will by now be familiar; however, it does have some new elements.

First, it contains a simulation model of the processor and memory **and** interface peripherals. One of the peripherals is a programmable interrupt controller (PIC), the other being a programmable counter/timer. By using these, simulations of interrupt functions and real-time operations can be made. It can also simulate input/output operations. Note that processor/memory simulation is necessary as the host processor is different from that of the target. This, by definition, is a cross-debugger. Where the debugger uses the same processor as that in the target unit, we have a native debugger. In such systems the code under test is usually executed by the resident processor. Clearly, where the host and target processors are different this would be impossible to carry out.

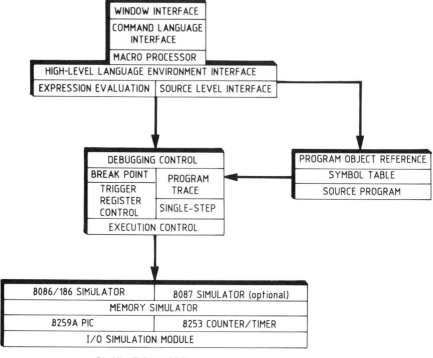

Fig.11.17 SoftProbe II debugger organization

The cross-debugger would appear to be inferior to the native debugger. In practice this isn't necessarily so, providing that the simulator is truly reliable. In such cases the confidence level of code correctness is much the same for cross and native debuggers. However, where simulation methods are used, the debugger designer has full control over the test environment. This makes it relatively easy to supply simulations of the types mentioned earlier. It also provides the facility to run a program trace-back (the 'how did we get here?' question) under all modes of operation, including interrupts. Execution control and monitoring can also be very comprehensive. Breakpoint settings can be extended well beyond the basic methods shown earlier. Conditional breakpoints can be incorporated, triggered on memory addressing, reading or writing data, the results of conditional expressions, and **combinations** of these (non-execution breakpoints). Trigger registers are used to set and control such operations.

A modern general-purpose debugger should also have the following hallmarks:

- Support for mixed language development.

- A straightforward command language, using window interfaces.
- Session recording, recall and replay facilities.
- On-line help.
- A library of useful facilities.

11.3.6 A closing comment —the pros and cons of host system debugging

Host system debugging has many advantages. With this we can test and debug most of the application program. In some cases this may be as high as 90% of the final product. We can interact directly with the program, seeing exactly how it performs. The effects of changes can be checked almost instantly. We save ourselves the time, cost and effort involved in producing reams of listings. Session recordings can be made, being useful for subsequent analysis. All this spells high productivity, reduced costs and faster development times. Some debuggers give information relating to execution times, allowing us to evaluate program performance.

So far, so good. But as with anything in engineering, there are practical limits to these techniques. These limitations arise as a result of three particular factors:

- Interaction of programs.
- Speed of execution.
- Host/target hardware differences.

(a) Interaction of source and debugger programs

Many debuggers are designed to run in a native environment. In such cases, during the debugging operation, three programs have to be considered. These are:

- The program being debugged.
- The debugger software.
- The host operating system.

These will be partly or completely resident in the host RAM. Hence they are not isolated from each other. It is normal for the operating system to be protected from application programs (Deitel, 1984); this same protection doesn't usually extend to the debugger. Thus the test program may alter the debugger itself, producing unexpected results. Further, experience has shown that in some less-than-robust operating systems, the same can occur. This interaction may seriously reduce the capability of the debugger.

(b) Speed of operation

One powerful aspect of the debugger is the facility to step through and interrogate the program under test. This means that the program runs at only a fraction of its normal speed. It might appear that we can minimize such problems by running at full speed to preset breakpoints. Unfortunately this can only be done with execution breakpoints. Any use of non-execution breakpoints means that the processor needs to stop regularly to check the break conditions. In practice this will result in the test program running quite slowly. In most cases, therefore, it isn't possible to debug at full operating speeds. Unfortunately, a program run slowly may behave very differently compared to its operation at full speed.

(c)   Host-target hardware differences
As a general rule target hardware configurations are different from those of the hosts (in fact that is almost always the case). We've seen that SoftProbe II goes some way to take into account specific hardware set-ups. Yet this only scratches the surface of the problem. That is, host system debugging cannot evaluate hardware/software interaction in real time.

In conclusion, a program which has been debugged on the host must give us great confidence in the software design. But until it actually runs on the target hardware it still remains unproven.

11.4 SOFTWARE DEBUGGING IN THE TARGET — SOFTWARE-BASED TECHNIQUES

11.4.1 General

The basic system configuration required for software debugging in the target is shown in Fig.11.18. Here the user interfaces to the target using some form of terminal/display device. This can range from a simple 'dumb' terminal to a VAX minicomputer. Communication with the target is usually done using a duplex (two-way) digital serial link. It is still necessary to provide communication and

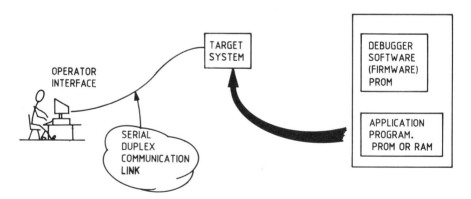

Fig.11.18 Target debugging – basic configuration

debugging facilities on the target itself. This is done by including a monitor or run-time support program in EPROM (firmware) on the target computer. Details of such firmware packages vary from supplier to supplier. However, within reason, it must be possible to locate it anywhere in the processor memory (i.e. be position independent). This prevents clashes with the program under test. The software to be tested can be resident in either ROM or RAM; the choice has a profound effect on the debugger capability.

This technique, software debugging in the target, implicitly assumes that the target board hardware works properly. The technique **can** be used for hardware testing when incremental development methods are used. Generally, though, it is meant to support software development only.

11.4.2 A simple monitor program

One of the earliest test/debug packages is the simple monitor program. Its purpose is to supply fairly basic support for target code test and debugging. Such monitors have usually been developed by users (not suppliers), especially where development support tools haven't been available. Interaction with the target occurs at a very low level, typically using absolute addressing and hexadecimal coding. All debugger software resides in the target, the operator interface being a simple 'dumb' terminal. This means that all target code is also located in ROM. Thus, using this debug method, it is impossible to change the program dynamically during the test session.

One would expect to find the following routines implemented as part of the monitor software:

- Display of program (code) memory.
- Display of data memory.
- Display of processor register contents.
- Modification of data memory and register values.
- Single-step control.
- Execute program with or without breakpoints.
- Return to monitor.

Implementing the single-step and breakpoint facilities can be difficult when the program is in ROM. In some cases it may be necessary to add extra hardware to the board design. This can be avoided where processors have a trap-flag facility in the instruction set (Morse, 1982).

Slightly more complex monitors have the ability to handle the downloading of object files from development systems (Syntel, 1987). These convert the downloaded files into binary format and load them into system RAM. Program debug is much the same as described above; now, though, it includes the facility to change program code. In this case the simple terminal is replaced by some sort of host system. Nowadays one would expect to find a PC being used for this function. To support such operations on a PC, extra software is needed for communication, terminal emulation and downloading functions.

Latterly, commercial products have been produced for a variety of micros. These, though, are generally designed for the more widely-used processors. Moreover, the delay between the arrival of a new machine and the production of a monitor package can be lengthy. Hence home-grown monitors are always likely to be with us.

11.4.3 Source level debuggers

There is one fundamental difference between target source level debuggers and host-based systems: where the program code is executed. Otherwise the major features are exactly the same. This can be seen from the organizational diagram for SoftProbe II/TX (Fig.11.19), the target debugger equivalent of SoftProbe II. It can be seen that the simulation package of SoftProbe II has been replaced by an execution monitor. The hardware and software structure needed to support the package is shown in Fig.11.20.

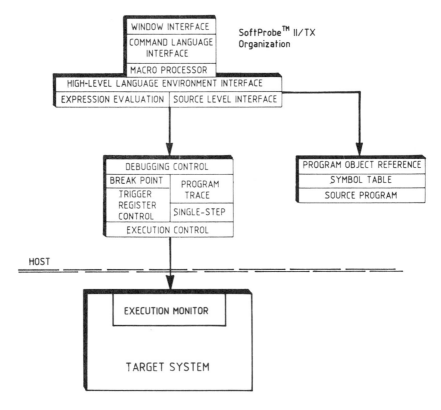

Fig.11.19 SoftProbe II/TX debugger organization

In this case the debugging software consists of two items, a source level debugging interface and an execution monitor. The interface is located on a host machine while the monitor is fitted to the target. So that these can communicate, extra software is needed. This consists of a target communication facility (in the host) and a host communication facility (in the target). Communication is carried out over a serial RS232 data link. A similar structure is used in the Logitech Modula-2 target debugger system.

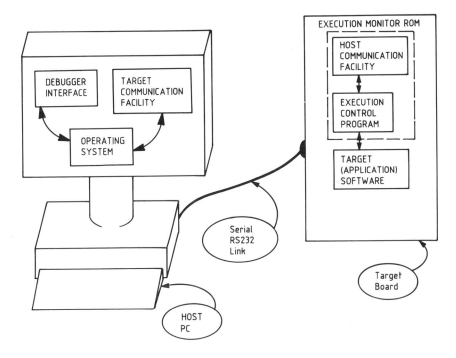

Fig.11.20 Target source level debugging – system configuration

The arrangement described here has many advantages. First, although debugging is done on the target, all symbol information is held on the host. Thus powerful user interaction and display facilities can be provided at minimal target memory requirements. Typically target run-time support packages occupy less than four kBytes of code. Second, recording of debugging sessions can be made on disk, useful for post-test analysis. Third, hard copy printout of active and recorded sessions can be obtained. Finally, the only target peripherals needed for debugging are those related to the serial communication system; all others are free for use by the application software.

Target run-time debuggers must be tailored to the target system under test. Pre-configured versions are sometimes supplied, as with SoftProbe II/TX; these are destined for use with Intel iSBC 86 series single-board computers and IBM PC/XT/AT motherboards. However, the monitor can be reconfigured for use with any Intel 86 processor-based system. Hardware interrupts present a particularly difficult problem for target system debuggers. Some make no

attempt at all to handle them. Others, like the Logitech 86 target run-
time support package, do provide software support. However, to do this,
assumptions are made about the interrupt structure of the target system and
its hardware configuration.

11.4.4 Debugging multitasking software

What distinguishes conventionally-written microprocessor programs from
multitasking software? The answer is that multitasking designs are fundamentally built up as a number of co-operating tasks which run concurrently.
Some are interrupt driven. Some need to respond to interrupt or non-interrupt
driven asynchronous external events. Data and signals have to be transferred
between tasks, and task execution must be carefully synchronized. And for
embedded systems this must be done predictably and fast (as needed by the
controlled process). Therefore a multitasking debugger must not only provide
all the features discussed so far; it should also have extra facilities to handle the
particular requirements of real-time multitasking systems.

   Basically what is needed is a tool which is distinct and separate from the
system executive. It must be capable of operating in a non-intrusive way
in parallel with the native code. That is, it should monitor and control
program execution without distorting normal inter-task behaviour. It must
allow the user to operate at two levels of debug. Consider the part-system of
Fig.11.21.

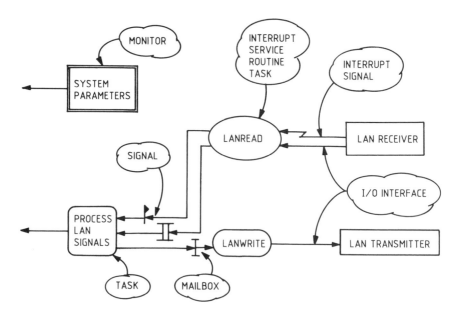

Fig.11.21 System structure – multitasking design

At the top level it is important to access and control system structures (e.g. tasks, mailboxes etc.) as logical elements of the multitasking design. Here we are concerned with system status, task status, tasks pending on signals, channel contents and the like. This method should provide a high level of abstraction; the user shouldn't need to know their internal structures to analyse system behaviour.

These functions are built on the use of register and memory data. Therefore the low-level debug features must let us interrogate and modify these in the usual way. This includes code analysis and disassembly both within tasks and system functions. In general, most of the debug operations at this level are similar to those met earlier. However, two points need a special mention: breakpointing and register accesses.

It must be possible to set breakpoints as and when desired. This includes an individual task, a number of specified tasks, or all tasks. But this raises a problem where breakpoints are set within code which is shared by tasks (typically a procedure). Using normal methods a break would take place each time the procedure is accessed. In some instances this is exactly what is intended by the debugger. In others we wish to view the execution path of a specific task, only breaking when the procedure is accessed by that task. Therefore we must be able to associate a breakpoint with a task identifier.

Another significant difference shows in the method by which the debugger interacts with registers. In a conventional debugger the register information available is the current, **actual**, status of the processor. Using this in a multitasking system would be quite limiting. It would be possible to check only the registers of the current executing task. Yet in many instances it is important to see the status of all tasks. So a multitasking debugger must also let the user get at the register contents of the task control blocks.

A multitasking debugger produced specifically for real-time embedded systems is RTscope (Ready Systems, 1986/87). This is designed to operate with their VRTX32-based operating systems. Like VRTX32 it is fitted into PROM, being independent of the hardware environment (though not the processor type). Given below (Fig.11.22) is an example of an RTscope debugging session provided by Ready Systems. The objective is to check a task's stack to see how much space the task uses. The operation includes the use of breakpoints, memory examination and modification, VRTX display and execution control. Full details of these debuggers can be found in the relevant data sheets. What **is** important though is that the debugger must be tailored to the operating system.

11.4.5 A last comment

Target-based software debuggers are powerful tools. They are especially useful where:

- Hardware is proven and fault-free.

● Software is not subject to asynchronous interrupts.

Even then it must be remembered that stepping and breakpoint control usually uses some form of invasive test technique. This disturbs normal program operation, resulting in reduced execution speeds. A program may check out

```
Multitasking output from application code(in this case each task's ID number):
Task 1    Task 2    Task 3    Task 2    Task 3    Task 1    Task 3    Task 2
Task 1    Task 3    Task 1

Task 3 hits breakpoint on using a VRTX qpost: multitasking output is frozen
At System Call Breakpoint
 Vrtx32 Call - qpost
SR = 3000              Trace = OFF        Active stack = MSP Interrupt mask = 0
                      N = 0   Z = 0    V = 0    C = 0
   PC   = 00F142EE  D0 = 0000000C     A0 = 000E28BC      VBR   = 00000000
   USP  = 00000000  D1 = 00000005     A1 = 000F854E      SFC   = 00000007
   MSP  = 00400600  D2 = 00000002     A2 = 00002004      DFC   = 00000007
   ISP  = 000E1A3C  D3 = 00000001     A3 = 000E8000      CAAR  = 12319C20
                    D4 = 00000000     A4 = 00F00306      CACR  = 00000000
                    D5 = 780CA257     A5 = 000F8000
                    D6 = 000FFFFC     A6 = 004005E6
                    D7 = 00000000     A7 = 00400600
00F142EE 4E40                         TRAP   #0

Display VRTX information on task 3 (Pri = Priority)
RC> dtask 3
Task Id    Priority        PC         TCB       State    Pending   Timeout
    3          1        00F142EE   <00407800>   RUN

Get address of this task's stack (byte offset 52 in TCB):
RC> show-   407856   02
00407856       0040    0600

Overwrite stack with "FF"s (stack is 100 bytes long):
RC> fill.b-   400600   &100   FF

Resume multitasking
RC> task

Switch to I/O channel for application
RT> <escape>
Task 3    Task 2    Task 3    Task 1    Task 2    Task 1    Task 3

Switch to I/O channel for RTscope
<escape>

Display the stack (100 bytes preceding address 400600)
RT> show.b-   400600   &100
00400600    E9 F7 03 E9 13 01 E9 E3 01 E9 19 01 E9 5F 01 E0   ................
004005F0    AF 01 E9 C6 01 0D 0A 71 75 65 75 65 20 31 30 20   .......queue 10
004005E0    66 75 6C 6C 20 00 0D 0A FF FF FF FF FF FF FF FF   full............
004005D0    FF FF FF FF FF FF FF FF FF FF FF FF FF FF FF FF   ................
004005C0    FF FF FF FF FF FF FF FF FF FF FF FF FF FF FF FF   ................
004005B0    FF FF FF FF FF FF FF FF FF FF FF FF FF FF FF FF   ................
004005A0    FF FF FF FF                                       ....

RT>

Bold letters represent user input
regular letters represent RTscope output or task output
italic letters represent comments
```

Fig.11.22 Sample multitasking debugger session – RT scope operation (courtesy of Ready Systems (UK) Ltd)

correctly and then fail at full-speed testing. What then? Moreover, the debugger uses a certain amount of target RAM as a workspace. It would therefore be possible for the application program to overwrite this (sloppy programming), causing chaos in the debugger. How do we locate such problems?

From this it can be seen that there is a clear requirement for hardware debuggers; this is the subject of the next section.

11.5 SOFTWARE DEBUGGING IN THE TARGET — HARDWARE-BASED METHODS

11.5.1 Introduction

Most of the tools described in this section were originally designed to tackle hardware problems in microprocessors. Similar items had previously been developed for minis and mainframes, but they weren't widely applied by computer users. The real-time microcomputer market is entirely different. Here equipment and system manufacturers predominate, not the major computer companies. Many, many users, operating in diverse fields, need to get microprocessor systems running correctly and delivered on time. And to do this they need to have the right tools for the job.

With time there has been a convergence of hardware and software test methods. As microprocessor software became more complex many such tools were adapted for use as software analysers. Some problems just couldn't be resolved without using hardware aids. And the difficulties were compounded by the almost exclusive use of assembly language programming in micros. One example which illustrates this point is that of a digital controller which occasionally (and only occasionally) crashed out. The problem was eventually tracked down to an interrupt occurring in the middle of reloading a programmable timer chip. The timer specification gave no warning of such a problem; in fact it seems likely that the chip manufacturer was unaware of such an event. This problem comes into the category of software-induced hardware faults; such problems are virtually impossible to detect using software debugging tools only.

Nowadays many test systems are seen primarily as software development aids. Such tools come in a variety of forms (Fig.11.23), the majority being plug-on units. The role, and effectiveness, of such units is discussed below. Emphasis is placed on their use as software rather than hardware test aids.

11.5.2 A basic test tool —the bus monitor

One of the simplest hardware test methods is to monitor the activity of the processor system while stepping through the program (Fig.11.24). Stepping can be done in a number of ways: clock cycle, machine cycle or instruction cycle. This depends on the design of both the single-step circuit and the processor itself. The technique is extremely useful for testing the operation of new (untried) peripherals. It is also particularly useful where device programming is complex (such as modern programmable communication controller chips). It has the advantage of being very low cost; thus it can be made readily available within design groups. It also illustrates two basic features of hardware-assisted software testing. First, program control is handled by a device separate from the processor. Secondly, monitoring is non-invasive.

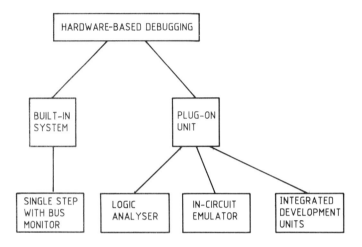

Fig.11.23 Hardware-based debugging methods

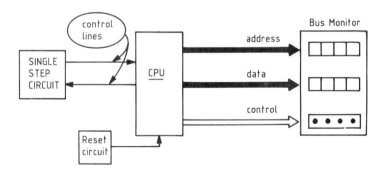

Fig.11.24 Simple hardware/software test method

This test configuration enables us to see that the right information appears at the right time. However, its main limitation is that operation is essentially static, i.e. one step and stop. A second problem is that only a fixed number of points are monitored; these are usually set by the design. What do we do then if a program executes correctly on single step but fails at normal run speeds? This problem highlights the need for a dynamic test tool.

11.5.3 The logic analyser

In its basic form the logic analyser is a data acquisition unit (Fig.11.25), gathering information from selected points within the micro system. Control of WHEN to record data is determined by the trigger signals. Control of WHAT to record is set by the connections into the micro system from the data pod. This includes address, data and control information. The amount of data recorded depends on the size of the RAM store within the analyser. Both WHEN and WHAT are open to user control via a keyboard interface. Information gathered during a test run is subsequently displayed for user evaluation. This may be viewed on either an alpha-numeric display (low cost) or a full screen unit (Fig.11.26).

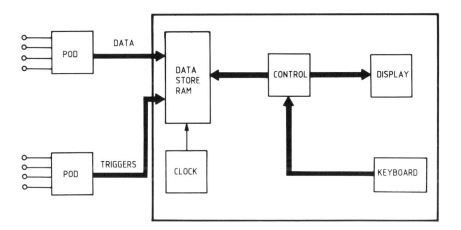

Fig.11.25 Logic analyser structure

The logic analyser doesn't control the micro; essentially it records what happens during a program run. Within a recording session the key point is the 'trigger'. This condition is set by the user as a marker for data collection. It may act as the start or finish of the recording session, being activated when the logic inputs on the trigger lines match the preset condition. Triggering may be set to correspond with instruction fetches, specific memory accesses, I/O device operation and suchlike. Information collected during the run can be displayed in a number of ways including:

- Timing waveforms.
- State diagrams.
- Graph diagrams.

(a) Timing waveforms
A typical example of a timing waveform display is shown in Fig.11.27. Although this is mainly used in hardware analysis it has its place in software

debugging. For instance, the problem described earlier was resolved using this display technique.

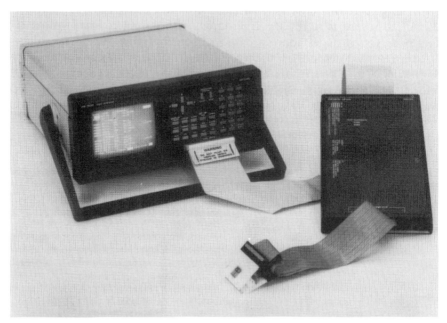

Fig.11.26 A modern logic analyser – Phillips PM3632 (courtesy of Phillips (UK) Ltd)

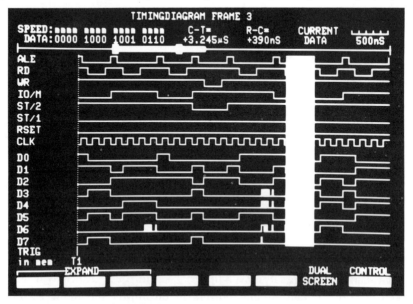

Fig.11.27 Timing waveform display – PM 3632

(b) State diagrams

Here the sequence of program operations relative to the trigger condition is displayed. This includes address and data information. Simpler units show these in hexadecimal or binary form; more complex types include disassemblers (Fig.11.28), giving assembly language mnemonics as appropriate.

(c) State graph diagrams

The main function of graph diagrams is to show data values as a function of another variable. Each recorded data value is defined as a point on one axis of the screen; this sets one of the display co-ordinates. The second co-ordinate is set by the other parameter. For instance, we could plot the digitized values from an analogue-to-digital converter on the vertical axis as a function of time (Fig.11.29).

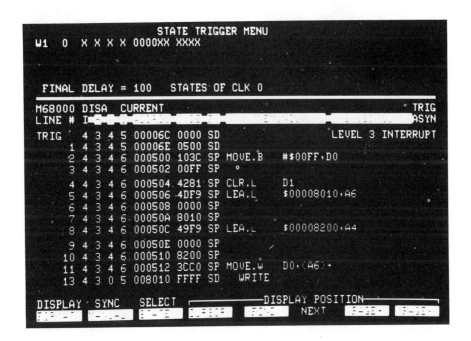

Fig.11.28 State analysis display – PM 3632

The logic analyser is a powerful tool. In fact, it is usually the second-last resort for analysing really difficult problems (the last line of defence is the oscilloscope). This, combined with single-step control, enables us to get to the bottom of any problem, hardware or software. It has one drawback. Analysis using the logic analyser is a time-consuming task, especially when the software is complex. This has led to the development of the in-circuit emulator (ICE).

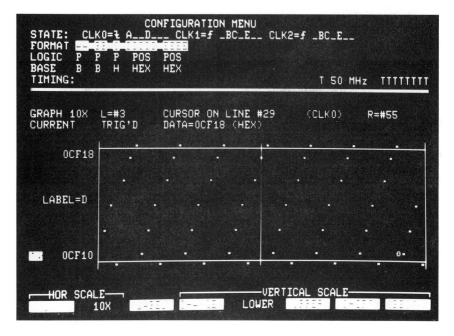

Fig.11.29 State graph display – PM 3632

11.5.4   The In-Circuit emulator

In-circuit emulation is defined to be 'the replacement of a microprocessor in a prototype by a piece of test equipment intended to provide all the functionality of that microprocessor, along with capabilities to assist in the integration of the hardware and software components of this prototype' (Tseng, 1982). ICE was originally designed by Intel (Tseng, 1982) primarily to tackle hardware problems. It has now become a major software debugging aid within the embedded systems community.

The facilities required of ICE are given in Fig.11.30, most of these by now being quite familiar. Resource mapping is the exception (described below). The important point is that all these features can be used in the target system at target speed of operation.

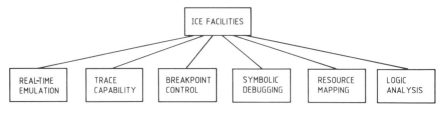

Fig.11.30 ICE facilities

Many variants of ICE now exist, ranging from general purpose units to those specific to manufacturer (Intel, 1987). However, the basic structure shown in Fig.11.31 is typical of modern designs. It consists of three major components:

- A host interface.
- An emulator module.
- The target board interface – microprocessor probe and trace pod.

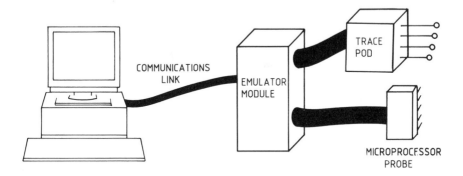

Fig.11.31 In-circuit emulator – basic structure

Their functions, in broad outline, are shown in Fig.11.32.

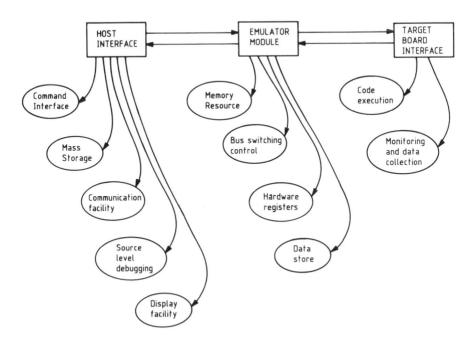

Fig.11.32 ICE sub-system functions

The microprocessor probe carries a microprocessor of the same type as the target. During emulation, the target processor is removed and the probe plugged-in in its place. All target software is subsequently executed by the emulation processor. At first sight this may seem odd. Why bother to take out one processor chip and replace it by an identical type? The answer is that the emulation processor can be controlled by the emulation module, something which can't easily be done with the original processor.

The trace probe is used for monitoring target board activities, such as address, data and control signals.

Direct control of the target board interface is carried out by the emulator module (Fig.11.33). It also acquires and records data sent to it from the trace pod. This module itself uses a microprocessor, sometimes called the control and interrogation processor. It does not have to be the same type as that in the target. The control processor is responsible for:

- Setting up the emulator module as commanded by the host.
- Uploading data to the host.
- Monitoring and controlling the emulator processor.
- Monitoring the target system for subsequent trace analysis.

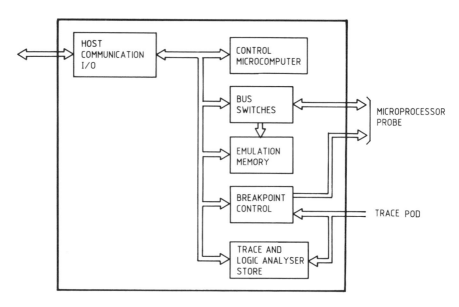

Fig.11.33 Emulator module functional diagram

Information transfer from the emulator processor to the control processor normally involves direct memory access communication methods.

The trace functions are handled by what, in this context, is best described as a software logic analyser. More powerful ICE units have a large acquisition store and an extensive analysis software suite to support this function. Using the recorded data the analysis software can create a thorough model of the microprocessor system. This includes internal registers, I/O devices and data structures. Such features are augmented by counters and timers which keep track of real-time events. Resource mapping is an important feature of in-circuit emulators. With this the emulator module allows the emulation processor to use its RAM-based emulation memory. This is done on a controlled, selective basis. It is thus possible to run an emulation without any components being fitted to the target board. In many systems it is even possible to execute target code without the target board being present. This has given rise to three modes of ICE operation, as shown in Fig.11.34.

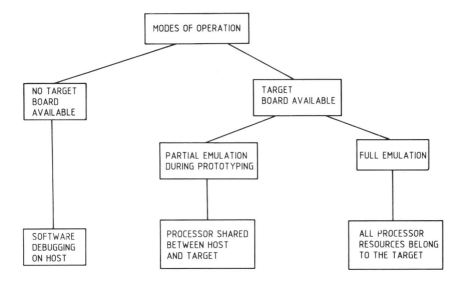

Fig.11.34 ICE modes of operation

It would be impossible to provide an ICE environment without a comprehensive control, display and interface software suite. Earlier systems used dedicated ICE environments. These, unfortunately, were extremely expensive. To meet the demand for lower-cost facilities, two particular configurations have emerged: single-user and shared systems.

In the first one the bulk of the software is housed on a PC host. PCs are relatively low-cost items (compared with special purpose ICE tools). Further, the PC can be used for other jobs, thus 'sharing' its cost amongst various users. Typical of these are the Thorn-EMI AVAL-ICE emulator (Fig.11.35) and the Intel i²ICE Integrated Instrumentation and In-Circuit Emulation System (Intel, 1987).

The drawback of this method is that only one ICE facility is available at any one time. One method designed to overcome this problem at a moderate cost is that of Fig.11.36. Here target boards are debugged using local emulators driven from dumb terminals. These emulators can be simpler (in software terms) than the stand-alone systems; use is made of the VAX host power.

ICE is one of the most powerful (and costly) tools of the microprocessor engineer. It lets us analyse software to a very great depth. Yet it still leaves one question unanswered; how good is the performance of our software?

Fig.11.35 Thorn-EMI AVAL-ICE emulator (courtesy of Thorn EMI Ltd)

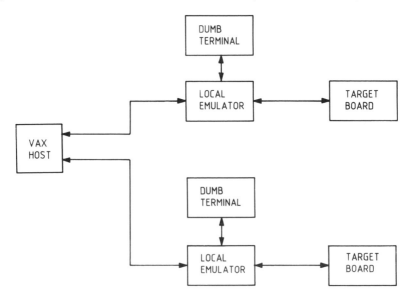

Fig.11.36 Use of local emulators

11.6 DEBUGGING IN HOST/TARGET COMBINATIONS

11.6.1 Background

In this context a host/target combination means one of two things. First, it describes schemes where the target uses the same (or similar) operating system as the host. Second, it includes designs where the host itself is used as the target. Both configurations are described below. The first is applicable to single board computer designs, using an adapted version of MS-DOS as the operating system. The second describes the use of the ubiquitous PC as a target machine.

The use of host-as-target is not new. Probably the most widely used general-purpose machines have been Digital Equipment Corp. (DEC) PDP, VAX and microVAX computers. More recently the PC, with over 10 million sales, has become a commercial standard. It is also finding its way into industrial applications in much larger numbers than DEC or similar machines. With such a large market vendors can expect high-volume sales of PC-based products. This, coupled with a standard operating system, has had some profound effects. These include:

- Very low-cost computing, mass storage and display facilities.
- Low-cost compilers, assemblers and development tools.
- A wide range of plug-in boards.
- A high level of compatibility in both hardware and software.

The PC is unlikely to make significant inroads into established embedded systems markets (packaging, environmental factors and operating system robustness are somewhat limited). On the other hand it is too important to be ignored.

11.6.2 DOS-based target

This approach aims to simplify application software development by providing a ready-made operating system. By itself this might not achieve much. But, by simulating MS-DOS, the system becomes extremely powerful and flexible. This is aimed at equipments typically designed around bus-based single-board computers (SBCs), Fig.11.37. The primary aims of this development method are twofold. First, it is used to debug application software, both in the host and the target. Secondly, it can be used for test and development of I/O hardware and device drivers.

Generally the software described here, the Appcom Software Suite (Hexatron, 1988), can be adapted to various hardware configurations. It does assume though that the processor is an Intel 16-bit model. Further, it also assumes that the processor board works correctly.

The development environment is almost identical to that of Fig.11.20. Just substitute the target operating system ROM for the monitor ROM. This OS is an emulation of MS-DOS. It thus makes the target system 'look' like a PC. Now both the host and target machines are (from the software point of view) almost identical.

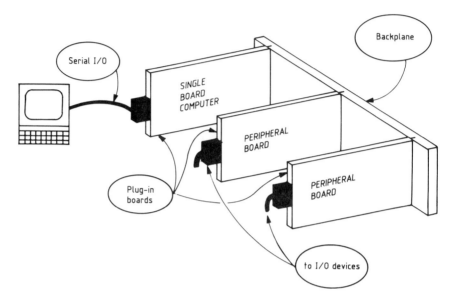

Fig.11.37 Bus-based target system

There are three distinct test, development and debug phases using this approach:

- Application software debugging on the host.
- Test of target hardware and drivers from the host.
- Application software debugging within the target.

There is nothing new to say about host system debugging. But before starting target software debugging one would normally get the hardware into a fully working state. This is done as follows:

- Set up a control and communications link between the host and the target processor board.
- Issue system-provided test commands from the host console to exercise the hardware.
- Generate specially-written hardware test routines in the target RAM, then exercise the hardware.

The application software may then be downloaded into the target. At this point the application program behaves as if it's running in a PC – though it's actually operating in its native environment. Therefore any implementation problems will quickly show up. Debugging can be done using the usual set of tools, with the added advantage of working within a familiar DOS environment.

The software described here is more than just a test/debugger tool. It forms the basis for a complete microprocessor development system.

11.6.3 PC as target

When a PC is used as the target machine one can usually assume that the basic hardware works correctly. There are pretty powerful PC software debuggers on the market; why then is there a demand for hardware-assisted debugging tools? It has been found that these are invaluable for the developement of:

- New hardware, especially plug-in boards.
- Complex software.

The first use is something we'd expect. The second, however, is quite surprising in view of the capabilities of software debuggers. But even in the PC environment, the limitations of software-based tools still apply (discussed earlier). In particular, monitoring and control of program execution while it runs at full speed is a virtual impossibility. And problems which show at that stage are usually the most difficult and obscure ones.

These are the reasons which resulted in ICE being developed. So we can regard PC hardware-assisted debuggers as being equivalent to dedicated emulators. The type described here, the ATRON AT Probe (Atron, 1986), Fig.11.38, is a good example of such devices. The tool itself consists of a single printed circuit board together with debugging software. The board plugs into any AT slot; it also has a probe plug for access to the numerical co-processor (80287) control lines. An external VDU can be connected to the board.

Fig.11.39 shows the outline structure of the AT Probe. Compare this with Fig.11.33; its similarity to ICE can clearly be seen. An external terminal/display unit is used for control of the debugging session. This eliminates interaction between the debugger display and that of the PC (note that the debugger **can** use the keyboard/display facilities of the PC).

Fundamentally the debugger monitors the address, data and control lines of the PC system, controlling the processor by the use of the non-maskable interrupt (NMI) line. Data collected from the PC is stored within a trace memory in real-time. This same information is sent to the breakpoint control section for evaluation and action. When a breakpoint is met, control is regained by the debugger by activating the NMI line. The information captured in the trace memory may, if desired, be displayed and interrogated using the remote VDU. This can be done both in assembly or high-level language form. Note that breakpoint control is set in hardware, thus supporting full-speed interrogation.

The control section carries the debugger software. This means that it is physically separate from the memory of the PC. Moreover it is write protected. Thus the application program cannot wipe out the debugger.

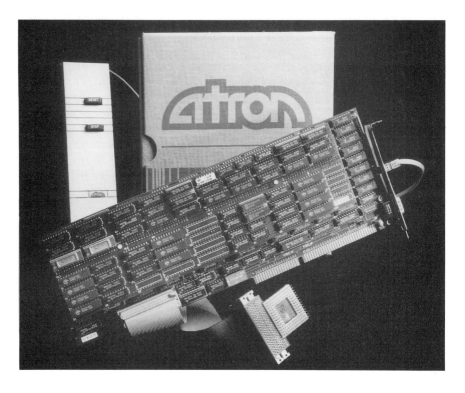

Fig.11.38 ATRON AT probe (courtesy of RPM systems)

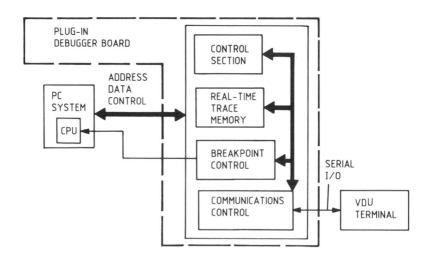

Fig.11.39 Atron AT Probe – outline structure

11.7 PERFORMANCE ANALYSIS TOOLS

What we have been doing so far is verifying the design of our software. That is, does it do what we expect it to (and conversely, does it not do unexpected things)? Let's assume that it has been tested to our satisfaction. Fine. But we still have little explicit data regarding the performance of the program. For instance:

- How long does the complete program take to run?
- How long do component parts (e.g. procedures) take to run?
- How often are individual procedures used?
- What sort of interaction do we have between procedures?
- What is the time latency in the servicing of interrupts?
- If parts of a program are slow, why?
- Are all procedures executed during verification testing?

These questions are not very important for many applications. After all, if a program which runs interactively on a PC is a bit slow, so what? And if it sometimes mysteriously crashes out, well, that's not so unusual. For embedded systems such behaviour may be disastrous; hence we do need some (if not all) answers to the above questions. Without the support of analysis aids, finding the answers is a long and laborious job.

Performance analysis tools (PATs) examine two main program factors, speed and code size (Fig.11.40). These sometimes come as part of a specific development tool, as in the AVAL-ICE in-circuit emulator. In other cases they are separate units which are integrated within the complete test setting. The Intel iPAT Performance Analysis Tool (Intel, 1987) is designed like this. iPAT is one of the most advanced tools currently available; thus it is used here as a reference vehicle for the description of performance analysis methods.

To tackle the questions set out above, program analysis must be conducted at a number of levels: module, procedure and line. Single events must be captured and analysed. Interrupt effects, both in terms of frequency and duration, need recording. Information display needs to be meaningful and clear, with the ability to work at a symbolic level **and** with absolute addresses. And finally, but most importantly, monitoring should be non-intrusive so as not to disturb the normal operation of the program.

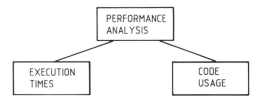

Fig.11.40 Use of performance analysis tools

Fig.11.41 shows the general functional structure of the Intel performance analysis tool. Address signals are picked up by a measuring probe and fed into a data acquisition function section. This is performed 'on the fly'. Selected information, as defined by the control section, is recorded here. It is then picked up for analysis and interrogation by the post-processor section. The results of this are input to the control section for onward transmission to the host computer. All operator commands are fed in from the host; all results are displayed on this same machine.

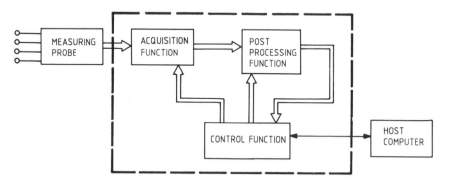

Fig.11.41 Intel performance analysis tool (iPAT) – overall structure

The basic operation of the acquisition section is shown in Fig.11.42. Input (measured) addresses are compared with those set by the user. If correspondence is found, two gates are opened and both the address value and the time of the event are recorded. A serial first-in first-out (FIFO) buffer memory store is used for this; thus all events are stored in sequence. This allows 256 specific address variables to be monitored simultaneously. The time-stamp interval settings range from 200 nanoseconds to 100 microseconds. The

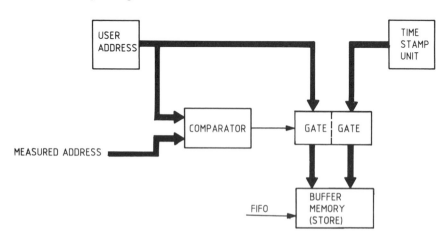

Fig.11.42 iPAT – basic acquisition function

post-processor (Fig.11.43) manages this data in accordance with the demands of the operator.

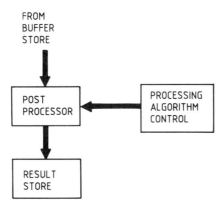

Fig.11.43 iPAT – post-processing function

Analysis of the information is carried out as set by the processing algorithm. The results are then stored in a temporary result store. This is constantly updated until the user requests a display; at that time it is extracted from the result store by the control section. Note that by using a FIFO the post-processor operation is decoupled from that of the acquisition function.

The overall control and display function (Fig.11.44) enables the operator to communicate with the analysis tool. In a typical session the operator defines (sets) the address accesses which are to be monitored, the processing to be carried out on the resulting recordings, and the form of display to be used for this information. The following figures show a specimen application using iPAT. This information is reproduced courtesy of Intel Corporation.

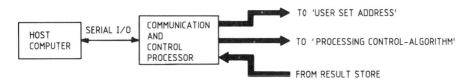

Fig.11.44 iPAT – control and display function

The first display (Fig.11.45) is a histogram record of procedure activation within an aero-engine test program. This gives a very broad view of program operation, showing how program execution time is consumed by individual procedures. In this case it covers a program run over 4188 msec. More detailed information concerning these procedures can be extracted from the recorded data. For instance, how many times did each procedure run in the record slot? And how much time did a procedure run consume (Fig.11.46)?

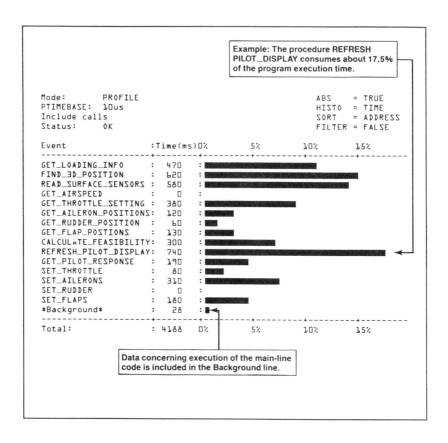

Fig.11.45 Time histogram display of aero-engine test program

Now let's suppose that more detailed timing information is needed. For instance, given that a procedure has a significant variation in its execution time, what is the statistical breakdown of this performance record? Or what is the latency performance between the arrival of an interrupt request and the execution of the interrupt service routine (Fig.11.47)? Finally, how can we be sure that all the code is actually exercised. In many applications, especially defence work, systems have a long life, being subject to upgrading modifications. It may be, for instance, that after a series of such changes some code is unused. Or we may have designed a test plan to check the code; how do we guarantee that it really does access all sections of the program? In these cases we can use a display (the 'coverage' mode, Fig.11.48) to show execution status of program elements. There are many other features of iPAT which are beyond the scope of this text.

From the preceding sections it can be seen that to perform detailed software analysis, special tools are needed. This approach also has an impact on the use of HLLs. Worries about speed/memory inefficiencies of compilers become less

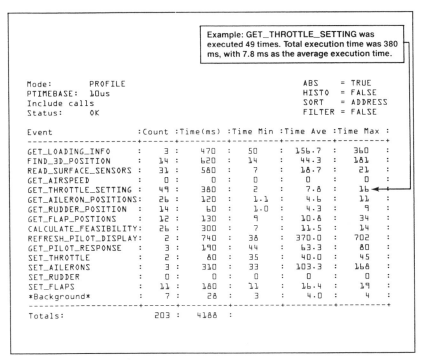

```
                                   +------------------------------------------+
                                   | Example: GET_THROTTLE_SETTING was        |
                                   | executed 49 times. Total execution time was 380 |-+
                                   | ms, with 7.8 ms as the average execution time. | |
                                   +------------------------------------------+ |
                                                                                |
   Mode:        PROFILE                             ABS     = TRUE              |
   PTIMEBASE:   10us                                HISTO   = FALSE             |
   Include calls                                    SORT    = ADDRESS           |
   Status:      OK                                  FILTER  = FALSE             |
                                                                                |
   Event              :Count :Time(ms) :Time Min :Time Ave :Time Max :          |
   -------------------+------+---------+---------+---------+---------+           |
   GET_LOADING_INFO   :   3 :    470 :    50  :   156.7 :   360  :              |
   FIND_3D_POSITION   :  14 :    620 :    14  :    44.3 :   181  :              |
   READ_SURFACE_SENSORS: 31 :    580 :     7  :    18.7 :    21  :              |
   GET_AIRSPEED       :   0 :      0 :     0  :     0   :     0  :              |
   GET_THROTTLE_SETTING: 49 :    380 :     2  :     7.8 :    16  <--------------+
   GET_AILERON_POSITIONS: 26 :   120 :    1.1 :     4.6 :    11  :
   GET_RUDDER_POSITION : 14 :     60 :    1.0 :     4.3 :     9  :
   GET_FLAP_POSTIONS  :  12 :    130 :     9  :    10.8 :    34  :
   CALCULATE_FEASIBILITY: 26 :   300 :     7  :    11.5 :    14  :
   REFRESH_PILOT_DISPLAY:  2 :   740 :    38  :   370.0 :   702  :
   GET_PILOT_RESPONSE :   3 :    190 :    44  :    63.3 :    80  :
   SET_THROTTLE       :   2 :     80 :    35  :    40.0 :    45  :
   SET_AILERONS       :   3 :    310 :    33  :   103.3 :   168  :
   SET_RUDDER         :   0 :      0 :     0  :     0   :     0  :
   SET_FLAPS          :  11 :    180 :    11  :    16.4 :    19  :
   *Background*       :   7 :     28 :     3  :     4.0 :     4  :
   -------------------+------+---------+---------+---------+---------+
   Totals:             203 :   4188 :
```

Fig.11.46 Table display of aero-engine test program

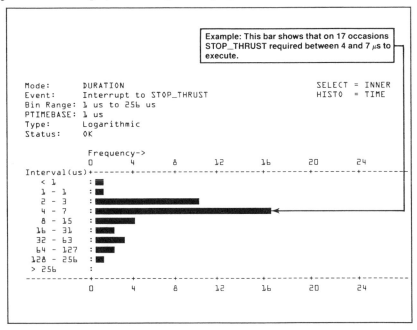

```
                                 +------------------------------------------+
                                 | Example: This bar shows that on 17 occasions |
                                 | STOP_THRUST required between 4 and 7 µs to |-+
                                 | execute.                                 | |
                                 +------------------------------------------+ |
                                                                              |
   Mode:        DURATION                          SELECT = INNER             |
   Event:       Interrupt to STOP_THRUST          HISTO  = TIME              |
   Bin Range:   1 us to 256 us                                              |
   PTIMEBASE:   1 us                                                        |
   Type:        Logarithmic                                                 |
   Status:      OK                                                          |
                                                                            |
                 Frequency->                                                |
                 0      4      8     12     16     20     24               |
   Interval(us)+------+------+------+------+------+------+------+           |
       < 1      :█                                                         |
       1 - 1    :█                                                         |
       2 - 3    :███████████                                               |
       4 - 7    :██████████████████████████████████████ <----------------+
       8 - 15   :██████████                                                
      16 - 31   :█████                                                     
      32 - 63   :█████                                                     
      64 - 127  :█████                                                     
     128 - 256  :█                                                         
       > 256    :                                                          
   ------------+------+------+------+------+------+------+------+
                 0      4      8     12     16     20     24
```

Fig.11.47 Duration mode histogram display

important once we can easily identify problem code areas. Consequently, the bulk of the program can be written in an HLL, limiting assembler to time-critical sections. As pointed out earlier, this has a major impact on reliability, development times and costs.

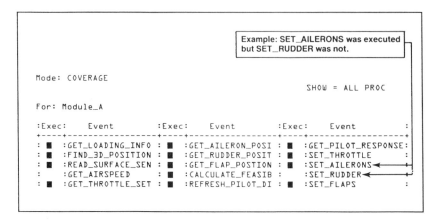

Fig.11.48 Coverage mode display

11.8 INSTALLING CODE INTO THE TARGET —NON-VOLATILE SOFTWARE (FIRMWARE)

11.8.1 Overview

Program environments can be described as volatile or non-volatile. The use of a PC as a target system typifies a volatile setting. Program behaviour in these situations can be broken down into two parts: start-up and application run (Fig.11.49). Here a boot program is carried in a non-volatile store, usually an EPROM. This first performs basic checks and housekeeping tasks, including hardware checks. It then loads part (or all) of the operating system into main, usually RAM-based, memory. To run an application program the user enters appropriate commands at the console. These are interpreted by the operating system, which proceeds to download the user program into main memory and execute the code. Note that the user may be excluded from the process by having an auto-execute feature.

This configuration is volatile because each time the computer is powered-down, all programs in main memory are lost. The system will respond correctly on power-up provided the disk is present and holds the correct programs. Sensibly then, we are talking about a hard disk. Such arrangements **are** used in real-time systems. For instance, they can be found in gas, oil and electricity control rooms, at the hub of a large distributed system; the control computer is usually a mainframe or mini. But they are not typical of the embedded market.

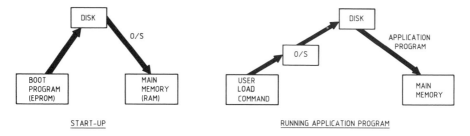

Fig.11.49 Program behaviour in a volatile environment

Nowadays almost all embedded functions use microprocessors, with the program code held in a non-volatile form. Various storage devices (Fig.11.50) are used, having one factor in common. They have to be programmed with the object code produced by the development process. This is where the PROM programmer is needed.

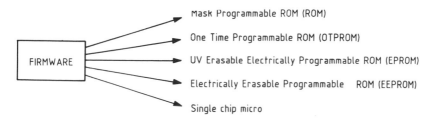

Fig.11.50 Non-volatile software – firmware storage devices

11.8.2 The PROM programmer

The basic requirement of a PROM programmer is that it must:

- Interface to various host development systems.
- Accept object code in specific file formats such as Intel Hex, Motorola S-Record, DEC-Binary, etc.
- Convert these to pure binary form.
- Program this data into PROM.

Fig.11.51 shows the overall structure of a general purpose PROM programmer. The final output from a compiler or assembler is an encoded file in, say, Intel Hex form. This contains not only the program code but also information concerning the location of such code in memory. It is downloaded to the PROM programmer over a communication link, typically using an RS232C serial channel. The control section acts on this input; it converts the program code to absolute binary form and loads it into RAM store. Its location within the store is defined in absolute terms by the linker. At this stage, if the EPROM is inserted into its programming socket, device programming can begin. This is usually done using commands from the local keyboard. The control section handles the programming process, 'copying' each data byte (or word) from RAM into EPROM. This is the only occasion when an EPROM is written to, and necessitates the use of relatively high programming voltages. When programming is finished this is indicated at the local display panel. Should the EPROM be faulty and refuse to program correctly this is also shown to the operator.

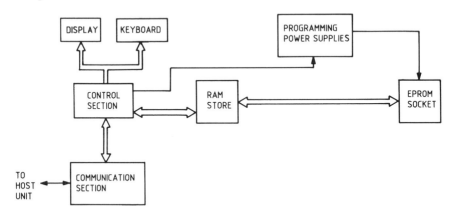

Fig.11.51 General purpose PROM programmer structure

Typical of the more powerful, advanced, programmers is the Stag PPZ, Fig.11.52 (Stag, 1987). Low-cost PROM programmers eliminate the need for local display and control facilities by using the host as an intelligent terminal. This assumes, of course, that the host is capable of operating in this mode.

The local control functions are split into two groups: RAM and EPROM operation. A typical set of operations is listed below; their value can only be appreciated after being heavily involved in program development.

(a) **RAM**

- **Fill** a section of memory with a data value.
- **Search** for a specified data string.
- **Replace** a data string with a new one.
- **Insert** and **delete** RAM values.
- **Copy** blocks of data within RAM.
- **Split** the RAM block into two or more sections for set programming (used where the object code is too large to fit into a single EPROM).
- **Merge** (or **shuffle**) RAM data (converse of SPLIT).

(b) **EPROM**

- **Blank** check of the PROM.

- **Program** the PROM with RAM data.
- **Verify** that the PROM and RAM contents are the same.
- **Store** the data from PROM to RAM.
- **Erase** – for EPROMs only.

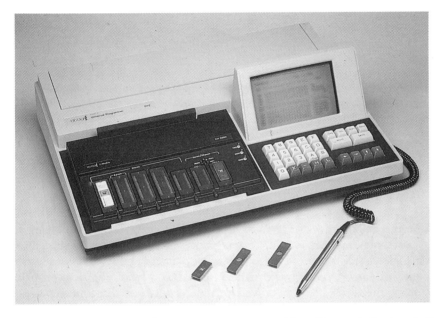

Fig.11.52 Stag PPZ Universal Programmer (courtesy of Stag Electronic Designs Ltd)

11.8.3 EPROM emulators

It has already been pointed out that program development and test can really slow down at the PROM programming stage. So we try to avoid using EPROMs until the final code is ready. Unfortunately there are cases where this just isn't possible. For instance, target system debuggers may not be available. Or in a small system it might be impossible to fit all the program code into the available RAM space. That, remember, is where the program is usually located for debug sessions.

This is where the EPROM emulator (Fig.11.53) comes into use. By using this, EPROM programming is eliminated, thus speeding up software development. Its similarity to the PROM programmer is obvious. What **is** different is that the RAM store is connected to a header plug instead of an EPROM socket. This header plug is connected into the EPROM socket on the target board.

The unit has two modes of operation, set-up and emulate. Commands from the host control the settings of the unit. When it is in set-up mode bus switches 'A' are closed, 'B' being open. Object files are downloaded (in their usual format) from the host to the emulator, translated to binary form, and loaded into the emulator RAM. In emulate mode the bus switches change state. These connect the emulator RAM to the header plug and hence to the target processor. Now the target system behaves just as if an EPROM is plugged into the EPROM socket; it will therefore execute the program contained within the RAM.

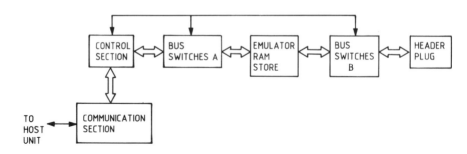

Fig.11.53 Block diagram of EPROM emulator

11.9 FINAL COMMENTS

When the microprocessor arrived it brought a new set of problems for the electronic engineer – with an enormous increase in complexity. New, sophisticated, tools were needed to develop microcomputer systems. This support, as you'd expect, was provided initially by the microprocessor manufacturers, the toolset being known as a microprocessor development system (MDS). Now there are two major sources of MDSs, microprocessor manufacturers and independent microsystems companies such as Ashling (1989). The facilities of MDSs vary considerably (as does the price), but fundamentally they integrate all the development aids discussed so far (Fig.11.54). Most modern MDSs are PC-based.

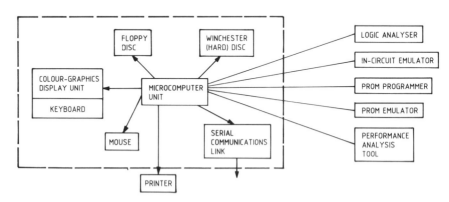

Fig.11.54 Configuration of a modern microprocessor development system

At the present time there is no such thing as a totally integrated toolset for real-time software development. One of the very few that makes a real effort to combine front-end and back-end tools is CARDTOOLS (Ready Systems, 1989); but even that fails to provide full coverage of the software life cycle. Even so, it is clear that the next generation of software tools intends to remedy this situation.

REFERENCES

Ashling (1989), Ashling Universal Microprocessor Development Systems, including ViewFinder and PathFinder, Ashling Microsystems Ltd., Plassey Technological Park, Limerick, Ireland.

ATRON (1989), *Debugging Tools from ATRON*, ATRON, 20665 Fourth Street, Saratoga, CA 95070.

Cooling, J.E. (1986), *Real-time Interfacing*, Van Nostrand Reinhold (UK), Wokingham, Berkshire, England, ISBN 0–442–31755–7.

Creative Data Systems (1987), *SoftProbe II – A Debugging Environment*, Creative Daten Systeme GmbH, Bahnhofstraße 103, 8032 Grafelfing/ München, West Germany.

DEC – Digital Equipment Corporation (1974), DDT – Dynamic debugging technique. Technical Report DEC-10-UDDATA-A-D, Maynard, Mass.

Deitel, H.M. (1984), *An Introduction to Operating Systems*, Addison-Wesley Publishing Company, ISBN 0–201–14502–2.

Digital Research (1983), *Concurrent CP/M-86 Operating System Programmer's Utility Guide*, Digital Research, Post Office Box 579, Pacific Grove, California, 93950.

Hexatron (1988), *Appcom Software Suite*, Hexatron Ltd., Unit 5, Business Centre, Avenue One, Business Park, Letchworth Garden City, Herts., SG6 2BB, UK.

Illingworth, V., Glaser, E.L., Pyle, I.C. (1983), *Dictionary of Computing*. Oxford Science Publications, Oxford University Press, Oxford, OX2 6DP, England, ISBN 0–19–853905–3.

Intel (1987), *Development Tools Handbook – Software, Tools and Systems*, Intel Corporation, 3065 Bowers Avenue, Santa Clara, CA 95051, USA, ISBN 1–55512–063–6.

Logitech (1987), *Logitech Modula-2 Version 3.0 User's Manual*, Logitech USA, 6505 Kaiser Drive, Fremont, CA 94555.

Microsoft (1987), *Microsoft CodeView and Utilities – Software Development Tools*, Microsoft Corporation, 16011 NE 36th Way, Box 97017, Redmond, WA 98073–9717.

Morse, S.P. (1982), *The 8086/8088 Primer*, Hayden Book Company, Inc., Rochelle Park, New Jersey, ISBN 0–8104–6255–9, pp87–89.

Pierce, R.H. (1974), Source language debugging on a small computer, *The Computer Journal*, **Vol.17**, No.4.

Ready Systems (1986/87), RTscope – Real-time multitasking debugger and VRTX32 system monitor – data sheet RSC-MC02053, Ready Systems, P.O. Box 61029, Palo Alto, CA 94306–9991.

Stag (1987). PPZ – The universal programmer, data sheet 803 2000 APC, Stag Electronic Designs Ltd., Stag House, Tewin Rd., Welwyn Garden City, Herts., AL7 1AU, UK.

Syntel (1987), *Download and Debug Monitor – DBO9*, Syntel Microsystems, Queens Mill Rd., Huddersfield, HD13 3PG, UK.

Tseng, V. (1982), *Microprocessor Development and Development Systems*, Granada
Publishing Ltd., St. Albans, Herts, UK, ISBN 0–246–11490–8.

Chapter Twelve

Documentation and testing

Documentation. Paperwork. Records. Words which induce instant apathy in any design team. Such things appeal to bureaucrats, not to creative designers. Maybe this is a slightly harsh judgement – apologies to dedicated bureaucrats – but it **is** true. Unfortunately, documentation is a key feature of all professional design and development activities. It can be regarded as the life-blood of the design body. Once it stops flowing properly, functions quickly deteriorate, eventually ending in rigor mortis. We just can't do without it. For some people, paperwork is an end in itself – but for the software engineer it is an essential component of the design process.

Now, what about testing? Its inclusion in this chapter is partly an example of coincidental cohesion – it had to go somewhere and this is as good a place as any. But there is an element of logic in this as well. Because testing and test documentation are very closely linked. Furthermore, it pulls together many aspects of software testing which have already been discussed in earlier chapters.

The approach adopted here is essentially a pragmatic one. It explains:

- Why documentation is necessary.
- How documentation fits into, and supports, the various phases of the software life cycle.
- The contents, structure and use of specific software documents.
- The underlying concepts of software testing.
- What static and dynamic testing achieve.
- The need for configuration and version control.

12.1 DOCUMENTATION —WHAT AND WHY?

12.1.1 The role of documentation

What precisely is the role of documentation in design engineering? Fundamentally it has three objectives: defining, communicating, and recording information.

In the first instance a prospective customer must define what he wants, why he wants it, when it's needed, and, ultimately, how much he's prepared to pay. Likewise, the supplier needs to define what he intends to do, how he intends to do it, what the delivered product will do, and when it will be delivered. Later, many other points need elaborating and defining, ranging from performance aspects to maintenance features. These definition aspects basically determine the **contents** of engineering documents.

The second aspect, communication, is self-explanatory. But this has an impact on the **style** of presentation. To be really useful, documents need to communicate information effectively. Text is not an especially good medium, as engineers have long realized. What does work well is a combination of diagrams and text, organized to meet particular needs.

Recording, the third objective, is here regarded as a formal operation to capture specific aspects of the design process. The purpose is to rigorously document the following:

- What was wanted in the first place.
- What the supplier promised to do.
- What the supplier actually did.
- Design and performance features of the finished product.
- Installation, maintenance and test aspects.
- The modification history of the product when in service.

The amount of paperwork produced in any particular job depends on many factors. However, one general observation can be made. Where customers set up procurement organizations to handle the acquisition of products, paper mountains abound. And frequently these do little to improve the design of the final product. What they really do, to quote one anonymous quality control engineer, 'is show why we got a lousy job in the first place'. Documentation for its own sake is pointless. Therefore what is discussed here is useful documentation, applicable to professional design organizations.

12.1.2 Documentation — its structure

When devising documentation we should ask ourselves three basic questions: who, what and when, Fig.12.1. This shows that the documentation structure is essentially a three-dimensional one. Unfortunately the axes are not independent ones.

Let's first consider who produces documents and who they're produced for. The answer to this is determined by two factors: the organizations involved, and the people concerned, with the project. Although the size of a project has some bearing on this, much more depends on the nature of the customer's organization. Consider defence projects. Here, whether we're dealing with large systems or small systems, the overall project structure is much the same. For instance, a typical naval project usually involves the bodies shown in Fig.12.2.

All are concerned with system specification, design and development – but they usually have quite different requirements when it comes to documentation. The operator, for instance, couldn't care less about the supplier's design standards as long as the product works properly. What is vital to him is the paperwork needed for operation and maintenance of the installed equipment. On the other hand, procuring agencies have the brief to ensure that proper design standards are maintained. Compliance with such standards must be shown by proper recording of design techniques.

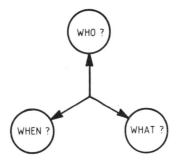

Fig.12.1 Documentation – the basic questions

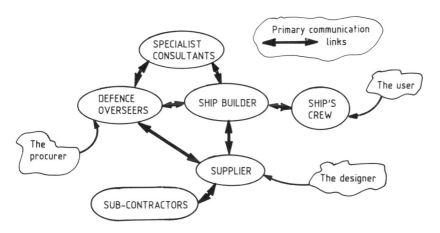

Fig.12.2 A complex project structure

In such developments the paperwork becomes complex because the structure itself is complex. By contrast, where the customer's organization is simple (Fig.12.3), the documentation requirements are less formal. Here the people involved are usually technical rather than administrative. They have a very **direct** interest to see that the supplier delivers the final product on time, within budget, and working as promised. The lines of communication are short and clear, involving few people. This example (like the previous one) also highlights the fact that generally the body acquiring (procuring) the system is not necessarily the end-user.

Projects like these, which generate least paperwork, are frequently the most successful ones. At first this may seem paradoxical. If documentation is so important, why is this the case? The answer is that documentation is a hygiene factor. If standards are poor, projects limp along in a disorganized, uncontrolled fashion. Improving these standards produces instant benefits – but only up to a point. Beyond this little is gained. In fact there may well be a fall in productivity, with more time being spent on paperwork than on the job itself. Therefore it is essential to get the balance right and match documentation standards to project requirements. Regrettably, cook-book solutions to this problem aren't available; it takes experience to work these out.

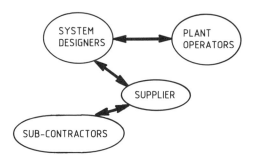

Fig.12.3 A simple project structure

12.1.3 A model for system documentation

In this chapter the reference model for system documentation is set at a fairly complex level, typified by those found in defence industries. Simpler models can be formed from this template by leaving out items which aren't needed in specific projects. Within this model three major bodies are concerned with documentation: the customer, the supplier and the end-user. Fig.12.4 sets out **what** such documentation contains and **when** it is produced within the project programme.

Although this chapter is devoted mainly to software documentation, software is only one part of a real-time system. It is essential to see it in this light to appreciate how it fits into the overall project development, Fig.12.4.

One of the first documents to be generated is the preliminary statement of requirements. This, originated by the customer, basically defines the purpose and intended function of the proposed system. The supplier evaluates these requirements in terms of technical feasibility, cost and timescales. This may be a funded study. More often it is part of a contract bid reply. Using the results of this study/bid, the customer eventually awards a contract to a particular supplier. Details of the required work is defined in a contract specification. At this point the supplier begins serious work, usually involving a preliminary design study.

During this period several documents are produced by the supplier. These form part of a major proposal document, and include the following:

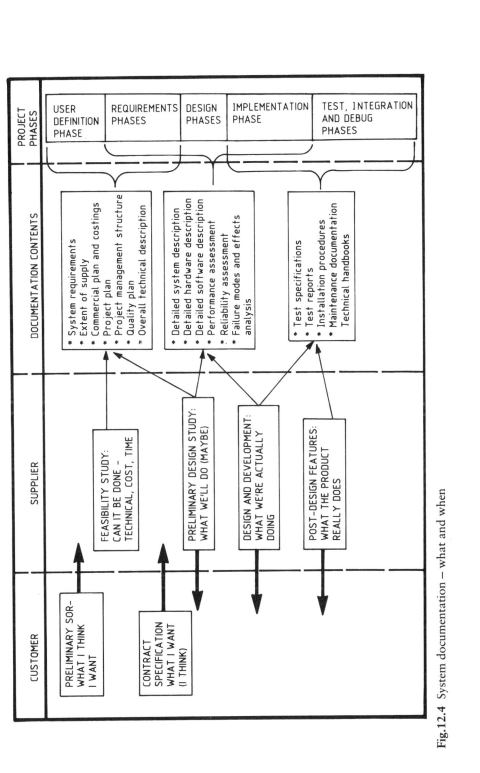

Fig.12.4 System documentation – what and when

- Extent of supply.
- Commercial plan and costings.
- Project plan and management structure.
- Quality plan.
- Overall technical description.

The first item, extent of supply, describes exactly what the supplier intends to provide to the customer. This includes:

- Hardware.
- Software.
- Documentation.
- Training.
- Post-design services.
- In-service support requirements.
- Environmental standards.
- Specialist ('type') testing of equipment.

The commercial plan defines:

- Overall costs.
- Estimated spend rates.
- Staging of payments.
- Contractual conditions.
- Arbitration procedures in the event of disputes.
- The company's commercial authority for the project.

The project plan details how the design, development, manufacture, test and installation of the specified system is to be controlled. It defines the:

- Project administration management and structure – contractual.
- Project administration management and structure – technical.
- Lines of formal communication with the company.
- Division of responsibilities within the company.
- Project control techniques.
- Progress-reporting mechanisms and meeting arrangements.

The quality plan (*STARTS Purchasers' Handbook*, 1987) is designed to show that the company complies with accepted quality assurance (QA) techniques. It describes the:

- Supplier's QA organization.
- Standards with which the QA organization complies.
- Formal QA systems and procedures of the supplier.
- Design and manufacturing standards used by the supplier.
- Specific details of quality verification techniques.

Finally, an overall technical description is produced. This is a wide-ranging and extensive document which includes:

- Overall system concepts.
- System design philosophy.
- System functional description.
- Equipment (hardware) description.
- Software structure.
- Software design techniques.
- System performance features.
- Testing and installation techniques.
- Man–machine interfacing.
- Maintenance and repair techniques.
- Reliability estimates.
- Failure mode behaviour.

This description represents what the supplier intends should happen (what happens in practice may be quite different). As design and development progress these items are translated from proposals to practicalities. The existing documentation is modified to reflect these developments; more detailed information is also produced. A substantial amount of design documentation is generated during this period, covering system, hardware and software aspects. Finally the post-design documentation is produced, relating to test, installation and maintenance functions. The ultimate document is a set of technical handbooks which, for large systems, occupies many volumes.

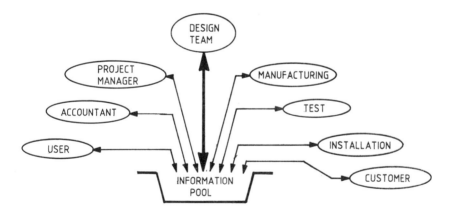

Fig.12.5 The information pool

A further consideration to be taken into account is how this information is used. We can visualize the situation as shown in Fig.12.5, where all information resides in a central 'pool' or store. Various bodies access this, providing inputs and obtaining outputs from the store. Note the following points:

- The major provider of information is the design team.
- All parties should have access to all information.

- Each party normally only uses specific sections of this information.
- Many parties use the same information, but need it presented in quite different forms.
- Consistency of the stored data is vital.
- Access to and use of the data store needs to be controlled to prevent unauthorized changes.

A centralized computer database is one of the most effective ways of implementing this information store.

12.2 SOFTWARE LIFE-CYCLE DOCUMENTATION — OVERVIEW

In real-time systems there aren't always clear divisions between documents relating to system, hardware and software features. A better distinction is to group items as they apply to specific aspects of the project development. In this chapter we're concerned mainly with the software life cycle and its associated documentation, Fig.12.6.

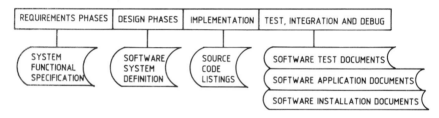

Fig.12.6 Software life-cycle documentation

As shown here each of the major phases has a set of associated documents – which are generated as work proceeds on the project. This point needs to be stressed. The information is produced and recorded as a result of performing analysis, design and development. It should not be confused with that produced specifically to support '. . . in-service use, maintenance, and subsequent development of the software . . .' (JSP188, 1980).

The system functional specification is created during the requirements phases. Essentially it is an extension of the earlier overall technical description, having two basic objectives. First, it defines the qualities of the proposed system from the customer's viewpoint: what it will do, how it will do it and how it is operated. Second, it acts as the design baseline for all subsequent work performed by the supplier.

During the design phases the software structure specification documents are drafted. These describe the functions, structure and operation of the software system at an architectural level, being primarily a design-working tool.

Program coding follows from this, using the structure definition documents as the design input guidelines. Source coding is documented in the usual form as a set of commented program listings.

During the final phase, that of test, integration and debug, several documents are produced. These relate to two major activities. The first is the software/hardware test and integration actions performed by the supplier, prior to delivery. The other is the installation and commissioning of the delivered software at the customer's site.

Documentation required for in-service maintenance etc., may readily be generated from the documents describe here.

12.3 SYSTEM FUNCTIONAL SPECIFICATIONS

12.3.1 Overview

System functions are described broadly in three ways: block diagrams, functional diagrams and requirements specifications, Fig.12.7.

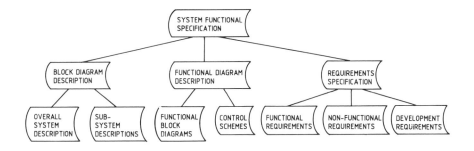

Fig.12.7 Documentation for the requirements phases

12.3.2 Block diagram description

These are high-level documents, designed to give an overview of the total system. They consist of a series of block diagrams, augmented with text, their primary purpose being to describe system operation. In large or complex systems these need to be expanded using a series of sub-system descriptions. Their purpose is to:

- Give a comprehensive description of the total system function and operation.
- Define the physical (hardware) composition of the total system.
- Identify the processor-based units within the total system.
- Define the operational features of all man–machine interfaces.
- Identify electronic communication methods used within the system.

12.3.3 Functional diagram description

This consists of block diagrams and flow diagrams – aided by text – describing precisely what the system is supposed to do. The block diagram depicts the overall system as a series of blocks, each one representing a particular function. Detailed operational aspects of each block (e.g. logic functions, sequencing, switching, closed-loop control, etc.) can be shown using control scheme diagrams. Specific details of all interfaces are given in text form. Individual blocks are connected to other blocks, hardware items or other systems.

In large systems a hierarchical diagram structure will have to be used. First, a single top-level diagram is produced. This is then decomposed by taking each block in turn and elaborating its functions on lower-level diagrams.

12.3.4 Requirements specification

These are described using three documents: functional, non-functional and development requirements specifications (see also chapter 3). These are text descriptions, but may be amplified using diagrams.

(a)   Functional requirements
These describe the behaviour of the system, and cover the following topics:

- System processing and processes.
- Input signals.
- Output signals.
- Start-up and shut-down operations.
- Fault identification and recovery mechanisms.
- Communication aspects of networked systems.
- Communication aspects of multiprocessor systems.

(b)   Non-functional requirements
These are concerned with details of system performance and data, interfacing and system constraints. They include:

(i)   System performance and data:

> Processor cycle times and throughputs
> Response time – asynchronous events
> Scheduling policy
> Context switch times
> Interrupt structures
> Self-checking features and diagnostics
> Fault detection and recovery techniques
> Exception-handling policy

Storage capacity – non-volatile
Storage capacity – volatile
MTBF, MTTR, reliability, availability

Specific time-critical functions
System-operating profiles
System parameters – types and range limits

Control laws
Computation times
Computation accuracy
Resolution and accuracy of digitized signals
Signal filtering and linearization techniques

Alarm functions
Data logging and storage requirements

(ii) Interfaces:

MMI screen display contents and format
MMI panel displays (status, warnings, alarms)
Monitoring, trend and logging display presentations
Hard copy facilities
Operator facilities
Operator access security
System modification (e.g. control loop tuning)

Analogue sensors:	Name, function, location, signal type, signal range, electrical levels, ADC resolution, accuracy and time, signal bandwidth, noise bandwidth sub-system (control, monitoring, alarm).
Digital sensors:	Name, function, location, signal type (serial, parallel), signal range, electrical levels, timing, frequency, sub-system type
On-off switches:	Name, function, location, electrical levels, response time to switch changes, sub-system type.
Processor output signals:	Generally specified in the same way as the input signals.

Data communications networks:
Network structure (e.g. bus, star,
ring), defining standard (Mil.Std.1553,
IEEE 802.4, etc.), name of data link
(control, surveillance, etc.), sources

and sinks of data, specific data items,
response times, network utilization,
message structure, fault handling and
recovery methods.

Software interfaces:

Real-time executives or operating
systems, data bases, screen formatters,
input/output device drivers, communication packages.

(iii)   System constraints:

Programming languages
Operating systems
Specific software packages
Development techniques (e.g. MASCOT)
Design tools (e.g. CORE)
Processor type
Maximum memory capacity
Size, weight, environmental factors
Maintenance philosophy
Maintenance facilities and resources

(c)   Development requirements

These apply to the methods and tools used in system design and development. As such there is some overlap with non-functional requirements; the boundary lines aren't always easy to specify. In essence they are a selective version of the original proposals, updated to reflect the current situation. They include:

- Deliverables: hardware, software, documentation.
- Test and installation procedures.
- Training, post-design services, in-service support requirements.
- Environmental standards, specialist ('type') testing of equipment.
- Cost monitoring, spend rates, staging of payments.
- Contractual conditions, arbitration procedures.
- Project administration structure – contractual and technical.
- Project control techniques (including configuration and version control, see later).
- Project milestones and progress-reporting mechanisms.
- Formal QA systems and procedures of the supplier.
- Design and manufacturing standards used by the supplier.
- Quality plan.

12.4 SOFTWARE STRUCTURE SPECIFICATIONS

As stated earlier, the software structure specification is a full and complete description of the software architecture. It is a dynamic, technical document, produced by the design team for, and as a result of, software design. It starts life as the software section of the initial proposal document. In its final form it becomes a major document in its own right, describing precisely:

- What the design does.
- Why it does it.
- How it does it.

The contents of the structure specification documents are shown in Fig.12.8. It can be seen from chapter 10 how modern design tools (such as YSM Analyst/Designer toolkit and JSD Network Builder/Speedbuilder) can play an important part here. Most of the required documentation can be produced automatically as part of the system design process. Chapter 10 emphasized the diagramming aspects of design methods, but now it can be seen that significant text input is also required. Such textual data is based mainly on the system non-functional requirements documents. Thus the total specification consists of text and diagrams describing the architectural and physical structures of the software.

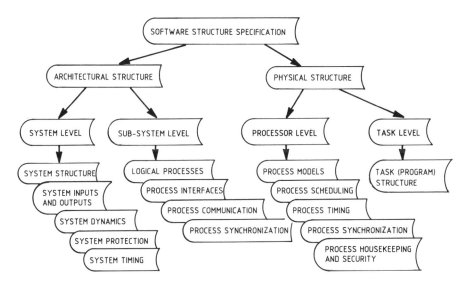

Fig.12.8 Documentation for the design phases

(a) Architectural structure
This is specified both at system and sub-system levels, as defined in Fig.12.8. The system level documents focus mainly on the interaction of the software and its external environment. Sub-system design relates more to the internal structure of the software system itself. Descriptions are produced for the full set of logical processes, their interfaces and interprocess communication and synchronization.

(b)   Physical structure
Here the software structure devised in the architectural phase is mapped onto the hardware. In multiprocessor designs functions are allocated to processors, every processor having its own description document. These processors each support one or more software processes. Thus a description of the individual process structures must be given, including:

- Process modelling technique.
- Scheduling, timing and synchronization of processes.
- Housekeeping and security aspects.

Finally, for each sequential task, a program structure document is generated.

How is information input to the design in the first place? How is it carried through the design from stage to stage? How is consistency maintained throughout the documentation? These depend almost entirely on the design methodology used − resulting in considerable variation at a detailed level. However, no matter which technique is used, the collective documentation should include the following:

(i)   General

- System and sub-system organization.
- Processing and processes.
- Input and output signals, system parameters − types and range limits.
- Start-up and shut-down operations.
- Fault identification and recovery mechanisms.
- Communication aspects (including networking).

(ii)   Performance

- Scheduling policy and interrupt handling.
- Processor cycle times, throughputs, response times, context switch times, specific time-critical functions.
- Self-checking features and diagnostics.
- Specific fault detection and recovery techniques, exception-handling policies.
- Storage capacity.
- Performance profiles.
- Control laws.
- Computation times and accuracy.
- Resolution of digitized signals.
- Signal filtering and linearization techniques.

(iii)   Detailed interface features

- Man–machine interfacing − content, format and facilities.
- Operator facilities and access security.
- System modification methods.

- Plant devices: name, function, location, signal type, signal range, electrical levels, ADC resolution, number representation, accuracy and timings, time response requirements.
- Data communication networks: network software model, name of data link, sources and sinks of data, specific data items, response times, message structure, fault handling and recovery methods.
- Software interfaces: hooks into, and use of, standard software packages such as real-time operating systems, data bases, screen formatters, input/output device drivers and network managers.

It should be obvious that without automated design tools this task is an immense one.

12.5 SOURCE CODE LISTINGS

Two particular documents are needed to describe the functioning of any program: program structure diagrams (chapter 6) and source code listings. In this text source code refers not only to executable code; it also includes many other aspects needed in a full description document. For each program unit the following information should be produced:

- General housekeeping (author, date, issue version, etc.).
- The function, logic and structure of the program unit.
- Detailed description of program functions (normally included as program comments).
- Inputs to, and exports from, the unit.
- Exception-handling procedures.
- Priority level (scheduled or interrupt-driven items).
- Initialization procedures.

Even where automated code generation is used, such information **must** be provided somewhere; without it it is impossible to gain a true understanding of the software.

In modern languages such as Ada or Modula-2 (chapter 9) most of this information is included in the package specification or definition module.

12.6 SOFTWARE TESTING — METHODS AND DOCUMENTATION

12.6.1 Introduction

Software testing is a general term which includes:

- Testing of sub-programs.
- Integration of these into larger units.

- Debugging at both sub-program and program level.

This section discusses both the methods used for, and the documentation produced from, software testing. In some ways it is a consolidation exercise, bringing together many points covered at different places in this text. Now though they are placed within a single context – testing.

What precisely do we mean by testing? Engineers generally take it to mean 'to make a trial of', implying practical or functional evaluation. However, in software terms, a better word is 'prove – to test the qualities of'. Software testing is the process used to show that program code:

- Fulfils its specification – VERIFICATION.
- Performs the required task – VALIDATION.

This can be done in two ways, defect prevention and defect detection (Fig.12.9). The first attempts to detect and remove defects in the source code by inspecting it – static analysis. The second aims to find and eliminate defects missed during static analysis by executing the code – dynamic testing. Both aspects have been discussed earlier: static analysis concepts in chapters 4, 7 and 10, dynamic analysis in chapter 11. This reflects very much how testing is generally carried out in practice – a rather *ad hoc* affair. But now the trend is towards formalizing test practices, especially for critical functions.

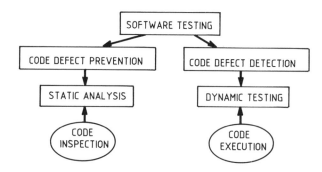

Fig.12.9 Software test techniques

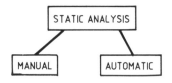

Fig.12.10 Static analysis techniques

12.6.2 Static analysis

Static analysis is a technique which has been practised within professional software circles for some time now – but mainly in manual form (Fig.12.10). These same principles were adopted early on by the safety-critical real-time software community. Very quickly they realized that manual methods were too error-prone for such applications; automated methods were needed. These two approaches are discussed below.

(a) Manual static analysis methods
Manual analysis is an informal process. That is, it isn't defined as a standard, formal set of rules or mathematical operations. Generally it consists of analysing programs by hand against particular design criteria. Further, the analysis should be performed by an experienced designer – who hasn't been involved in the original work.

The following guidelines are typical of those used in manual static analysis checks. They don't claim to be comprehensive, and will probably need modifying to suit individual applications.

(i)   General

- Does the program fulfil (or appear to fulfil) its intended purpose?
- Can the input/output relationships be clearly established?
- Are there unwanted relationships present?

(ii) Standards check

- Have the overall design rules (e.g. YSM) been complied with?
- Are the program constructs safe?
- Is the overall structure sensible?
- Are non-standard language features present?
- Have the project naming rules been adhered to?

(iii) Program and data structures

- Is all code reachable?
- Are all variables initialized before use?
- Are all declared variables used?
- Are all inputs read as intended?
- Are all outputs written to as intended?
- For sequences:
    - (a) Are all statements listed in correct order?
    - (b) Are these executed ONCE only?
    - (c) Are sequence groups executed from a single entry to a single exit point?
    - (d) Do the statements represent the solution to the problem?
    - (e) Does the order of execution produce the required result?

- For iterations:
  - (a) Are the controlled statements executed at least once (post-check)?
  - (b) Can control pass through the operation without ever executing the controlled statements (pre-checks)?
  - (c) Is iteration guaranteed to finish (that is, are the loop termination conditions correct)?
  - (d) Has the correct number of iterations been carried out?
  - (e) Has the control variable been altered within the loop itself?
  - (f) What is the state of program variables on exit from an iteration?
- For selections:
  - (a) Are all alternative courses of action explicitly taken into account (including answers that don't fit the question)?
  - (b) Are the alternative statements constructed using the basic structures of SP?
  - (c) Have the questions relating to sequential operations (and, where appropriate, iteration) been considered?

(b)   Automated static analysis methods

Automated analysers attempt to answer the questions set out above – with minimum human intervention. The factors to be analysed can be grouped into two major categories: program attributes and program verification, Fig.12.11.

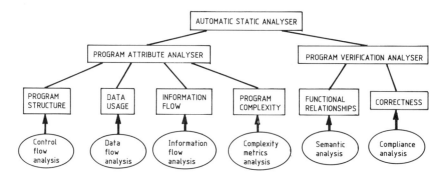

Fig.12.11 Automated static analysis tools

Program attribute analysers evaluate:

- Program structure (control flow analysis).
- Data usage (dataflow analysis).
- Information flow (information flow analysis).
- Program complexity (complexity metrics analysis).

Verification analysers evaluate:

- Program functional relationships (semantic analysis).
- Program correctness (compliance analysis).

In the UK the most widely-used static analysis verification and validation tools are Malpas (1989) and SPADE (1989).

(i)   Control flow analysis

The purpose of this test is to indicate the general quality of the software. It evaluates the control flow through the program, both locally and globally. It also assesses the use (or abuse) of the basic control structures (sequences, loops, selections). Results may be presented in flow-graph form, this being derived by:

- Identifying specific points within the program as nodes.
- Connecting these using arcs or edges.
- Labelling all nodes and arcs.
- Using this information as input to a graph-drawing package.

The resulting directed flow graph:

- Illustrates program complexity.
- Identifies multiple entries and/or multiple exits from program control constructs.
- Indicates redundant paths or unused code sections.
- Shows unreachable code.
- Identifies dynamic halts in the program (black holes).

The results may also include a call graph display, showing procedure call sequences and structures.

(ii)   Dataflow analysis

This analysis tool is used to check that data within the program is used correctly. Typically the following items are highlighted:

- Use of undefined variables.
- Uninitialized variables.
- Unused variables.
- Redundant operations (reads and writes).
- Data reads from locations not previously written to.
- Data reads and writes within the directed graph structure.

(iii)   Information flow analysis

The objective here is to establish the dependencies between input and output variables. The information may be presented as follows:

From Node	To Node	Output Variable	Depends on (Input Variables)
BEGIN	END	StartPump	LowOilPressure PumpSelect
		OpenVent	HighPressureAlarm

It also identifies:

- Unused data.
- Use of undefined data when forming output values.
- Use of incorrect input variables when constructing an output value.
- Specifying an incorrect output variable from specific input variables.

(iv) Complexity metrics analysis

'Difficult' software is more likely to have a greater number of defects than simple code. Therefore, if the complexity of a piece of code is known, probable error rates can be deduced (so goes the theory). Thus complexity metrics analysis is used to measure the intricacy of the software under test. Results are usually presented using well-known software complexity metrics (STARTS, 1987). Which is fine. Except that, as stated in chapter 4, precisely what these techniques show is open to question. Therefore the benefits of this analysis method are questionable.

(v) Semantic analysis

The semantic analyser determines the functional relationship between program inputs and outputs. It does this in two stages. First it derives all possible executable paths through the program. Then it applies the full range of input variables to these paths and evaluates the resulting output responses. Thus it is a primary tool for the verification of program code against its specification. It has another particular use – pointing up paths which the programmer may not have been aware of. In many cases such paths exist only for inputs which lie outside their normal range. The programmer should cater for such events using defensive programming techniques. However, if he hasn't, and should out-of-range inputs appear, the software response may be most unexpected (and even catastrophic). But by highlighting these at the analysis stage, disasters can be averted.

(vi) Compliance analysis

This is used to verify formally that a program conforms to its specification. Where discrepancies occur the analysis tool should identify the cause of such differences. The basis for the analyser is a comparison between a formal specification of the program and its performance (as deduced from semantic analysis).

The most common technique is to develop a formal specification of the program – typically using VDM, Z or OBJ (chapter 7). This is input to the compliance analyser together with the output from the semantic analyser. By comparing the two, non-compliances of the program can be identified.

12.6.3 Dynamic analysis

In real-time systems dynamic analysis is a widely-used technique. The basic concept – shown in Fig.12.12 – is that of stimulating the software to be tested and measuring the resulting responses. Most of chapter 11 was devoted to this topic, but there the emphasis was on methods and tools. Here we intend to look at some of the underlying concepts and practical problems of dynamic analysis.

Fig.12.12 Basis of dynamic testing

Dynamic test methods are classified as either specification-based ('black box') or program-based ('white box') (Gilbert, 1983). Two extremes of these groups can be easily defined. At one end, only the function of a program unit is defined; no information is available concerning its internal structure. This is a pure black-box item. Test conditions are thus set to evaluate the function in question. At the other extreme the complete program structure is known. Here white-box test conditions are devised to exercise both the function and the structure. In practice any software unit being tested will usually lie somewhere between these two end-points.

When devising a set of dynamic tests the following questions need to be considered:

- What input stimulus (test data) should be applied?
- What results should be produced (result predictions)?
- How should the actual results be compared with those expected (results analysis)?
- How should discrepancies be reported (fault diagnosis)?
- How effective are the tests (coverage analysis)?
- How do we measure software performance (performance analysis)?
- What sort of environment must be provided to support such testing?

The relationship of these various components (with the exception of performance analysis) is shown in Fig.12.13. The complete structure is called a 'test harness' (note: there are variations on this definition). Tests are carried out as follows. First the test data is created by a test data generator. This is applied via a driver unit to the software under test, subsequent responses being recorded. The input data is also fed to a prediction generator, which outputs a set of predicted responses. These are compared with the actual responses by a results analyser, errors being flagged up. Errors are further analysed by a fault diagnostician, to provide detailed information and identify likely causes of code defects. The input and output data, together with details of the test software, are evaluated by a coverage analyser. Its function is to generate statistics concerning the test effectiveness – the extent to which the software has been exercised during the test run.

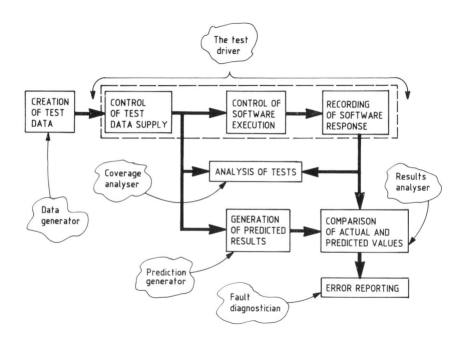

Fig.12.13 Specific aspects of dynamic testing – the test harness

The scenario described here may be automated. In all known cases the harness is run on a host machine and may include facilities to emulate target systems. Such systems may also provide performance analysis, but these are derived from the emulated system. To obtain true performance figures, target system performance analysis tools must be used (chapter 11).

Many software developers implement the test harness manually (apart from executing the software, that is). A typical test document has the following format:

X.GENERAL
   X.1 General description and rationale of tests.
   X.2 Software resources needed.
   X.3 Hardware resources needed.
Y. TEST PLANS
   Y.1 Test 1
      Y.1.1 Test conditions.
      Y.1.2 Input data.
      Y.1.3 Global data conditions.
      Y.1.4 Expected output data.
      Y.1.5 Expected procedure calls.
      Y.1.6 Expected global data conditions.
      Y.1.7 Special conditions for this test.
   Y.2 Test 2
etc.

12.6.4 Integration and acceptance testing

In very small projects the code often consists of a single unit – even though the software may have been developed on a modular basis. In large systems sizeable chunks of software are developed and coded separately by separate design groups. Integration is the process of combining these separate software units into a single composite item.

Individual software units, when tested in isolation, may work correctly. This is no guarantee that the total software package will do the same. Thus the basic function of integration testing is to verify that it does work as planned. All the tools and processes discussed earlier are applicable to this activity; it's just that the job is a more difficult one.

Acceptance testing is how the supplier demonstrates that he has met the customer's requirements. This usually takes place in a number of stages. First, after integration testing has finished, a preliminary acceptance test is performed. Normally this is carried out at the supplier's site, prior to delivery/installation of the software. For most real-time applications this has to be conducted in a simulated system environment – the software cannot sensibly be demonstrated in isolation from its intended application. The second stage of testing, conducted at the customer's site, initially involves installation testing. This leads onto commissioning testing, system testing and finally, full system trials. It is recommended that the IEE guidelines are followed concerning acceptance-testing documentation (IEE, 1985).

12.7 CONFIGURATION AND VERSION CONTROL

These apply both to the product itself and to its documentation. Computer configuration is defined as 'the functional and/or physical characteristics of hardware/computer software as set forth in technical documentation and achieved in a product' (EIA, 1982). 'Version' refers to a specific variant of the software or hardware system.

Configuration control is 'the discipline which ensures that any proposed change (modification or amendment) to a baseline definition (or build level) is prepared, accepted and controlled in accordance with set procedures' (IEE, 1985). When configuration control is implemented properly it:

- Ensures that the current design and build state of the software and hardware is known and recorded.
- Provides an accurate historical record of system development (useful in debugging).
- Enables users to formally and safely record all change details including reasons for change, change requests and corresponding approvals or disapprovals, authorization for change, and dates.
- Ensures that documentation can be produced which truly describes the system as supplied to the customer.
- Enables the system to be rebuilt correctly in the event of catastrophes.

Version control is the activity of controlling the development and build of system components: hardware, software and documentation. Documentation control is only one aspect of the complete subject. Yet the only way version control can be implemented is by using and controlling documentation. This starts right at the beginning of the project with the SOR, leading into the functional specifications, finally ending with acceptance testing.

12.8   READING MATERIAL — REFERENCES, BIBLIOGRAPHY AND GENERAL GUIDANCE

This subject matter is essentially a practical one, being much less prescriptive than descriptive. The reason is simple. Test and documentation procedures are heavily influenced by many factors, including:

- The nature of the project (e.g. defence systems).
- Size of project.
- Current practices.
- Current tool support.
- Company philosophy, structure and standards.
- Costs.

The following documents provide more than sufficient information for the implementation of effective test and documentation systems. The presentation of such information ranges from mildly exciting to rivetingly boring; but then, that's life.

British Standards 5515 and 6488, BSI, UK.

DOD-STD-2167A (1988), *Military Standard – Defense System Software Development*, Department of Defense, Washington, D.C. 20301, USA.

EIA (1982), Configuration management definitions for digital computer programs, *Configuration Management Bulletin No.4-1*,Electronic Industries Association, 2001 Eye St., N.W., Washington, D.C. 20006.

EIA Bulletins on Configuration Management, EIA, Washington, D.C. 20006.

EQD Guide for Software Quality Assurance, UK Ministry of Defence Procurement Executive, Software Quality Assurance Group, EQD, Aquilla, Bromley, Kent, UK.

Gilbert, P. (1983), *Software Design and Development*, Science Research Associates Inc., Palo Alto, ISBN 0–574–21430–5.

IEE (1985), *Draft version – Documentation guidelines for computer software in control, automation and monitoring systems*, Institution of Electrical Engineers, Savoy Place, London, UK.

IEEE Software Engineering Standards 729, 730, 828, 829, 830, 982, The Institute of Electrical and Electronic Engineers Inc., New York 10017–2394, USA.

JSP188, Joint Services Publication 188 – *Requirements for the Documentation of Software in Military Operational Real-time Computer Systems*, Procurement Executive, UK Ministry of Defence, 3rd Ed. March 1980.

MALPAS (1989), *Malvern Program Analysis Suite*, Rex, Thompson and Partners, West St., Farnham, Surrey, GU9 7EQ, UK.

SPADE (1989), *Southampton Program Analysis and Development Environment*, Program Validation Ltd., 34 Bassett Crescent East, Southampton, SO2 3FL, UK.

STARTS (1987), *The STARTS Guide – A Guide to Methods and Software Tools for the Construction of Large Real-time Systems*, NCC Publications, Manchester, ISBN 0–85012–619–3.

STARTS (1987), *The STARTS Purchasers' Handbook*, NCC Publications, Manchester, ISBN 0–85012–585–5.

UK Defence Standard 00–16/1 (1983), *Guide to the Achievement of Quality in Software*, Procurement Executive, UK Ministry of Defence.

UK Defence Standard 00–55 (1989 – interim), *The Procurement and Use of Software for Safety Critical Applications*, Procurement Executive, UK Ministry of Defence.

Index